D1216848

FROM A KANSAS FARM TO THE ENGINEERING HALL OF FAME

The Legacy of Walter E. Hanson, P.E., S.E., Hon. M. ASCE

By

Janice A. Petterchak

With Writings and Presentations

By *Walter E. Hanson*

Walter E. Hanson

Rochester, IL: Legacy Press

ISBN: 0-9777897-0-5

Library of Congress Control Number: 2007905667

Book Design: Polly Danforth
Morning Star Design, Springfield, IL

Printing: Phillips Brothers Printing
Springfield, IL

i

INTRODUCTION

Walter E. Hanson is well known and respected as a civil and structural engineer as well as a civic and church leader. When a colleague recommended me to Mr. Hanson for his biography, I felt privileged to participate in the project.

Over several months he and I met, often at his Springfield home and sometimes at his "retirement" office at Hanson Professional Services Inc., the firm he founded more than fifty years ago as W. E. Hanson & Associates. In that office are file cabinets of correspondence, speeches, publications, slides, and photographs relating to his lengthy career. He permitted access to that collection, which, along with the reminiscences and recollections he taped for my use, provided the basis for his wonderful story.

In the library at Hanson Professional Services, Betty Lou Hicks, Mike Rogers and Amy Matzke helped locate other pertinent materials. I appreciate their assistance as well as the contributions of Mr. Hanson's family, friends, and business and academic associates. Together those resources have resulted in this life story of Walter E. Hanson.

One of the company executives described Mr. Hanson as "a peach of a guy." Others who know him would heartily agree.

Janice A. Petterchak

PREFACE

A Family Remembers

Karen Hanson Pletsch

To reminisce about my father is, of course, to remember the good times of my childhood. We were a very close threesome, Mother, Dad, and I. I remember Dad tying a rope to an outside faucet and patiently turning one end so I could jump rope in the driveway. I remember the Sunday afternoon games of Pollyanna and Go Fish and the trips for ice cream. I remember mornings at the museum and movies downtown. There were picnics, lots of books, lightning bugs in summer and fireworks on the 4th of July. How idyllic it now seems, and it was. Dad was never too busy or too tired to give abundant attention to a young girl secure in the knowledge that he would always be there for her.

When I think about Dad's legacy, I think about my children and grandchildren and the role model their grandfather has been for them. My children will recount, among other things, wonderful times at the lake during summer visits to Springfield. Our family memories are individual and collective. However, Dad is, for all of us, a man of intellect, integrity, great good humor, and infinite patience.

Others will give testimony to Dad's substantial accomplishments in the engineering field. As I look through papers from past years, I continually find notes and letters expressing appreciation for a lesson learned or a personal kindness shown. He touched so many in one way or another. His contributions to the community have been a source of enjoyment to him over the years and have left us with shoes too large to fill. He has always been committed to giving back in recognition of how well served we as a family, and he as a businessman, were over the years. In all endeavors, he has been modest and acknowledged the efforts of others before he has taken credit for himself.

So much dinner conversation during my youth revolved around business. Dad would talk to Mother about his work day. I listened as decisions were made and personnel issues were explored. I watched Hanson Engineers grow strong under his wise direction. Never did I think then that those would be lessons I could carry through the years.

He could have written a book on Business Practice as well as Foundation Engineering, and we strive today to continue his tradition of high ethical standards. Dad was always an advocate for women in business. He has been, and continues to be, my staunch supporter. He is unfailingly generous with praise and inevitably sends an email or a visit with a word of compliment or encouragement.

Dad's most recent lesson to all of us may be one of his most valuable, his lesson on aging. It has been uplifting to watch his continued involvement and interest in projects and current events. We discuss global economics, college basketball, and Washington politics. He uses his "tricycle" walker without a trace of self consciousness. He continues to make new friends, keep in touch with old ones, and carry his age with a well deserved dignity earned through all of his 90 years. I am truly honored and blessed to be Walter Hanson's daughter.

Jonathan M. Pletsch

For most of our lives, David, Amy and I did not have a true appreciation for the professional success of our grandfather or the incredible significance of his engineering projects and partnerships. As we have grown into adulthood, we've continued to learn amazing things about his hardships as a boy in Kansas, his unwavering commitment to his country and his family as a young man, and the seemingly endless number of lives that he has positively impacted through his professional abilities and his outstanding character.

We remained oblivious to our grandfather's professional successes for so long because he was always just "Bampa" to us—the wonderfully loving man with a smile on his face and an infinite supply of kind and insightful words. Bampa was not an engineer in our eyes. He was the man who taught us to fish with cane poles on the shores of Lake Springfield. He was the man who pulled us around the yard in a trailer behind the lawnmower. He was the man who took us to baseball games, gave us history lessons in New Salem and played Chutes and Ladders. He was just Bampa.

When I was a little boy, I loved nothing more than watching big machines digging holes in the earth, hauling dirt and moving heavy objects. Bampa would often pack a lunch for the two of us and we would picnic at the edge of a construction site, spending the entire day watching the bulldozers and the cranes. Even during these times, which are some of my fondest childhood memories, I did not understand Bampa's contribution to the world of structural development. He was just good company as I marveled at the powerful and mesmerizing machines in front of me. It was just a day hanging out with Bampa.

Bampa's humbleness kept him from discussing his success and the success of his company with his three grandchildren. Instead, through his wisdom and insight, he taught us about the world around us as only a grandfather can, helping us truly believe that we could accomplish great things in life. He provided us with an education—giving

Walt Hanson's grandchildren during their high school and college days. Left to right are David, Amy and Jonathan Pletsch, with friend Bandit.

history lessons, teaching us to build model structures with our Erector sets, and reading children's stories to us. And most importantly, he showed us how to be kind and honorable human beings, simply by being a kind and honorable man himself.

Now that David, Amy and I have grown into our thirties and two beautiful great-grandchildren have entered Bampa's life, it is still difficult to fully understand the professional side of our grandfather that others know so well. Nowadays when we take him out to lunch, the conversation is much more inclined to be an in-depth discussion about the Fighting Illini's basketball team rather than a lesson in foundation designs. His intelligence, wit and well-defined perspective of current events, sports and politics always provide the opportunity to discuss any topic with him. And he always takes an interest in what we have to say.

The respect and admiration that Bampa's coworkers, partners and friends have for his valuable professional impact is impossible to ignore. His ingenuity, hard work and business successes have improved the lives of so many people, many of whom will never personally know him. His three grandchildren have a great appreciation for this, too. But first and foremost, to us, he's our loving grandfather. He's a family member who has always been there for us, cared so dearly for us, and above all else has given his heart and soul to guiding the lives of his daughter and his grandchildren in a positive direction. His successes in his profession are minor in comparison to his successes with his family. After all, he's just our Bampa, and he always will be.

Amy E. (Pletsch) Schoenoff

Several things stand out in my mind when I think about my grandfather. In addition to the fact that he is a wonderful man and grandfather, he is unobtrusively intelligent and has always been forward thinking and a strong advocate for new technology. As a headstrong pre-teen, I remember the irony of him patiently telling me that I should be open-minded as I complained about the "annoying beeps of the new answering machine things that people have." I remember spending hours playing games, drawing pictures, and typing countless stories and meaningless documents on his new version 1.0 Macintosh computer. Not only did he recognize the innovation of this new computer with the strange controller called a "mouse," he willingly and happily allowed his young grandchildren to make full use of it.

Above all, I agree with Jon. Bampa "showed us how to be kind and honorable human beings, simply by being a kind and honorable man himself." One of my favorite childhood memories is spending the afternoon of one of my birthdays at the kitchen table with Bampa, building a doorbell out of wires, plastic pieces and a battery from my new electronics set. That afternoon I had so much fun with him, learning and building and wrapping wire around cardboard tubes. When it was completed, I was very proud of our accomplishment. I distinctly remember writing in my diary later that evening that "we couldn't have done it without each other." Looking back, I know that obviously was not the case, but he made me feel that way. Even as a child, I felt I was an important and integral part of our team. It still warms my heart and brings tears to my eyes. For Bampa, this type of kindness and warmth toward others is second nature, and something as adults, we can now objectively recognize and aspire to. As children, this was the Bampa we always knew with all the understated honorable qualities one can have. He always has been, and always will be, "just our Bampa."

David A. Pletsch

I was never close to my father growing up, but Bampa has always been there for me. Perhaps there was a generation gap chronologically, but I was not aware of it. I remember hiking at New Salem with our sandwiches carefully packed in my NFL lunchbox. When we lived in Kentucky, Bampa and I trekked through the Daniel Boone forest. We even got "lost" on one occasion. In retrospect, I feel certain Bampa had things under control, but what a sense of adventure! I didn't realize then how many lessons there were in those times together.

One summer on a visit to Springfield, the two of us constructed a tree house in an apple tree in the backyard of their lake home. We fished with our cane poles off the dock. We swam in the lake and went for rides in the Jon boat. As busy as he surely was, I never felt there was anything more important to him than spending time with me.

Like Jon, I remember visiting job sites, listening to Bampa joke with the construction workers. Bampa has such a kind yet respectful way about him that he makes everyone feel comfortable and interested in the conversation. It makes no difference whether the person is a CEO or someone simply checking his coat. His genuine interest is apparent. What an important lesson for me to learn, and it was a lesson learned by example.

It is a privilege to be able to thank Bampa for his greatest gifts to me found in the small pieces of advice and the loving conversations we have shared over the years. I thank him from the bottom of my heart for everything he means to me. I cannot possibly put it into words. I can only say that there is more love and admiration than he can imagine. And, after all, this fine man is "just our Bampa."

FROM A KANSAS FARM TO THE ENGINEERING HALL OF FAME

CONTENTS

APPENDIX

In 1917, Walter Hanson sits in his little red wagon in the front yard of the old family home, four miles south of Lyndon, Kansas. Three rooms on the right of the photograph were the home of grandparents Hans and Anne, following their immigration from Denmark in 1878. The three-room home was the birthplace of Mettie and Andrew, children of Hans and Anne, in 1878 and 1880. In the early 1900's, a large two-story addition was built and became the birthplace of Walter and Etta, children of Andrew and Laura (Mickelson) Hanson.

Summer of 1918, Walt Hanson sits on a shock of wheat in the northwest 40 acres of the old farm home.

ONE

From the Farm to Kansas State College
1916-1939

As a young farm boy in eastern Kansas, Walter Edmund Hanson enjoyed learning how things were made and how they worked. He carried that interest through college and graduate school, earning degrees in civil and structural engineering and becoming a university professor. Then in 1954 in Springfield, Illinois, following three years as Engineer of Bridge and Traffic Structures for the State of Illinois, he and two partners founded the engineering firm W. E. Hanson & Associates. Today, Hanson Professional Services Inc., still headquartered in Springfield, with many branch offices, provides a variety of engineering, scientific, architectural, telecommunication, program management and land acquisition services to a worldwide scope of clients.

And throughout his career, Walter Hanson has participated in the activities of professional and educational entities, especially the American Society of Civil Engineers and his alma mater, the University of Illinois.

1

Walter Hanson's paternal ancestors and maternal grandfather were natives of Denmark. Hans Hanson, son of Hans Hendriksen and Mette Larsdatter, was born in Karlslunde on April 21, 1842. Hans attended the local school, completing the elementary course in 1856, attaining "very good" and "excellent" grades in reading, religion, writing, arithmetic, and conduct. He worked for several years as a farmhand, and in 1864, with Denmark at war with Prussia, was conscripted to military service.

After the conflict, Hans returned to farm work, maintaining his legally required Servant's Conduct Book. "Every servant should be equipped with a Servant's Conduct Book," according to Danish law, with fines levied for a lost, deliberately damaged, or falsified book:

Walter Hanson's paternal grandparents: Hans Hanson and Anne (Andreasen) Hanson

> Before such a book may be used it shall be sealed, in Copenhagen and incorporated cities by the police authorities, but in rural districts by the parish pastor. . . .
>
> Every employer who hires a servant is entitled to enter in his/her Servant's Conduct Book from what date to what date he/she was hired, and the wages to be paid or paid therefore.
>
> Every employer shall, before a servant leaves his employ, enter in the Servant's Conduct Book from what date and to what date the servant has served him, and in what capacity he/she has served.
>
> It is up to the employer whether he will add any remarks concerning the behavior of the servant during the time of service.[1]

After four years as a farmhand, Hans decided to leave Denmark "to go to America," according to the local pastor, "in order to make for himself a better external position in life than the one he believes he can attain in this country. The best wishes for his future's happiness go with him from here."[2]

Hans and his brother Ole Hanson immigrated to the United States in spring of 1868. After a brief stay in Illinois, they moved to Kansas and began homesteading in Osage County. The brothers were among thousands of new settlers arriving after the Civil War to farm the fertile Kansas prairies.

Acquired from France as part of the 1803 Louisiana Purchase, Kansas in 1861 became the thirty-fourth state in the Union. Many of the Kansas newcomers emigrated from the eastern and central states, while others were foreigners newly arrived in America. "Nearly all of them were poor," reported one historian. "But they were full of hope and ambition, and were willing to undertake the toil and privations of pioneer life for the chance to make real their dreams of a home on the Kansas prairies."[3]

Turning the bare plains into fertile fields was a heavy task, fraught with hardship and discouragement. Severe droughts, hot winds, and insect invasions often destroyed the wheat, corn, and alfalfa crops. But the intervening prosperous years attracted still more immigrants to Kansas, who gradually developed towns and built many schools and churches.

For several years Hans Hanson homesteaded in Osage County, four miles south of the little town of Lyndon. He built a small house and a barn and broke the sod on eighty acres of farmland, then traveled to Copenhagen, Denmark, where on February 24, 1878 he married Anne Andreasen (or Andreasdatter).

Anne was the daughter of Andreas Nielsen and Birthe Jorgendatter, whose farm outside the village of Tune was near the farm home where Hans Hanson was reared. Born on May 10, 1843, Anne completed elementary school in 1857. She was confirmed in Tune Church, "with rather good knowledge of the scriptures," reported her pastor, "just as she also during the preparatory classes always was industrious and of good moral conduct."

Grandfather Hans Hanson and Grandmother Anne, Aunt Mettie, and Father Andrew.
The photograph was taken before their marriages to Hans Larson and Laura Mickelson.
Note original small house circa 1905, prior to addition shown in the top photograph on the frontispiece of this chapter.

3

Walter Hanson's maternal grandparents: Lottie (Plowman) Mickelson and Newton Mickelson

After elementary school, Anne became a servant for several area farmers. One of those employers, for whom she worked from 1869 until her marriage nine years later, reported in her Servant's Conduct Book that Anne was "dependable, faithful and good; she has become so dear to all of us that it hurts us all much that we must part."[4]

The newly married Hans and Anne Hanson settled on the Kansas farm, where their first child, Mette ("Mettie") Marie, was born on December 2, 1878, followed on May 26, 1880 by Andrew Carl Hanson. Hans developed the homestead, adding to the original house, building sheds, and cultivating an additional eighty acres.

"There had to be a tremendous talent in the minds of the homesteaders in Kansas," Walter Hanson recently remarked,

> *to be able to construct such magnificent things as their big barns, which were well built and well reinforced, and also the wells and cellars and granaries and housing for the cattle and chickens and pigs. Those involved real structural engineering, as well as knowledge of groundwater hydraulics and flows through the streams and rivers. Today, colleges and universities give degrees in agricultural engineering. The homesteaders were doing it back then with an eighth-grade education.*

By the time of Hans Hanson's death on February 15, 1904, he had accumulated some 320 acres, "one of the most substantial farmers of Osage County," according to his obituary. Anne remained on the farm until her death on August 15, 1913.

A nearby family also with Danish roots was headed by Newton Mickelson. Born on October 18, 1859 in Bårup, Denmark, he had arrived in the United States at the age of ten with his parents, Lars and Bodyl Mickelson. The family settled on a farm south of Lyndon, and on February 1, 1887, Newton married Charlotta "Lottie" Agnes Plowman, daughter of Hanna and the Rev. J. T. Plowman, who officiated at the ceremony.

Lottie had been born on June 6, 1866 in Mifflin County, Pennsylvania of English

Andrew and Laura (Mickelson) Hanson, married November 25, 1913

and German ancestry. Her grandfather Wilhelm Strunk had been a soldier in the Revolutionary War, and a family genealogist suggests that he was probably a third- or fourth-generation American. The Plowmans, too, had come to America in the previous century, and several family members supported its war for independence from Great Britain.[5]

When Lottie was four years of age, her family settled in Miami County, Kansas, later moving to Melvern. Lottie and Newton Mickelson became parents of six children. Daughter Laura Bodyl Mickelson was born on October 5, 1889.[6]

Andrew Hanson, who maintained the family homestead, on November 25, 1913, at age thirty-three, married twenty-four-year-old Laura Mickelson. They became members of the Lyndon United Presbyterian Church and were parents of two children born at the farm home, Walter, on July 14, 1916, and Etta, on November 24, 1917.

Walter and his sister attended the one-room Widney grade school, located 1½ miles from the family farm. According to the Kansas State Historical Society,

> *For a hundred years, white frame or native stone one-room schoolhouses dotted the section corners across Kansas. They were called names like Prairie Flower, Buzzard Roost, and Good Intent. The children who attended ranged in age from five to 21 and endured dust storms, prairie fires, and cattle drives eddying past the school house in order to get an eighth grade education. . . .*
>
> *The school teacher, sometimes scarcely older than her pupils, was a renaissance individual. She had to be a nurse, janitor, musician, philosopher, peacemaker, wran-*

Main Street in Lyndon, Kansas, 1917, later to become part of U.S. Highway 75—extending from Minnesota to Texas

gler, fire stoker, baseball player, professor, and poet for less that $50 a month. Equipped with little more than a blackboard and a few textbooks, teachers passed on to their pupils cultural values along with a sound knowledge of the three Rs.[7]

"Those one-room schools were scattered about every six or eight miles all over the county," Walter recalled:

> "Widney" evidently had been named for John Widney, who had given the land for the school a decade or more earlier. My mother attended the Grandview school-house several miles west, and there was even one called Jackrabbit. That was the way the children of the Kansas homesteaders received eight years of education, by means of those one-room schoolhouses. We had one teacher for eight grades; six of us in my grade, right through graduation.
>
> The two principal library books in our one-room school were the Book of Knowledge *and issues of* National Geographic. *They were our main reading material, along with our textbooks. I always enjoyed the arithmetic games, because I was pretty good in arithmetic and generally came out the winner of any arithmetic contest.*

During fifth grade, Walter's essay "Blackie the Cat" won the *Topeka Daily Capital* newspaper's weekly "Best Story" contest. The essay is reprinted here:

> When I was two weeks old, my mother moved my sisters and brothers and myself from the barn to the wood pile. She did this so we could see the outside world better and catch rabbits and other animals. We liked our new home better than the barn.
>
> I lived at the farm till I was a year old and then my master moved to the city and took me along, also one of my brothers. I didn't like the city life at all because there wasn't any place to hunt. I lived in the city six months and then my master moved

6

to a smaller town.

I liked it better there because there was more room and I could hunt some. I lived in this town six months. Then one day my master picked me up and put me in a box. We drove several miles and then I was taken out and, what do you suppose, there I was back at the farm.

My—wasn't I glad to see my mother again.

Walter E. Hanson

As the contest prize, Walter received a copy of *Making Things with Tools*, a 1928 book for youngsters published by Rand McNally & Company. He cherishes the volume, "which told you, among the projects, how to make chicken coops and how to brace them so they wouldn't collapse. I often said it was my first structural engineering textbook."

The Hanson Family: Walter's mother, Laura; father, Andrew; sister, Etta; and Walter.

For many years, Arthur Capper, publisher of the *Daily Capital* as well as Kansas Governor from 1915 to 1919 and later a U.S. Senator, sponsored an annual children's celebration in Topeka, known as the Capper Birthday Party. Capper's birth date, July 14, was the same as Walter's. "I remember well my trips with my father to those events for several years in the 1920s," said Walter. "It was always in July, with crowds of fifteen to twenty thousand. The ones we attended were on the state fairgrounds."

One of the reasons that Walter became directed toward civil engineering were the trips to town with his father to deliver eggs and cream, sometimes in the family's Model T Ford, sometimes in a horse-drawn wagon pulled by a team of horses.

Construction workers on new bridge over Salt Creek, one mile south of Lyndon, Kansas, circa 1923. Young Walt Hanson observed the building of the bridge and believes that the experience influenced his decision to study civil engineering at Kansas State College, where he majored in bridge design and construction. (Photo courtesy of Osage County Historical Society)

For a time, we detoured over Salt Creek, about a mile south of Lyndon, where the state highway department was building a new bridge. Every time we made that trip we watched the progress of the construction. I remember asking my father, "Who decides how long that bridge will be, and the details of it?"

He told me that the highway department was in Topeka, and that most of the highway department employees were civil engineers. I learned later that the Salt Creek bridge was a Warren-type truss, a popular design at that time for steel bridges with riveted joints.

When Walter was eleven years old, his father became ill and was hospitalized for several weeks in Ottawa, about twenty miles from Lyndon. Transferred to a Topeka hospital, he died on March 26, 1929. The death, according to the hospital, was a suicide, although Walter is not certain of the circumstances:

> The morning after Mother received word, she called my sister and me into the living room of our farm house. I was in the sixth grade, and she told us we had to continue, the three of us, running the farm, continuing our lives.
>
> I remember that same morning, going out to feed the cows, horses, chickens, and doing the farm chores—all that work before school. Mother, my sister, and I developed a close partnership to carry on.
>
> I just could not believe that my father had committed suicide. It was a lingering stigma, although I didn't let it affect my relations with others or my school work. He had always been there for us.
>
> Some years later, as a young graduate engineer, I experienced excruciating pain from a condition that may have been similar to my father's. Fortunately, my problem was cured by surgery, a possibility not available to him.

Prior to receiving the eighth-grade graduation certificate, each student was given the Osage County examination. "I remember," said Walter, "that I made the Honor List on my county exams. The local newspaper printed the list."

The Great Depression that began in the late 1920s caused great economic hardships for the next decade. Walter entered Lyndon High School in 1930, with his five Widney School classmates. "My mother and sister and I got along fine during those years":

> Fortunately, we had no mortgage on our property. Many farmers around the community lost theirs because of large mortgages. We had plenty to eat, although those years were not good, economically.
>
> I drove our 1926 Model T to high school when it ran, a pretty good car. Mechanically, it was not very complicated, but the three bands—low, reverse, and brake—were always wearing out. On the clay and mud roads, when reverse was the only band that worked, I sometimes had to back up our hill.
>
> I was not into athletics; I was not very good, but also as a farm boy I had to take care of the chores, with no time for practice. On the farm land that we owned, other farmers planted and harvested crops on a share-crop basis.

During high school, Walter was hired for summer jobs by other farmers and on Saturdays clerked at the Lyndon IGA—carrying groceries to cars and running errands.

Elected President of the 1934 senior class, he ranked second of the thirty-six students. Scheduled to speak at the graduation ceremony, he was homebound after contracting mumps. "I regretted it very much, but about a week later Superintendent Paisley brought my graduation certificate."

Old Lyndon High School building, which Walt Hanson attended during his freshman year. A new building was under construction from which he graduated in 1934. (Photo courtesy of Osage County Historical Society)

After completing high school, Walter expected to remain on the family's well-developed 160-acre farm. But 1934 was a drought year, killing the corn crop, while chinch bugs ruined the wheat fields. When the drought conditions continued into 1935, he began to seriously consider entering college. "While in high school I had begun to think about engineering if I went to college. My math and science teacher and Lester Paeris, a farmer with some college education who had been a schoolteacher, advised me to go to college. The farmer said that even if you did nothing after getting a college degree but sit on a fencepost, you would enjoy it more."

In the spring of 1935, Walter inquired about requirements for entering Kansas State College of Agriculture and Applied Science (now Kansas State University) in Manhattan. Deciding to pursue a degree, he sold his pigs for $60 and left the family farm in August. Superintendent Paisley drove him to Manhattan, where he enrolled in the civil engineering curriculum—the first in his family to work toward a four-year college degree.

Locating a room in an off-campus home, "I knew absolutely no one: no students, no faculty, no residents of Manhattan. The first few days and nights were kind of a lonesome period, until I started to attend class. And the $60 didn't last long":

> *I knew in the first semester that I would study civil engineering. I had read a little about civil engineering and had talked it over with my high school advisors. It seemed like it was engineering that I would most enjoy and be best in, although we had a lot of mechanical gadgets on the farm. If civil engineering hadn't been available, I would have probably enrolled in mechanical engineering.*

Walt Hanson, 1939, as a member of the college of engineering council at Kansas State, where he was president of the student chapter of the American Society of Civil Engineers, as well as a member and officer of several honorary societies.

Throughout the college years, Walter found jobs to pay for his tuition and expenses. For one semester he worked with a professor through the National Youth Administration, a Depression-era federal program of the Franklin Roosevelt administration. "My first task was to fill out the professor's attendance book with the names of the students for the several classes that he taught. At the same time I got a job at the college cafeteria, washing dishes and helping during mealtimes."

Transportation for the few occasions Walter returned to the family farm was hitchhiking. "I got through the first semester and the second semester, both financially and scholastically, and made the Phi Kappa Phi honor group for freshmen."

Most Kansas State students mailed their laundry "for our mothers to do. We sent it parcel post monthly in a little suitcase-type container, with a place to slip in the address: To Mrs. Laura Hanson, Rt. 3, Lyndon, Kansas. When she sent it back, she would flip over the paper to read: Mr. Walter Hanson, at my Manhattan address."

During sophomore year, he continued rooming at the same house. "By that time I'd become well acquainted with the other boys, and we were a compatible group. I worked for another professor on some consulting work and also continued in the cafeteria."

Walt Hanson (right), and K-State classmates Harold Brown and Bruce Roberts, work on a railroad design problem in the spring of 1939.

For junior year, Walter and Harlan Bull, another student in the home, decided they wanted to work in a sorority house. After interviews, both obtained jobs with the Pi Beta Phi sorority. "That was my best job, because the housemother favored us over the girls,

Engineering building (circa 1930's) at Kansas State University. The civil engineering departmental offices were located in the far left section, and Walt Hanson attended classes and laboratories in various locations of the building.

and the cook always made certain that 'her boys' had plenty of good food."

Then as a senior, he moved to a residence that had been remodeled for student housing. There he became acquainted with two other senior civil engineering students, Harold Brown and Bruce Roberts. Bruce and Walter were roommates, and all three obtained part-time work with civil engineering professors. For many years, Bruce and Walter remained close friends, and for a time they would become business associates.

Between semesters, Walter tried to find work as a draftsman, "and thought I had a job one summer between my junior and senior years at the state highway department in Topeka. But somebody with a little more experience or a little more pull got the job."

Instead, he went home as he had in previous summers and worked for area farmers. "The main summertime job involved threshing":

> *Two brothers named Nelson had a steam engine and a thresher. Farmers would load their hayracks with bundles of wheat. Driving alongside the threshing machine, they threw the bundles into the thresher, and out came the grain, caught in wagons next to the machine.*
>
> *There were lots of jobs associated with the threshing operation. The farmers would arrange to help each other, bringing their hayracks and horse-drawn wagons.*
>
> *Many of the farmers, including ours, raised alfalfa hay and clover to enrich the soil with nitrogen. After growing alfalfa for four or five years, the farmer would plow up the field and then could raise a good corn crop.*

11

There were always hay harvesting operations: mowing the hay and letting it dry—hoping we wouldn't have rain. When the hay was dry, we would rake it into rows. The farmer came in with the hayrack and hay loader. My two uncles (more my brothers than uncles)—Uncle Earl and Uncle Ray Mickelson—owned a hay bailer. The three of us did a lot of hay business, not only the alfalfa hay but also prairie hay, which we bailed and used in the wintertime to feed the horses and livestock. That's how I spent most of my summers when I was at Kansas State.

Active in student engineering organizations, Walter served as president of the Kansas State student chapter of the American Society of Civil Engineers. "I've been an ASCE member ever since my chapter presidency in the fall of 1938. As a senior, I was our representative on the Engineers' Open House committee, comprised of students from all engineering departments, civil, mechanical, electrical, agricultural, and chemical." He was also president of Steel Ring and a member of Sigma Tau, both honorary engineering organizations.

In the summer of 1939 Walter graduated with honors from Kansas State College with a Bachelor of Science degree, ready to begin a career in civil engineering. "I must give much credit and thanks to my cousin Shannon DeWeese, who came to live with my mother and sister and became a partner in the farm operations while attending Lyndon High School. He became a second son to mother."

Walter's achievements in obtaining a college education were a motivation to others of his family. Recently a cousin wrote: "Thanks for being my inspiration, via my father. Looking back on family conversations, it is evident to me that my father, Ray, was quite proud of his nephew Walter, and from my earliest school days my father's plan was that I should go to Kansas State and study engineering, like cousin Walter! And so I did."[8]

Endnotes

1   Servant's Conduct Books of Hans Hanson and Anne Andreasen, translated by Ingvar Schousboe, held by Walter E. Hanson.

2   Hans Hanson, "Servant's Conduct Book," final entry, April 5, 1868.

3   Anna E. Arnold, *A History of Kansas*, Topeka: State of Kansas, 1919, p. 119.

4   Anne Andreasen, "Servant's Conduct Book," final entry, Feb. 7, 1878.

5   Eldon Mickelson to Walter Hanson, Dec. 11, 2005.

6   Newton Mickelson died on September 6, 1946, Lottie Mickelson on June 18, 1952. Both are buried in Lyndon Cemetery.

7   www.kshs.org/portraits/county_schools.htm

8   Mickelson to Hanson, May 23, 2006.

While working on a seismograph crew in Durant, Oklahoma, Walter Hanson met Sue Roling, a senior at Southeastern Oklahoma College, and they married on September 14, 1940. Following a weekend honeymoon in Dallas, Texas, Walt reported for work in Wichita Falls, where the newly married couple resided until they moved to Kansas City, Missouri, the following year.

TWO

Doodlebugging for Oil
in Texas and Oklahoma
1939-1941

*The business is so new [in the 1930s] that small towns haven't adjusted to oil people
and regard them with suspicion and concern. We try to keep a good reputation. . . .
Life isn't too monotonous and even has an element of adventure in it. The crew is like a
family—our joys and sorrows are shared. . . . We always see and learn about something new
or different, and can put away a nice nest egg for the future. Such is the doodlebugging life.*

Ida Green, *Life in the Oil Patch*

Graduating from Kansas State College after the 1939 summer session, Walter found
that, because the country was still recovering from the Great Depression, jobs were scarce.
His roommate Bruce Roberts accepted a position as county engineer in western Kansas,
and their friend Harold Brown joined his uncle's construction company.

In the neighboring state of Oklahoma, however, rich oil fields had been discovered in the mid-1920s, and both
Oklahoma and Texas prospered
from enormous oil production.
Walter was invited to interview
with the Petty Geophysical Engineering Company in San Antonio,
Texas. The position involved drawing contour maps of subsurface
rock formations as well as inter-
preting and computing seismograph records.

"The Petty Company was at
that time under contract to the
Sinclair Oil Company," Walter ex-

*Although most of Walt Hanson's work on the seismograph crew
entailed the drawing of subsurface contour maps, he took to the field
occasionally. Above, he sits in a 1939 Plymouth seismograph truck.*

15

plained, "to try to locate oil fields for Sinclair. Petty had crews in several areas in northern Texas and southern Oklahoma, and even overseas. I had a loan to pay off from senior year at Kansas State, so during the interview I agreed to foreign travel. I doubt that I would have gotten the job if I had not said that I would go to Burma."

That oil-exploration work is known as "doodlebugging." Named for an earth-burrowing insect, a doodlebug is an electronic device that records the elapsed time between the explosion of a small underground dynamite charge and the return of energy from the rock layer. Doodlebug crews traveled from town to town, staying for weeks or a few months, mapping the earth's subsurface in search of oil. The doodlebug workers transmitted their recorded information to a nearby instrument truck, for later interpretation by geologists.[1]

Because of threatening war conditions, the Petty firm did not receive the Burma contract, and Walter was instead assigned to a doodlebug crew for work in Nacona, Texas. "We arrived during an August sandstorm. Our crew numbered about ten or twelve, including office and field personnel":

> The Texas climate and overall environment were quite different from Kansas, but the crew members and local people were friendly, even though I soon became affectionately known as a 'damn Yankee.' But I was not alone; there were two other Wildcats from Kansas State on the crew, and even a Badger from the University of Wisconsin.
>
> My roommate was Norm Davis, an electrical engineering graduate from the University of Oklahoma. Norm and I attended the 1939 Cotton Bowl game in Dallas, between the University of Texas and the University of Oklahoma. Each team had an All-American player. The game was close, won by the University of Texas in the final quarter. One of the Texas half backs was a native of Nacona, Texas, and I think nearly all of the population of that small northern Texas city attended the game.

In late 1939, the seismograph crew moved to southeastern Oklahoma, to explore and evaluate the oil potential in the Durant area. "We stayed in Durant just long enough for me to fall in love with (Mattie) Sue Roling, a senior student and beauty queen at Southeastern Oklahoma State." For their first date, the couple drove to nearby Ardmore to see the popular movie "Gone with the Wind." "I was completely overwhelmed by the whole Roling family," Walter recalled. "Sue had two beautiful sisters; Edna was older, Freda younger, and their parents appeared to gra-

Days of courtship, Walt and Sue Hanson in Durant, Oklahoma, spring of 1940

ciously welcome me into their family, despite my being a 'damn Yankee.'"

Sue's parents, Earle Godden and Lela Coker Roling, and grandparents, Charles and Mattie Coker, had moved to Durant from Amity, Arkansas shortly before Sue's birth on November 19, 1919. Earle Roling was the son of Henry Jackson and Mattie Ann Pricilla Runyan Roling. The Runyan family lineage has been traced to Isaac Barefoot Runyon (1757-1875) and to the French Huguenot Protestants of the sixteenth and seventeenth centuries.[2]

Earle Roling became station manager in Durant and Tulsa for the Midland Valley Railroad.

Walter's seismograph crew, not finding favorable conditions for oil reserves in the Durant area, returned to Texas, to the town of Wichita Falls. "I found it most inconvenient to make the trip back to Durant every weekend. So, I proposed marriage. Sue and I were married in the First Methodist Church of Durant on September 14, 1940. We began our 67-year partnership in a small two-room apartment in Wichita Falls, Texas. I remember the soggy messes when I'd forget to empty the drip pan beneath the icebox in our apartment."

Above: *Laura Hanson (left) and Lela Roling on the day of the wedding of Walt and Sue, September 14, 1940, in Durant, Oklahoma.*

At Left: *Walt and Sue's first home— a small apartment on the left side of this Wichita Falls residence.*

Before graduation from Kansas State a year earlier, Walter had applied for employment with Ash, Howard, Needles & Tammen, a prominent bridge engineering consulting firm in Kansas City, Missouri. In December, 1940, he received an offer to join the firm as a structural draftsman and junior designer. "Sue and I yearned for more stability and considered this a good opportunity," he explained. "Furthermore, it was the kind of work that I dreamed of all during my college years." He accepted the position, and the couple began planning their move from Wichita Falls, Texas to Kansas City, Missouri.

Endnotes

[1]   Ida Green, *Life in the Oil Patch*, www.ti.com/corp/docs/company/history/lifeinthe oilpatch.shtml

[2]   Marie Runyan Wright, *Up the Runyon/Runion/Runyan Tree*, Baltimore: Gateway Press, Inc., 1993, pp. 393-94.

The Mississippi River bridge between Dubuque, Iowa and East Dubuque, Illinois was Walter Hanson's first experience with the design of bridges while employed with Howard, Needles, Tammen & Bergendoff in Kansas City, Missouri. The design was completed in 1941, received a high war-time priority, and was completed in 1943. The bridge has received numerous awards for its advanced structural design and beauty, and is registered as a National Historic Landmark.

Aerial view of the bridge and Dubuque areas; the city of Dubuque, Iowa on the right, and Illinois to the left.

THREE

Detailing and Design of Bridges in Kansas City
1941-1942

*Even in the depths of the Depression's worst years, Kansas City was enjoying
a building boom. A new thirty-four-story Power & Light Building, the tallest
skyscraper in Missouri, stood over the city like a shining statement of faith. . . .
Compared to other cities, the Kansas City outlook was confident and expansive.*

David McCullough, *Truman*

When Walter and Sue Hanson arrived on January 2, 1941, this large Missouri city
had emerged from a politically corrupt era to become a commercial, industrial, and
transportation center of the midwest. Future President Harry S. Truman represented the
state in the United States Senate, as European nations struggled to survive the onslaught
of German tyranny.

After German bombers attacked British ports, airfields, and London, Truman supported President Franklin Roosevelt's promise of aid to Great Britain. And as a member
of the Military Affairs Committee, Truman voted for the first peacetime draft of young
American men.[1]

Concerned but not yet affected by the impending world crisis, the Hansons decided on a two-room apartment in a large brick building on Warwick Boulevard. "The
apartment was not much larger than the one we had in Texas," Walter recalled, "and
neither Sue nor I was very happy with that rather lonesome apartment living":

> It was quite a change from the fellowship of the seismograph crew. However, we
> became friends with Charles and Gladys Newman. He was a pilot for the Trans
> World Airlines, and Gladys was a charming southern lady from Roanoke, Virginia.
>
> Sue and Gladys soon found a nice duplex for the four of us on South Charlotte
> Street, a great improvement over the apartment building. The only disadvantage
> was that the duplex was four or five blocks from the Troost streetcar line, my trans-
> portation to and from work. The Ash, Howard, Needles & Tammen office was at
> 1012 Baltimore in downtown Kansas City.

The firm, founded in 1914, specialized in transportation projects, including the design of long-span bridges. As junior designer and draftsman, Walter's responsibilities at the firm included the detailing of various sheets of bridge plans. His first assignment was helping complete the plans for a bridge across the Mississippi River at Dubuque, Iowa. "The task was not easy for me, especially since it had been nearly two years since my graduation from Kansas State. However, I saved my college books and solutions of design problems in concrete and steel, and with a concentrated nighttime review and much help from associates I was able to do the job."

Residents of the Dubuque area had agitated for a number of years for replacement of the 1887 "High Wagon Bridge," so named because tall smoke-stacked steamboats could maneuver under its structure. Economic conditions resulting from the Great Depression, however, delayed the project. By 1940, though, with European nations embroiled in World War II, a new bridge was considered critical for facilitating military transportation within the United States.[2]

The planned structure on U.S. Route 20 would join the Iowa city with East Dubuque, Illinois. During the contract drawings, Walter recalled, "I was very pleased when Mr. Harper, the chief draftsman, asked me to prepare the cover sheet, commonly called the General Plan and Elevation. There were probably more than fifty sheets in the set of plans, covering the entire Iowa to Illinois project. I was not qualified to analyze and design much of the main spans of the bridge, but I can claim responsibility for several of the smaller piers and retaining walls."

Construction on the three-span, truss-arch Julien Dubuque Bridge (named for a French fur trader and Dubuque-area lead miner[3]) began in 1942, as America became involved in the World War. Upon completion the following year, the American Institute of Steel Construction judged the structure "The Most Beautiful Bridge of 1943." It has since been registered as a National Historic Landmark.

After completing the Dubuque bridge plans, Ash, Howard, Needles & Tammen turned mainly to defense and war-related contracts. One such project was design of an Army proving-ground in Hope, Arkansas. "I was notified that I would be transferred there," Walter recalled, "but at the last minute the plans were changed for me to remain in Kansas City":

> Sue and I had already given notice of leaving to our landlord on Charlotte Street, so we found a small apartment on Wornall Road, near the famous Plaza shopping area at 49th Street. We continue, sixty-five years later, to consider the Plaza and Kansas City the most attractive and well-planned city and suburban shopping center in the world. We learned later that we had lived a few blocks from the famed newscaster Walter Cronkite.

While employed with Ash, Howard, Needles & Tammen (later called Howard, Needles, Tammen & Bergendoff and today known as HNTB), Walter became acquainted with two civil engineers whose friendships would become significant and continue for years. Dr. Jacob Karol, one of the firm's lead design engineers, had attained his Ph.D. at the University of Illinois in 1938. James G. Clark, a young professor in the U. of I. civil engineering department, spent the summer of 1941 at the firm to gain practical experience in bridge design.

"Jim and I became friends, and I told him about my need for graduate studies and even showed him my transcript from Kansas State College. From both Jake and Jim, I learned about the great reputations of such University of Illinois structural engineering professors as Hardy Cross, Thomas Clark Shedd, and other recognized giants on the faculty there."

An engineering professor at Illinois from 1921 to 1937, Hardy Cross had previously taught at Brown University and practiced structural and hydraulic engineering in Boston and New York. He was known for insightful writings, including a monograph on arch structures that became a text at Harvard University's Graduate School of Engineering. Thomas Shedd had also taught at Brown, then worked for a New York bridge company before joining the University of Illinois engineering faculty in 1934.

In January 1942, James Clark contacted Walter about a position as instructor in the University of Illinois Civil Engineering department. He was very interested in the opportunity to teach while also completing his graduate studies. "The teaching position would allow me to carry a half-time schedule of graduate course work," he explained. "Jim advised that, if interested, I should write to Professor Whitney Huntington, head of the Civil Engineering department. Sue and I agreed that this was an opportunity I should pursue":

> I sent my credentials to Professor Huntington and soon was offered the job. So, in February, as a result of those acquaintances and friendships in Kansas City, we packed our belongings in a two-wheeled trailer and crossed the Mississippi for the first time in our lives, on our way to Urbana/Champaign, Illinois.

Endnotes

[1]   David McCullough, *Truman*, New York: Simon & Schuster, 1992, pp. 196, 254.

[2]   Mary Charlotte Aubry Costello, *Climbing the Mississippi River Bridge by Bridge*, Vol. 1: Mary Charlotte Aubry Costello, 1995, p. 152.

[3]   Robert P. Howard, *Illinois: A History of the Prairie State*, Grand Rapids, Mich.: Eerdmans, 1972, p. 166.

In 1943, Walt and Sue Hanson stand near the Alma Mater statue at the University of Illinois with the new student union building in the background. Walt was soon to leave his graduate studies and teaching to serve in the U.S. Navy and to return in 1946.

FOUR

University of Illinois before U.S. Navy Service
1942-1943

Engineering does not tell men what they should want or why they want it.
Rather it recognizes a need and tries to meet it.

Hardy Cross, *Engineers and Ivory Towers*

The Hansons arrived in Champaign on a cold, damp day during the first week in February, 1942. Walter was about to become an instructor in civil engineering at the University of Illinois. He also intended to register for one unit of graduate coursework. On that first day, he telephoned Professor James Clark, with whom Walter had worked the previous summer in Kansas City. He and Sue wanted Clark's advice on housing in Champaign/Urbana.

> *The next day we found an apartment at 819 Vine Street on the west side of Champaign. The landlords were Mr. and Mrs. MacMurray, who had just remodeled their house to add a small apartment, consisting of a kitchen in the basement and the living room and bedroom on the second floor. That was not the most convenient arrangement, but being young, Sue and I didn't mind running up and down the stairs to get from where we ate our breakfast to where we dressed to go to work. Since the house had been recently remodeled, everything in our apartment was quite new, and that appealed to us.*

The following day Walter reported to Professor Whitney C. Huntington, head of the civil engineering department. Huntington at that time was a dominant influence in the University's national leadership in civil engineering education. He referred Walter to Professor Jamison Vawter for his graduate course schedule and to Thomas C. Shedd, professor of structural engineering, to enroll in his graduate course in steel design (C.E. 107).

23

Thomas Clark Shedd, Professor of Structural Engineering, was Walter Hanson's advisor during all of his graduate studies, before and following his military service in WWII. Shedd was widely recognized as an excellent teacher of both theory and practice. He was the author of two seminal books in analysis and design of structures used in undergraduate and graduate courses. For a decade or longer, he served as chairman of both the professional and structural committees for Illinois licenses. Professor Shedd also served as president of the Central Illinois Section of Civil Engineers and as a director of the national organization.

I was also asked to report to Professor William Rayner, head of surveying, for assignment to teach a surveying course, known as Civil Engineering 15, for students who were not in the civil engineer curriculum.

At that time nearly all of the civil engineering faculty had offices in Old Engineering Hall, where the Dean of the entire College of Engineering also had his office. I was assigned an office on the fourth floor, vacated by a professor in the Army Reserves who had been called to active duty.

The surveying class contained a diversity of students with wide interests and ambitions. There were several excellent students, including Jerry Dobrovolny in the mechanical engineering curriculum. Jerry stayed in the U. of I. academic world, later becoming head of the General Engineering department. We remain friends, and he has often reminded me that the reason the students stayed long after my surveying classes ended was not because they wanted to gain more information from me, but because they wanted to see my beautiful young blond wife when she arrived in our car to drive me home.

Because of Walter's bridge design work in Kansas City, he adjusted readily to Professor Shedd's steel design course. Shedd's work experience with a New York bridge firm added a practical perspective to his teaching. He had authored two engineering textbooks, *Theory of Simple Structures* and *Structural Design in Steel*, used in both undergraduate and graduate courses at the University.

While enrolled in Professor Shedd's class, Walter wrote a technical article that he titled "Secondary Stress in Bridge Members Due to Their Own Weight." He explained:

The chord and diagonal members of a bridge truss are usually proportioned from a calculated combination of tension or compression without considering the stress in the member due to its own weight. Secondary stresses due to distortions of the truss

24

under loads are not usually considered if the depth of the member is less than one-tenth of its length. On the other hand, if this depth-to-length ratio is greatly decreased, it may be entirely possible that the stress due to the member's own weight should be considered.

He described a method for finding the stress resulting from the weight of a primary member, in terms of its length, radius of gyration, and depth. Impressed with its content, Professor Shedd advised Walter to submit the article to the American Society of Civil Engineers' *Civil Engineering* magazine, and it was printed in the "Engineers' Notebook" section of the March, 1944 issue—Walter's first published article.[1] (By that time, Walter was in the U.S. Navy, learning about airborne radar.)

"Many of the students in that first class of my graduate work became lifelong friends," he said.

The spring of 1942 is also memorable for another reason. Professional engineers in Illinois were trying to get legislation passed requiring the licensing of practicing engineers, and a group of them formed the Illinois Society of Professional Engineers. Professor Harold E. Babbitt, head of Sanitary Engineering in the U. of I. Civil Engineering department, became president of the new organization. He was internationally known in the field, primarily because of several textbooks that he had authored.

Professor Babbitt needed a secretary to handle some of the correspondence related to the fledgling ISPE and employed Sue to fill the position. I've always affectionately introduced Sue as the first secretary of the Illinois Society of Professional Engineers, and she doesn't hesitate to relate some interesting accounts of meetings in Professor Babbitt's office.

In 1943 the Illinois legislature passed the first law regarding professional engineer registration, but later the courts would declare the law unconstitutional. It became necessary to start over, and the legislation was accomplished by the time I returned from the Navy in 1946.

University salaries for graduate students and instructors were distributed over a twelve-month period, even though the work period was nine months. "There was no opportunity to obtain additional salary on campus during the summer months," Walter said, "so many of the Civil Engineering faculty sought summer work elsewhere."

The Kansas City firm that had hired Walter in 1941 offered a temporary summer position, and the Hansons' Champaign landlords agreed to hold the apartment for their autumn return. At Howard, Needles, Tammen & Bergendoff, Walter helped design the Harry S. Truman vertical-lift railroad bridge across the Missouri River at Kansas City. The project had received a high-level wartime priority, although some steel reinforcement bars in the concrete piers were salvage from other projects. "Those summer months of 1942 were most interesting, because I worked directly for Ernest E. Howard, senior part-

In 1942, when Walt Hanson joined the faculty of the University of Illinois, Engineering Hall (above) contained most of the offices of the civil engineering faculty, in addition to those of the Dean of the College of Engineering. Walt's first office was located on the top floor. When he returned in 1946, following military service, his office was more conveniently located on the second floor.

ner of the firm, on the design and plans for the railroad bridge. Sue and I have always remembered with gratitude that Mr. and Mrs. Howard invited us for dinner the night before we were to return to the U. of I. What a thrill for a couple of kids."

During the 1942-1943 school year, both students and faculty were leaving campus for military service; some were drafted and others volunteered. For the fall semester Walter was assigned to teach classes in engineering drawing and assist in upper-undergraduate civil engineering courses. "The classes were full of students who expected their draft notices any day, a situation certainly not conducive to concentration on classwork." In addition to teaching, he completed two courses in structural analysis and design taught by Professor Shedd.

Although most engineering faculty members were exempt from the draft process, Walter felt an increasing obligation for military service. After discussions with Sue, he met with a Naval recruiting officer and volunteered to join the U.S. Navy at the end of the spring semester. "I indicated to the officer that my preference for service was with the Navy Seabees. I made that request because I knew the Seabees, as the construction arm of the Navy, would be as close to civil engineering experience that I could possibly get while in service."

In July, University of Illinois President Arthur Cutts Willard sent a letter on Walter's behalf to the Office of Naval Officer Procurement in St. Louis, Missouri. Willard, former head of the University's Mechanical Engineering department, indicated his approval of Walter's decision "to join the Armed Services of his Country . . . with the understanding that he shall continue his services to the University until such date as he is called to active duty by the Navy."[2]

Endnotes

[1]   Pp. 114-15.

[2]   A. C. Willard to the Office of Naval Officer Procurement, July 19, 1943, Hanson office files.

In January, 1945, Walt Hanson, one of three airborne radar officers with Carrier Air Group 88, left San Francisco aboard the U.S.S. Antietam *for service in the Pacific. Upon completion of additional training at Hilo, Hawaii, Walt was reassigned to the Night Attack and Combat Training Unit (NACTU) at Barbers Point Naval Air Service, Hawaii, where he remained until the end of WWII.*

FIVE

Service as an Airborne Radar Officer, USNR
1943-1946

*For America, World War II began on Dec. 7, 1941, when Japanese planes bombed
Pearl Harbor. Americans who remember back to that Sunday can summon up the exact
moment when they heard the news, which shattered a Sunday afternoon listening to a
football game or a Sunday afternoon concert on the radio: We interrupt this broadcast to
bring you a special news bulletin. Pearl Harbor has been attacked by the Japanese.*

Norman Polmar and Thomas B. Allen, *World War II:
Encyclopedia of the War Years*

Having volunteered for military service in spring of 1943, Walter passed the physical examination at the Naval Recruiting Office in St. Louis, Missouri. In October, upon receiving his commission and orders, he wrote to Associate Dean Harvey H. Jordan of the University of Illinois Engineering Department, formally requesting a leave of absence from his teaching position.[1]

Included with the commission were orders for indoctrination as well as radar and communication training. Radar (Radio Detection and Ranging) had been developed in the 1930s as a method of "seeing" objects at night and in inclement weather; during daylight in clear weather, radar extended the range of sight. The ability to detect aircraft and ships by the reflection of high-frequency electromagnetic waves became a crucial technical development in the war.

Disappointed at not being assigned to the Navy Seabees, as he had indicated to his recruiting officer, Ensign Walter E. Hanson readily accepted the orders "and later was glad for the radar experience."

He was assigned to two months of indoctrination training at Fort Schuyler, New York. He and Sue traveled from Urbana, Illinois to Tulsa, Oklahoma, where she would remain with her family while he participated in the instruction program:

On October 5 I began a two-day train ride from Tulsa to New York. Proud to be wearing the Navy uniform, I was also somewhat uneasy to be entering an unknown phase of my life. Whenever we traveled by train during the war the passenger cars were filled to capacity with military men and women. Some were fortunate to have seats, but often we just sat on our luggage.

From Chicago to New York, I had a seat on the New York Central, and I was quite thrilled to see Grand Central Station for the first time. My destination, Fort Schuyler, was an additional fifteen or twenty miles by streetcar.

Fort Schuyler, which dated from 1833, was constructed on Throgs Neck, a narrow peninsula that extends from the southeastern Bronx into Long Island Sound. Named in honor of General Philip Schuyler of the American Revolution, the fort was built to protect New York from sea attack. It was garrisoned during the Civil War, then abandoned in 1870, and in 1934 transformed into headquarters campus for the New York State Merchant Marine Academy.

During World War II Fort Schuyler was converted to a military facility. Hanson recalled his arrival in October of 1943:

I was one of a hundred or more newly commissioned officers destined for service in various branches of the U.S. Navy.

We had drills on the parade grounds at Fort Schuyler. The platoon leader, who was as inexperienced as we, often led us frightfully close to the sea walls before giving the command "to the rear, march."

The entire company had unexpected air raid drills, involving practice evacuation of the barracks. Once I slept through the blaring of sirens, wakened by the

officer on duty: "Ensign Hanson, are you sick?" I immediately sat up in bed, and to my astonishment was alone in the barracks, except for the officer. He said, "Hanson, you're supposed to be out of here." Needless to say, I felt fortunate to receive no more than a mild reprimand for sleeping through the bomb raid alert.

After the Fort Schuyler training, each officer was assigned to preliminary radar school—at Princeton University, Harvard University, or Bowdoin College in Maine. Walter received orders to Princeton. Although the officers were required to live in a college dormitory during the four-month training, they were permitted off-campus on weekends. Sue rented an upstairs bedroom in a house owned by a

Walter and Sue relax during a weekend in 1943 at Princeton, New Jersey. Walt lived in the university dormitory in the background while attending the Navy radar school. Sue worked at the LaVake jewelry store and lived on Mercer Street across from Albert Einstein and his sister.

couple named Smythe on Mercer Street in Princeton. Mr. Smythe was a headmaster in a private boys school "and quite a pompous man," Walter recalled.

"Our classes did not commence at Princeton until after January 1, 1944," he said, "so Sue and I enjoyed Christmas and New Year's at Rockefeller Center and saw a Broadway play. We were two country kids in Times Square for the first time. What excitement!"

Most of the pre-radar class members were Naval officers with recent degrees in engineering, mathematics, or science. "The main prerequisite apparently was mathematics through integral calculus":

> I was the only civil engineer in the group, but that was immaterial, because most of the electronics was new to everyone. My course in elementary electrical engineering at Kansas State served me well, though, because I knew that, according to Ohm's law, current was equal to voltage, divided by the resistance. And, I learned that some of the mathematics Professor Shedd had taught in structural engineering at the University of Illinois applied equally well in the electrical and communications field. For example, the principle of superposition, Maxwell's law of reciprocity, and some of Coulomb's work were mentioned frequently.

Sue found a job at LaVake's jewelry store in Princeton, and the Hansons became friends with Mrs. LaVake and her son Myron. Sue accompanied Mrs. LaVake to New York to purchase diamonds, "which was quite an experience for a country girl, and along with the LaVakes we visited Atlantic City, where we ate raw cherrystone clams for the first—and last—time."

The Smythe house was directly across the street from the home of physicist Albert Einstein and his sister, Maja, at 112 Mercer Street. Einstein had joined the Institute for Advanced Study in 1932, located near the Princeton campus. With an endowment from philanthropist Louis Bamberger, the Institute continues its primary purpose of pursuing "advanced learning and exploration in fields of pure science and high scholarship."

> Often Sue and I observed Albert and his sister in their gray sweaters and flowing gray hair, enjoying their stroll on the sidewalk of Mercer Street. We never mustered enough self-confidence to introduce ourselves and have regretted our reluctance. I might have been able to ask Albert for help on my radar problems and various experiments, but fortunately I squeezed by on my own.
>
> Also at Princeton at that time were the British author and philosopher Aldous Huxley and his brother. Aldous wrote the controversial Brave New World a few years earlier. We would see the brothers at a neighborhood restaurant on Saturdays and Sundays.

Upon completion of the Princeton program, Walter reported on June 1, 1944 to the Massachusetts Institute of Technology in Boston for four months of advanced radar training. He and Sue rented a house in nearby Brookline "from a Miss Johnson, a schoolteacher and cousin of John F. Kennedy, who went to Cape Cod for the summer." MIT, which had begun radar research and experiments in the 1930s, provided the Navy with lecture and laboratory facilities in the Harbor Building in downtown Boston. Every month a new class of approximately 150 officers would begin Radar School, learning to operate and maintain advanced radar equipment.

Sue's younger sister, Freda, stayed with the Hansons after her husband, Bill Barbe, left for Europe as a navigator in a bomber squadron. Sue's older sister's husband, Truman Wester, came to Harvard as a new ensign to study pre-radar, as Walter had done at Princeton, and joined the Hansons on weekends. "So for a few months in the summer of 1944, Boston became a gathering place for a number of family members."

> *The four months in Boston were enjoyable for Sue and me in many respects. It was our first opportunity to see historic sites of the Revolutionary War. We also enjoyed canoe rides on the Charles River and the Boston Pops on the grass along the river. We read about the war in Europe and the Pacific, and we appreciated the contrast between our situation and that of the Marines and other military, for example, on Iwo Jima and other Pacific islands.*

Completing their MIT radar training, the officers were asked to choose a specialty in airborne, battleship, or submarine radar. Walter chose the airborne specialty:

> *I reported to Quonset Point Naval Air Station, Rhode Island, for assignment to a carrier air group. That assignment, to Carrier Group 88, did not come until December, so during the two months between Boston and Quonset Point, Sue and I rented a room in Warwick, Rhode Island. It was a restful period after the nine months of concentration at the radar schools.*
>
> *We took a bed-and-breakfast trip along the Delaware River between Pennsylvania and New Jersey. The October foliage was spectacular, just like what we had seen two years before in southern Illinois and Indiana. It was a good substitute for autumn in the Midwest.*

Carrier Air Group 88 formed and trained at Otis Field on Cape Cod, Massachusetts, a Naval Air Station adjacent to the Army's huge Camp Edwards training base. As a Radio-Radar Officer, Walter reported to Otis Field on December 11, 1944. He and Sue rented a summer cottage in West Falmouth, a few miles from Otis Field. "Sue's brother-in-law Truman Wester had just finished his pre-radar class, and his wife, Sue's sister Edna, had joined him in Boston. The four of us celebrated Christmas and New Year's on Cape Cod in our cottage equipped only for summertime living. Except for some frozen plumbing and subsequent water problems, our two months on Cape Cod were uneventful and enjoyable."

Carrier Air Group 88 consisted of four squadrons: fighter, fighter-bomber, dive-bomber, and torpedo. Walter was assigned to the group's commander staff, and in turn to the torpedo squadron. "Our training missions included navigation, communication, and practice bombing."

In January, 1945 Carrier Air Group 88 left Otis Field, assigned to further training at the Naval Air Station in Hilo, Hawaii. "Sue and I drove from Cape Cod to Tulsa, Oklahoma, where she planned to stay with her family while I was overseas. During our few days in Tulsa, we received the news that Sue was pregnant. She joined her sisters Edna and Freda, who were also at home awaiting babies while their husbands were in military service. Grandparents Roling never received appropriate credit for their caretaker contributions during those days."

Carrier Air Group 88 re-formed at Alameda Air Station near San Francisco, California. The air group was transported on the newly commissioned aircraft carrier *Antietam* to Pearl Harbor, Hawaii. "This was a memorable experience; I was amazed at the huge size of our *Essex*-class carrier *Antietam*. I'm sure that others had the same qualmish feeling as we passed under the Golden Gate Bridge to an unpredictable future."

Essex-class ships served as the Navy's primary mobile air striking force in the Pacific theater of World War II. Considered the "workhorses" of the war, each ship had steam turbines that could produce speeds of 32.7 knots. Most were at least 870 feet long and carried heavy armor and armaments, with crews of some 3,450 officers and enlisted personnel.

After disembarking Navy personnel at Pearl Harbor, the *Antietam* departed for the western Pacific war zone.[2] Walter and the other members of Carrier Air Group 88 flew in DC-3s to Hilo, where they trained until April, 1945. During that period, he was promoted from Ensign to Lieutenant (j.g.).

In addition to serving as a navigation bomber on the TBS (torpedo planes), he was assigned other duties by the air group commander, S. S. Percy, Jr. "The most un-enjoyable job was censoring all letters mailed by members of our Air Group. I quietly pondered whether my acceptance of that assignment and the quality of my work might have been reasons for my promotion. But it was also a joke among junior officers that if we lived long enough we'd all receive promotions."

Ensigns Truman Wester and Walter Hanson, brothers-in-law and both in radar schools in Boston, 1944, Truman at Harvard and Walt at MIT.

In April, Air Group 88 was ordered to combat in the Pacific, aboard the aircraft carrier *Yorktown*.[3] "It was then that I had a great disappointment. Commander Percy announced that only one of the three radar officers would accompany the group, which

Sue and baby Karen Sue, born September 28, 1945, in Tulsa, Oklahoma. Walt waited almost a month before receiving a letter from grandmother Lela Roling, that Sue and baby daughter were doing fine. Another four months passed before Walt was able to return home to meet his daughter for the first time.

meant that the other two would receive orders to other duty. I, being most junior, was not assigned to combat. Commander Percy explained that these were orders from Washington that he could not change."

Instead, Walter was transferred to Barbers Point Naval Air Station, a few miles from Pearl Harbor and Honolulu, assigned as an "airborne radar instructor" for the Night Attack and Combat Training Unit (NACTU). The air station, constructed in 1941, had become a busy hub of Naval aviation activity for forces amassed in Hawaii to carry the war across the Pacific.

In response to brutal Japanese kamikaze air attacks, the Navy ordered a fleet of twin-engine airplanes with advance-warning radar to find and destroy enemy targets at night and in bad weather. One such aircraft was the Northrop P-61, a huge, glossy-black carrier-based fighter plane. Known as the Black Widow, the P-61 was the first American plane designed specifically as a radar-equipped night fighter. The pilot could be directed to targets by radio communication and radar pictures from carriers and other ships.

Walter's responsibilities included training the pilots, radar operators, and gunners in operating and maintaining the P-61's air-intercept radar equipment. He continued that assignment for five months, until the Japanese surrender in September, 1945.

Christmas, 1945. Walt plays Santa at a party for the night fighter squadrons at Barbers Point Naval Air Station, Hawaii. The war had ended and very little military activity was being continued. Walt taught a G.E.D. course for enlisted personnel and reviewed an engineering textbook while waiting for transportation home.

The most anxious month of my military years was from mid-September to the first or second week in October, 1945. The war had ended, but I had not yet heard whether I had become a father in Tulsa, Oklahoma. I was told that there was very little mail delivery from the states, because all of the ships were carrying troops home. Finally, I received a long envelope from Sue's mother containing her letter that Karen Sue Hanson had been born on September 28, along with a beautiful picture of mother and daughter. All was well. I sat down and immediately wrote a letter to Karen—which was more for Sue than for Karen.

Once war ended in the Pacific, Barbers Point served as a demobilization center for more than six thousand military personnel. "Priority for transportation was arranged according to service time," Walter said, so he remained at Barbers Point until January, 1946. While there, he enrolled in an engineering correspondence course, and although he couldn't locate a book on structural engineering, he found one on aircraft structures, "my introduction to what civil engineers today call LRFD design."

For Christmas, he helped arrange a special celebration for the officers and enlisted men awaiting discharge. "I later learned that my original Air Group 88 had returned to the United States several months earlier. The crew suffered only one casualty, a fighter pilot who had been one of my good friends."

In January, 1946, after his ship arrived in San Francisco, Walter had a three-day rail trip to Chicago and on to Great Lakes Naval Training Station, north of the city. "I was discharged and left Great Lakes on February 3, then traveled by train to Tulsa, where, after more than a year's absence, Sue was waiting. Without a doubt, I thought that daughter Karen was the prettiest baby in the world."

Endnotes

1   Walter E. Hanson to H. H. Jordan, Oct. 15, 1943, Hanson office files.

2   The *Antietam* was en route to a combat zone when Japan capitulated in late summer, 1945. The ship operated in Far Eastern waters during the first years of the post-war era, returned to the United States in 1949, and was sold for scrapping in 1974.

3   The *Yorktown's* aircraft inflicted heavy losses in Pacific action and supported American troops in the Philippines, at Iwo Jima, and at Okinawa. After service in Korea and Vietnam, the *Yorktown* was decommissioned in 1970 and is designated a National Historic Landmark, the centerpiece of a fleet of ships at Patriots Point Naval & Maritime Museum in South Carolina.

In 1949 - 1951, Ralph Peck, Thomas Thornburn and Walter Hanson collaborated to write the
Foundation Engineering textbook. They produced a second edition twenty years later.
Both editions of the book have been translated into many foreign languages.

SIX

From Graduate School to Associate Professor
At the University of Illinois
1946-1951

The design of a steel bridge or building presents a many-sided problem.
A successful solution requires a thorough study of the service the proposed structure is
intended to render as well as the layout and proportioning of the frame of that structure.

Thomas Clark Shedd, *Structural Design in Steel*

Foundation Engineers are responsible for joining superstructures, having great strengths
and reasonably known stress-strain properties, to their substructures, whose ultimate support
is either soil or rock, having large variations in both strength and deformation.

Therefore, we must strive to be wholistic engineers, possessing knowledge limited by neither
geotechnical nor structural specialization, but loyal to both. We must be geo-structural
engineers, or else we may design failures.

Walter E. Hanson

While at Barbers Point, Hawaii, in late 1945, awaiting transportation to the States, Walter corresponded with Professor Whitney Huntington, head of the University of Illinois Civil Engineering department in Champaign/Urbana. "My graduate work had been cut short there when I entered the service in 1943," Walter explained. He had also received a letter from Reben Bergendoff, partner in the Kansas City bridge engineering consulting firm where Walter had worked before entering graduate school.

Both Huntington and Bergendoff expressed interest in Walter's returning, and he contemplated which offer to accept. "I didn't make up my mind," he said, "until I talked to my wife, Sue, who was still in Tulsa with our six-month-old daughter, Karen, whom I hadn't seen yet. Sue and I agreed that we would return to the University of Illinois, so that I could finish the master's degree":

One problem in Champaign/Urbana at that time was housing for the influx of veterans that were coming back to school, some as students, some as faculty members. For two months I roomed with a professor friend and his wife in Urbana until Sue and I found a small house to purchase at 709 South Grove Street. We moved in with our baby daughter and stayed for more than five years.

Returning to the University, Walter was pleased to learn that Professor Huntington had arranged an assistant professorship position for him. "I was surprised, because I hadn't yet finished my master's degree," he explained. "I was also permitted to continue my graduate studies while teaching, so I enrolled in the remainder of Professor Thomas Shedd's graduate courses, C.E 106 and 108":

All through my master's work, my advisor was Professor Shedd, and half of my classes toward my master's degree in structural engineering, a special discipline of civil engineering, were taken from him. He was a great teacher, both in academics and application of theory in practice.

I met with the head of the electrical engineering department to discuss my Navy airborne radar experience in the Pacific, as well as my education at Princeton University and MIT before I went overseas. He decided that I was eligible for one unit of graduate work in

Walter and Sue Hanson's first home ownership, South Grove, Urbana, Illinois. The house was purchased in 1946 with the benefit of the G.I. loan when Walt returned from military service to resume graduate studies and teaching at the University. It remained their home until 1951 when they moved to Springfield, Illinois.

electrical engineering, which turned out to be beneficial as far as completing my master's degree work.

I may be the only individual who received a master's in civil engineering with one unit of credit in electrical engineering, while also teaching in three different departments: general, aeronautical, and civil engineering. Some of my civil engineering teaching consisted of help to the more senior professors in their courses.

We had large classes of veterans under the G.I. bill. They were excellent students, some of whom had been in my classes before we went into service. There was a great bonding among the students and the faculty who returned to the University after the war.

While continuing his graduate studies in structural engineering, Walter did independent study in foundation engineering under Professor Ralph B. Peck, renowned in the field of geotechnical engineering. "From 1947 to 1951," Walter wrote in a later testimonial to Peck, "I was the structural engineer in Ralph's geotechnical team. It was my privilege to teach courses in both structures and foundations to junior and senior students of civil engineering. During the summer months I worked with Ralph on consulting jobs."[1]

In August, 1947, after obtaining the master's degree in engineering, Walter wrote a lengthy report published in the 1947 *American Yearbook*, describing structural engineering projects throughout the United States. "Professor Huntington had written for the *Yearbook* in several previous years, and I think he just wanted to get out from under the responsibility. But it was good experience, and I didn't hesitate to accept the assignment."

With encouragement from Huntington and Shedd, Walter also wrote several discussions for the *Transactions of the American Society of Civil Engineers* and was appointed chairman of the departmental monthly faculty meetings. "The entire faculty would get together for dinner," Walter said of the monthly meetings, "and then one of the faculty or a visitor would make a brief presentation":

> For one of the programs, I asked Professor Nathan Newmark of the Civil Engineering department to discuss the engineering research that was being done at the University for the state highway department and other clients. Professor Newmark was head of structural research in the civil engineering department, with an interest in electronic computation.
>
> Since I had had radar experience in the Navy, I knew something about electronics and microwaves. That gave me enough nerve to ask Newmark to talk about what might be the future in the use of this new computing technology to solve complicated engineering problems.
>
> Nate stood there before us and showed how a person could express a quantity in the thousands in the binary language of zeros and ones. Then he solved a simple problem or two in the binary system. We were amazed!

Newmark was among the engineering, physics, and mathematics professors who promoted the University's involvement in computer development and use. In 1948 the Board of Trustees appropriated $150,000 for the purchase of a computer from Reeves Instrument Company of New York. As chair of the digital computer laboratory, Newmark headed a committee to deal with the new project, but by the end of the year they determined that Reeves could not meet the contract terms.

A computer designer at the Institute for Advanced Study in Princeton, New Jersey, suggested that the researchers at Illinois build their own computer. In the early 1950s, Newmark and the Illinois team succeeded in designing the first ILLIAC computer, "whose combination of speed and memory was unmatched in the world," according to a University historian.[2] That achievement marked the beginning of applying computer science to engineering and establishment of the new digital computer department.

1947, Sue Hanson and daughter Karen, dressed for Easter Sunday services at First Presbyterian Church in Urbana, Illinois.

Faculty colleague William J. Hall credited Newmark with attracting young students to the field of civil engineering. "There grew up around him," said Hall, "one of the most active research centers in civil engineering in the country."[3]

Walter and Sue became friends and bridge partners with Newmark and his wife, Anne. Walter also had a close professional relationship with Professor Peck and Professor Thomas H. Thornburn, both members of the soils and foundation (now called geotechnical) engineering section of the civil engineering department. Along with colleague Karl Terzaghi, Peck had recently completed the textbook *Soil Mechanics from Theory to Practice*. Thornburn taught classes on rock mechanics, soil stabilization, soil testing, and soil mapping. Peck, Hanson, and Thornburn developed a course dealing with soil mechanics and foundation engineering, and in June, 1949, signed a contract with John Wiley & Sons Publishing Company to produce the work in textbook form.

Peck taught the first course, in September, 1949, from his and Thornburn's mimeographed notes, handed out as the semester progressed. Walter assisted with the example designs and proofreading the notes, sometimes lecturing in class, grading the student quizzes and examinations, and participating in developing the book. "I suspect that the main reason I was asked to participate was because of my definite interest in the structural aspects of the foundations of civil engineering projects":

One of Ralph Peck's most important original decisions regarded the organization of the book. He decided that it would consist of four parts, with the introductory material in Part A and the descriptive material in Part B—covering types of foundations and methods of construction. Part C would be devoted to the selection and proportioning of foundations, in chapters according to particular soil types. In my opinion, that was a logical organization of material that no other author has undertaken. Part D would be devoted mainly to the structural aspects of various kinds of foundations.

During the summer of 1949 I spent considerable time in helping develop the chapters and the design plates in Part D, as well as all of the design plates dealing with the proportioning of foundations in Part C.

The typescript was completed by fall of 1950, and while the book, titled *Foundation Engineering,* was being prepared for publication, the authors contracted with a small publisher in Champaign to produce two spiral-bound volumes for use in their courses that semester. The booklet covering Part A was titled "The Properties of Subsurface Materials," and the one for Parts B and C was divided into "Types of Foundations and Methods of Construction" and "Selection of Foundation Type and Basis for Design."

Dr. Peck recently recalled the circumstances of their developing the textbook:

While Walt Hanson was in the armed services during World War II, I had come to Illinois and was developing an elementary course in foundation engineering based on the relatively new field of soil mechanics. Several of the younger faculty members were interested in teaching the course, but their background was in structures and they did not share my interests in the soil mechanics aspects. When Walt returned, however, he was greatly interested. We arranged that he would spend a summer working in the soils laboratory and participating in consulting activities.

The principal project at the time was a vertical lift bridge for a railroad in Cleveland. This type of structure had two towers, one on each side of the river with a bridge span supported by cables that passed over large pulleys at the top of each tower. This project was to determine the appropriate foundations for the two towers. Walt set up the soil boring program, examined and described the samples, conducted tests and concluded that the most appropriate foundations would consist of long timber piles founded in the relatively stiff clay located near the bottom of the bedrock valley. He conducted the required consolidation tests, made the estimate of settlements, and essentially designed the foundation.

The bridge engineer for the railroad was not satisfied. He felt that the structure should rest on concrete piers extending to bedrock. He doubted the validity of the calculations that indicated that the settlements would be moderate and quite acceptable. The railroad was not paying for the bridge, and the engineer seemed to be making unreasonable demands. He called for a meeting in Cleveland that Walt and I attended and to which he had invited Shortridge Hardesty, partner in the firm of

Waddell and Hardesty, the designer of the bridge itself. He had invented the vertical lift bridge and had seen it established as a very economical and useful type of structure. When the bridge engineer made his presentation, concluding that deep foundations were necessary to avoid undesirable differential movements, Hardesty pointed out that the tall steel towers of such bridges were subjected to daily cycles of movements of the sun as it first shone on the east side of the towers, then on the south side, and finally on the west side in a daily pattern. These movements were substantially greater than the calculated settlements of the structure, but they did not cause any difficulty in the operation of such bridges. Hardesty concluded that Walt's timber pile design was perfectly adequate.

The unique feature of Foundation Engineering *was its amalgamation of soil deposits (Tom Thornburn's specialty), soil mechanics (my specialty), and structures (Walt's specialty). Without Walter's skill in structures and without his willingness to immerse himself in soil mechanics over that critical summer, the book would not have happened.*

In mid-1950, Walter prepared a discussion essay to a paper written by a University of California civil engineering professor, "Successive Approximations for Beams on an Elastic Foundation." Walter supplemented Professor E. P. Popov's analysis with a discussion of potential pitfalls when using the author's method for analyzing foundations on soil. Both Popov's paper and Walter's discussion were published by the American Society of Civil Engineers.[4]

Walter's contract for the 1950-1951 class year at the University of Illinois indicated his promotion from assistant professor to associate professor, with tenure. In addition to his scheduled University classes, he taught several extension and refresher courses in Champaign/Urbana as well as other locations in the state:

Several of those courses involved engineers from the Illinois Division of Highways. I traveled to Carbondale, headquarters of Highways District 9, to teach an elementary course on foundation engineering, describing some of the up-to-date methods for taking soil borings and using data from laboratory tests for design.

I would teach a class in Champaign/Urbana in the morning, then drive 200 miles to Carbondale, teach there in the evening, stay overnight, get up very early the next morning and drive back to Champaign/Urbana in time for my afternoon class. Those were long days, but they were very satisfying.

The refresher courses, which I taught in Champaign/Urbana and once in Chicago, were for engineers who had accomplished the necessary practice requirements for professional registration but had never taken the examination. The courses provided a review of material covered in the exam.

In both 1950 and 1951, Walter was honored by the student organization "Illinois Technograph—The Engineering Council." He received the majority of student votes for the most effective teacher award. "This recognition was one of the best and most significant that I received in my teaching career. I was proud to be considered the 'most effective instructor' of civil engineering in the judgment of students, even though some of the other professors may not have agreed."

In addition, students of the Chi Epsilon engineering fraternity elected Walter an Honor Member of the chapter. Appreciating the award, he attended the meetings and participated as a chapter trustee for a number of years.

Endnotes

[1] John Dunnicliff et al., eds., *Judgment in Geotechnical Engineering; The Professional Legacy of Ralph B. Peck*, New York: John Wiley & Sons, 1984, p. 8.

[2] R. A. Kingery, R. D. Berg, E. H. Schillinger, *Men and Ideas in Engineering; Twelve Histories from Illinois*, Urbana: University of Illinois Press, 1967, pp. 112, 116.

[3] In 1981 the University of Illinois officially renamed the civil engineering building the Nathan M. Newmark Civil Engineering Laboratory. Richard G. Weingardt, *Engineering Legends; Great American Civil Engineers*, Reston, VA: American Society of Civil Engineers, 2005, p. 129.

[4] ASCE *Transactions*, Paper 2457, Vol. 116, 1951.

*1952 condition of the suspension bridge over the Kaskaskia River at Carlyle, Illinois.
The bridge was built in 1859 on the old Vincennes Trail which connected Indiana to Missouri. By 1924,
most of the traffic had been diverted onto newly constructed highways, of which U.S. Highway 50 was one.
In 1952, when Walter Hanson was the Illinois Engineer of Bridges, this old bridge received its
first restoration to a pedestrian bridge and was renamed the General Dean Memorial Bridge.
Photo courtesy of the Abraham Lincoln Presidential Library, Springfield, Illinois.*

*The General Dean Bridge has received additional restorations since 1952. As shown above, it represents a significant
part of a park development and is listed on the National Register of Historic Places.*

SEVEN

From Academia to State Government
As Illinois Bridge Engineer
1951-1954

There can be little doubt that in many ways the story of bridge building is the story of civilization. By it we can readily measure an important part of a people's progress.

Franklin D. Roosevelt

While on the civil engineering faculty at the University of Illinois, Walter obtained Illinois licenses as a professional engineer and as a structural engineer. His P.E. license was issued in 1946 by a "grandfather clause" based upon education and experience prior to passage of the state law. In 1951 he passed the S.E. written examination with a grade of 93.

Through teaching extension courses around the state, Walter had become acquainted with engineers at the Illinois Division of Highways, the largest division in what was called the Department of Public Works and Buildings, in Springfield. One of the division employees was bridge engineer George Birch, with whom Walter served on a committee of the American Society of Civil Engineers.

Professor Ellis Danner, who headed the highway engineering section of the civil engineering department at the University, learned of Birch's pending retirement in the summer of 1951. Danner encouraged Walter to apply for the position and arranged an interview in Springfield with the Division of Highways' chief engineer, Frank N. Barker, and his assistant, Elmer Knight. "Following that interview," Walter recalled, "I was offered the job as successor to George Birch, who had been the bridge engineer since 1917. It was a difficult decision, because I was certainly well satisfied in the academic world, but I did have a strong desire to return to the practical world, similar to the work I had done in Kansas City ten years earlier."

He accepted the position, which the Illinois Society of Professional Engineers an-

Illinois River Bridge, Beardstown, Illinois.
First major bridge built during Walter Hanson's tenure as Engineer of Bridges, 1951-1954.

nounced in its monthly newsletter. "Mr. Hanson has many friends among the students and alumni of the Department of Civil Engineering, University of Illinois, and all of his friends both in and out of the Society wish him every success in his new undertaking."[1]

Sue and Walt Hanson stand proudly in front of their first home in Springfield from 1951-1957, 1917 Whittier Street.

The Hanson family moved from Urbana to Springfield during Illinois State Fair Week, in August of 1951. "I remember the 90 degree temperature, no air conditioning in the car, while we slowly progressed to the fair, which of course we weren't interested in attending at that time." The Hansons purchased a small house at 1917 South Whittier, just north of Ash Street.

At the time of Walter's appointment, with Illinois Governor Adlai E. Stevenson supporting a massive road-building program, the General Assembly passed two bills that increased motor fuel taxes and truck license fees to fund the new construction. In 1951 the State Division of Highways awarded road construction contracts that exceeded $44 million.[2] The initiatives would increase substantially over the next few years, with Walter's bridge group assuming responsibility for the state's nearly 1,300 primary, county, and township bridges, as well as traffic structures:

> *I reported to the fifth floor of the Centennial Building (now called the Howlett Building), where many of the employees of the Division of Highways were located. Others were at the District 6 office on Ash Street.*
>
> *I was a pretty naïve thirty-five-year-old college professor, now more or less responsible for all the bridges in the state of Illinois. That meant not only a lot of bridge design but also approval of the bridges that were designed by private engineering firms for cities and counties. Any new, proposed bridge had to pass through my office for approval. I had a good assistant, Robert Murphy, who had been working in the Division of Highways for a number of years, along with twenty-five or thirty other engineers and technicians in the bridge section. They were most cooperative and helped me feel my way.*

Walter's first assignment was to accompany the assistant chief highway engineer to Chicago. "There were some problems during the construction of a new bascule bridge across the Chicago River. I met some of the city's and Cook County's good qualified, experienced bridge engineers. And during my tenure in the position, I became better acquainted with many Chicago engineers, a number of whom came to be personal friends."

> *When I became bridge engineer, there was a general feeling within the bridge section and throughout the entire Division of Highways that some reorganization was necessary. During the first month or two we worked out a reorganization establishing five groups within the section: bridge planning, bridge design, shop inspections, inventory and ratings, and outside plans review. For all that we needed to do, the work had to be pretty well organized as far as responsibility and authority.*

To assist in the division, Walter hired Tien H. Wu, a recent University of Illinois engineering Ph.D. "I asked him to design and supervise an embankment stabilization project near LaSalle, Illinois, on Route 51. We accomplished the stabilization by sand drains and installed numerous settlement platforms to monitor the rate and amount of settlement. That was the first use by the state of Illinois for staged embankment construction and sand drains for subsoil stabilization." Dr. Wu later became head of geotechnical engineering at Ohio State University.[3]

One of Walter's most interesting projects was restoration of an early American suspension bridge that spanned the Kaskaskia River near Carlyle, on the old Vincennes Trail from Vincennes, Indiana to St. Louis, Missouri. The small bridge, with a 12-foot wide, 264-foot span, was built in 1859. Although most traffic was diverted in 1924, the bridge remained in a badly deteriorated condition.

In 1951, after the Historic American Buildings Survey recommended preserving the dilapidated span, the Illinois General Assembly appropriated $20,000 for rehabilitation work. Walter and his staff designed the conversion to a pedestrian bridge, reducing the bridge deck to six feet and adding new cables. On Veterans Day, 1953, officials dedicated the structure, renaming it to honor Korean War hero and Carlyle native General William F. Dean. The bridge is now listed on the National Register of Historic Places.[4]

Walter and others on his staff also implemented new methods of soil exploration and testing, which they used extensively for designing foundations. "That resulted simply because of my involvement at the University of Illinois, testing and teaching classes and even writing the *Foundation Engineering* textbook."

He reviewed galley drafts of the text while bridge engineer in Springfield. "I returned to Urbana several times to continue the final work on the galley proof. One such trip was during Christmas vacation in 1951, when Sue, Karen, and I were guests of the Pecks. Ralph and I worked on the book, while our families enjoyed the more common festivities of the season."

Published just prior to the 1953 fall semester, *Foundation Engineering* became widely adopted by engineers in practice as well as in academia. Authors Peck, Thornburn, and Hanson defined the book's purpose as an introduction for the undergraduate student

> to the field of foundation engineering and to provide him with the ability to investigate and evaluate subsurface conditions, select the most suitable types of foundation for a given site, judge the performance of each type in service, and design the structural elements of the type finally selected. Where soil mechanics contributes to these purposes it is introduced, but it is nowhere presented merely for its own sake. Experience in the classroom has indicated that this approach develops in the student an excellent comprehension of the successful practice of foundation engineering.[5]

As Illinois bridge engineer, Walter supervised the design and construction of bridges using welded steel girders. The first was located at Lake Decatur, across the spillway of the dam. Another first in Illinois was a post-tension concrete bridge in Montgomery County, about a half-mile east of U.S. 66 (now Interstate 55), near Litchfield.

> We took one of the beams to Talbot Laboratory at the University of Illinois and tested it until we were satisfied that they would safely support the design loads.
>
> After the bridge was built, the county engineer, Jake Whitlock, and the consulting engineer firm arranged for a dinner at a nearby church to celebrate the dedication of this first post-tensioned concrete bridge. Jake had been one of my students at the University of Illinois.
>
> I don't think many post-tensioned concrete bridges have been built, because they require a lot of field work to carefully gauge the tension in the cables and reinforcements.
>
> Then we began using precast concrete bridges. The beams were built in a casting yard and allowed to cure. The tensioning of the reinforcement was introduced before

the concrete beams were cast and allowed to cure. After a few weeks they were hauled to the site and placed on the piers and abutments.

During his tenure with the state of Illinois, Walter wrote several papers that he delivered at professional meetings. In 1952 he presented "Developing of a Bridge Maintenance Program for Highway Bridges" at an annual highway conference held at the University of Illinois. With the focus of his division on new bridge construction, he expressed the critical need for a long-range program to maintain existing bridges within the state.

One of his most extensive writings, on bridge girders, began while he was teaching at the University of Illinois. Later, Wallace F. Wiley, an engineer in the Bridge Office, became interested in the subject and assisted Walter in developing the final typescript. "That paper," he said, "entitled 'Constant Segment Method for Analysis of Nonuniform Members,' required many hours, at night and during vacations. It was published by the American Society of Civil Engineers in 1956, and was considered favorably by a number of structural engineers, including the bridge group of the Federal Highway Administration. I was told that the paper was used as the basis for developing their first computer program to analyze bridge girders having non-uniform cross section."[6]

Endnotes

[1]   *The Illinois Engineer,* Oct. 1951, p. 3.

[2]   *Illinois Blue Book, 1951-52,* pp. 554-56, *1953-54,* pp. 594, 597.

[3]   Hanson communicated frequently with Wu at Ohio State University, and in the mid-1990s they collaborated on a paper, "Uncertainties in the Geologic Environment," published in the Nov. 1997 issue of *Journal of Geotechnical and Geoenvironmental Engineering,* pp. 1083-1084.

[4]   David Plowden, *Bridges: The Spans of North America,* New York: Viking Press, 1974, p. 121.

[5]   *Foundation Engineering,* New York: John Wiley & Sons, 1953, p. x. By 1966 the textbook was in its eleventh printing, and the second edition was published in 1974. The book has been translated into many languages, including Russian, and the latest (1997), Indonesian.

[6]   ASCE *Transactions,* #2842, Vol. 121, 1956.

*Interchange of Kansas Turnpike south and east of Wichita. During the first six months of
W.E. Hanson & Associates (1954-1955) the new firm worked with Wilson & Company to design the bridges
from Wichita to the Oklahoma line. Walter traveled the Kansas Turnpike often between Kansas City
and the U.S. 75 interchange in subsequent years to visit family and friends in Lyndon, his hometown.*

EIGHT

Birth of W. E. Hanson & Associates
1954-1955

*Though most of America's more than half a million highway bridges are small and anony-
mous, they may not be any less important to the local traffic than the Golden Gate and
Brooklyn bridges are to their hordes. . . . Every bridge, small or large, is also an aesthetic
and environmental statement. Its lines are important beyond its span; every bridge must not
only bear its burden, whether cows or coal trains, but must also be able to withstand the
burden of proof that, in the final analysis, society is better served, tangibly and intangibly, by
the bridge's being there at all.*

Henry Petroski, *Engineers of Dreams*

Working as bridge engineer for the Illinois Division of Highways, Walter in August, 1954, received a telephone call that within a matter of a few months would lead to a new career—the formation of a consulting engineering firm that specialized in bridge design.

The phone call came from his Kansas State College roommate and close friend, Bruce Roberts. "After graduation in 1939 we became widely separated in quite different types of jobs," Walter said. "Bruce became a county engineer in western Kansas and I was a member of a seismograph crew in Texas and Oklahoma. During World War II we both volunteered for the Navy. After the war, Bruce accepted a position with Wilson & Company in Salina, Kansas, and by 1954 had advanced to senior partner."

Exchanging greetings over the telephone, Bruce then asked Walter whether he intended to remain in his position with the State of Illinois. When Walter replied that he hadn't given much thought to any other job, Bruce went on to explain that Wilson & Company had just signed a contract with the Kansas Turnpike Commission for design of the turnpike from Wichita to the Oklahoma state line. With the project including fifty-six bridges, Bruce suggested that Walter return to his home state of Kansas to head a bridge section in the Wilson firm. "I told Bruce that his offer was most interesting and that I would call the next day with my response."

He and Sue spent a sleepless night discussing the proposal, then decided that they were too deeply rooted in Springfield and Champaign/Urbana to relocate as a family to Kansas. Nine-year-old Karen was about to begin fourth grade, and the couple had made many friends in Springfield, both professionally and at the westside Westminster Presbyterian Church.

They agreed that he could commute to Kansas to work with Wilson engineers on the Turnpike bridges. Further, Walter wanted to invite two of his former University of Illinois students, Roland D. "Dean" Collins and Marcus J. Rice, both then state bridge designers, to join in forming a new engineering company in Springfield. He intended that the three would perform the Kansas work and eventually seek bridge contracts within Illinois.

"Walt and I got together and made plans," recalled Collins, who said that they telephoned Rice "to ask if he would be interested in joining us. Without a moment's hesitation, he said 'Yes.'" Walter knew that they would need at least six months for the Kansas work and would not have much time for other projects, "even with the help of three or four engineers at the Wilson company."

The following day Walter spoke again with Bruce Roberts, discussing the proposed new firm in Springfield. The two men, along with Wilson senior partner Nathan Butcher, agreed to meet in Kansas City to formulate terms between the two engineering firms.

On a hot summer day, Walter, accompanied by Sue and Karen, drove to Kansas City, where he, Roberts, and Butcher discussed terms for preliminary work, then signed an agreement that Walter's firm would design the Turnpike bridges.

Anticipating future work for his new firm, Walter prepared a formal paper to "1) set forth my qualifications to establish and head a consulting engineering firm in the fields of bridges, foundations, and other structures, and 2) justify the firm's chances for a successful business in these professional fields of structural engineering." He listed personal data and his professional experience, publications, professional affiliations, and described potential clients:

> The professional engineering fields of bridges, structures, and foundations are very specialized; however, the sources of business for a consulting firm in these fields are plentiful. The following list gives some of the prospective clients of the proposed firm.
>
> 1. Public agencies responsible for highway construction. These include states, counties, cities, and toll road commissions.
> 2. Consulting engineering firms in other fields and architects who have frequent need for specialized consulting services in these fields.
> 3. Other private companies, such as railroads, oil companies, contractors, and manufacturers of construction materials.

The original office of W.E. Hanson & Associates was located in two rooms on the second floor of a building at the corner of 4th and Capitol streets, Springfield. The building has long since been replaced by a modern structure housing the Illinois Association of Community Colleges.

> *The many contacts that I have developed throughout Illinois and in other states, as a result of my present position and my publications, would be invaluable in the establishment of a private engineering firm. These contacts include many governmental agencies as well as private companies.*
>
> *The 1954 Highway Act authorized an increase of some 75 to 80 percent in expenditures of federal aid to highways. This amount is exclusive of proposed toll road expenditures. Therefore, it is inevitable that in the future more bridges on all classifications of highways will be designed and built.*
>
> *At the present time there are no consulting engineering firms in Springfield specializing in the engineering fields of the proposed firm.*

Walter estimated income for the first year at $24,000, based on fees established by the Illinois Society of Professional Engineers and the American Society of Civil Engineers, with an additional $8,000 in special services fees. "Thus," he concluded, "the total gross income during the first year is estimated to be at least $32,000."[1]

For the Kansas Turnpike project, Walter traveled by train to Salina in October and remained there until the following January. On November 1, he, Collins, and Rice formalized their partnership agreement, under the name "W. E. Hanson & Associates." He would contribute 40 percent of needed cash contributions, with Collins and Rice each providing 30 percent.

The partners rented a small second-floor office in the Hagler Building, on the northeast corner of Fourth Street and Capitol Avenue in Springfield. Walter estimated $11,310 in office expenses for the first year, including rent and a part-time secretary at $100 per month each.[2]

The Kansas project involved bridge designs for a 52-mile segment of the Turnpike, the first controlled-access highway in mid-America. Walter and his partners designed four-span continuous steel girder bridges with concrete decks and piers. He remembers one Turnpike bridge in Wichita that crossed over Oliver Street at a very large skew angle, requiring long haunched girders. To analyze the Oliver Street structure, he used the theory and procedures contained in his paper that had been published in the ASCE *Transactions* when he was the Illinois engineer of bridge and traffic structures.

The partners traveled to Kansas on Gulf, Mobile & Ohio and Missouri Pacific trains from Springfield to St. Louis, to Kansas City to Salina—a lengthy, tiring trip. Thus, in November, Walter recommended by memo to Collins and Rice that the firm purchase a company car. "After the first of the year," he wrote,

> *we will undoubtedly go on some kind of rotating basis for taking care of this job. If we could get a jitney for $500 or $600 that had some good miles in it, we could probably pay for about half of it by savings in transportation. It would come in mighty handy to the man here in Salina. Also, the man here could drive back to Springfield on Saturday and the next man could come back to Salina on Sunday or Monday. Why don't you look around a little to see what can be purchased for say $200 down plus monthly payments. Of course, if our account has grown, which I doubt, maybe you would decide to pay cash.[3]*

For a few days at Christmas, Walter joined Sue and Karen at Sue's parents' home in Tulsa. "During those three months, together with the Wilson engineers, we designed some fifteen to twenty bridges. At the same time, Collins and Rice were completing another four or five bridge designs in our Springfield office. Our daily rates of pay were very, very small, compared to today's salaries."

In January, Collins arrived in Salina to relieve Walter, who returned to Springfield. The three men agreed to purchase a used Chevrolet, and "Walt worked out a deal," Collins recalled, "where we would have two people in their Kansas office at all times. One of us would stay in Springfield, work on the project as time permitted and try to drum up work. One of us would stay for three weeks, with one person overlapping the first week and the other overlapping the last two weeks."

They alternated working in Salina through March of 1955. "I remember one weekend," said Collins,

> *Marc and I drove to Springfield for a bridge game on Saturday night and back on Sunday—a thousand mile weekend.*
>
> *As I remember, we were paid $2500 a month, which took care of office rent, miscellaneous expenses and a draw for the three of us. At the end of the project, the*

money was divided equally between the two firms, minus each firm's direct ex-
penses. We had a nest egg to start.
. . . The rest is history.

On completing the Kansas project, the partners returned to Springfield in the company Chevrolet. "We were full of self-satisfaction for having completed the design and preparation of contract documents for the fifty-six bridges, as scheduled," recalled Walter. "For several months through the summer of 1955 we were in intermittent contact with Wilson & Company during the letting of contracts and construction."

Through the ensuing years, engineers with the two firms continued working together on projects. The association would culminate in a formal joint venture in 1969, Hanson-Wilson, Inc., combining the surveying and transportation expertise of Wilson & Company engineers with the bridge design capabilities of Hanson engineers.

While working on the Kansas Turnpike, Walter and his partners had virtually no time to consider other projects. "However, several small engineering design assignments just seemed to walk in the door during that period. We were recognized as good bridge designers, and after the Kansas project was completed, we had to start promoting our qualifications in Illinois."

Endnotes

[1] Walter Hanson, "To Whom It May Concern," Sept. 1, 1954, Hanson office files.

[2] Hanson, "To Whom It May Concern."

[3] WEH to RDC, MJR, IMH, Nov. 27, 1954, Hanson office files.

Shoal Creek Bridge, located near Breese, Illinois, built in 1820, rests on its original native limestone piers following restoration of its superstructure in 1956. Located on the old Midland Trail between Vincennes, Indiana and St. Louis, the bridge served thousands of pioneers in covered wagons on their westward journeys. Today, it continues to serve county and township traffic.

NINE

Getting Established in Illinois
1955-1960

Bridges and dams are bound by a common heritage. Both are among the most visible and most important manifestations of civil engineering in our environment, and both are essential components of the public works foundation that supports America's transportation, electric power, agricultural and water supply systems.

Donald C. Jackson
Great American Bridges and Dams

After completing the Kansas Turnpike bridges in the spring of 1955, Walter and his partners, Roland D. Collins and Marcus J. Rice, returned to Springfield—and began planning for the future. "Although we had designed three county bridges in Kane County, Illinois, concurrent with the Kansas work," Walter recalled, "our backlog was essentially zero":

> *We recognized that our immediate future would be in structural engineering, mainly bridges, and probably with county governments in Illinois. But we also wanted to promote projects in the geotechnical area, such as dams and foundations requiring expertise in both below- and above-ground structures. So, we set up a crude soils laboratory, with only the fundamental and most inexpensive testing equipment available.*

Walter's experience as Illinois bridge engineer and as co-author of the *Foundation Engineering* textbook were assets in business development. He knew many of the county engineers on a first-name basis; in fact, he had taught several of them at the University of Illinois prior to and after World War II.

59

He and his partners traveled the state, meeting with the county and city engineers to discuss planned road and bridge projects. "Many county engineers were well qualified to perform the surveys and road plans," he said, "but they needed help on the bridge designs. Staff at the central bridge office in Springfield were pleased that we were working with the counties, because they had more than they could handle on the state and federal highways." Consequently, in the first year and continuing for a decade and beyond, the Hanson firm designed many of the county and township bridges in Illinois.

One of their first county bridge projects, in 1955, was a 200-foot three-span, steel-I-beam structure over the Little Wabash River in Wayne County. The consulting engineering firm of Marbry and Johnson held the contract, primarily for the surveying and road design, and subcontracted with Hanson for the bridge plans.

Two other early bridge projects were located in Macoupin County. One was handled directly by agreement with the county, and the other as subcontractor to Shepard, Morgan, and Schwaab, in Alton—a joint venture relationship that has been maintained for many years. "On some projects," Walter explained, "their firm was the prime engineer, and in other cases ours was the firm with primary responsibility to the client."

Walter continued his involvement in professional activities, serving in 1955 as president of the Central Illinois Section of the American Society of Civil Engineers. He represented the Section on the Illinois Engineering Council, a statewide association of some twenty professional engineering societies. In 1960, after election as IEC president, he would monitor bills in the Illinois General Assembly with potential impact on the engineering profession. When one of the IEC member associations withdrew over concern that it would lose its tax-exempt status, Walter helped the IEC attorney resolve the issue.

Donald D. Oglesby, who had joined the firm after high school graduation in 1955, worked part-time while pursuing civil engineering degrees at the University of Illinois. As business continued increasing, the Hanson partners agreed in 1956 to change the company name from W. E. Hanson & Associates to Hanson, Collins & Rice. They relocated the firm from downtown Springfield to a remodeled residence some ten blocks south, at 1622 South Fifth Street.

Later that year, Leo "Lee" J. Dondanville joined Hanson, Collins & Rice to begin his professional career with the firm and eventually to follow Walter as president and CEO. A civil engineering graduate of Notre Dame, he had been a University of Illinois master's degree student majoring in soil mechanics and foundation engineering under Professor Ralph Peck. He had also served in the Air Force in Alaska. "With Lee's arrival," said Walter, "we began to build a clientele of architects and engineering firms that needed soil mechanics and foundation engineering in connection with their design of above-ground structures."

In 1957, "Sue and I stretched our net worth to purchase a house at on Lake Springfield. That would be our home for the next thirty-two years. Then Karen and her family assumed ownership, and in 2005 it became the home of grandson David and his family, which includes our great-grandchildren, Jessica and James David ("J.D."). The comfortable and happy living for four generations is a memorable accomplishment for Sue and me."

Aerial view of the new home of Sue, Walt and Karen Hanson on Lake Springfield, purchased in 1957. It has been the location of many company picnics in addiiton to hundreds of family events. The property is presently the home of Walt's grandson David Pletsch and family.

One of Hanson, Collins & Rice's unusual projects was in Clinton County, a bridge north of Breese that spanned Shoal Creek. For more than a century, travelers crossed the bridge on the trail from Vincennes, Indiana to St. Louis, Missouri, but by the 1950s it was in serious disrepair and unsafe for traffic. The County Superintendent of Highways, James G. Cooney, asked Walter whether several "war surplus" steel I-beam girders the County had in storage could be used in rebuilding the bridge.

Precast concrete planks were designed for the roadway resting on the surplus girders, and workers repaired the original limestone piers that were anchored on bedrock. After completion of the project, Cooney reported, "Thus this 137-year-old structure has neither died nor faded away. Dressed in new outer garments, it looks forward to the wonders of a changing world and backwards to a glorious and fruitful past."[1]

In the fall of 1957, Nathan Newmark, then head of the University of Illinois Civil Engineering department and a longtime Hanson friend, arranged to meet with him in Springfield. Professor Thomas C. Shedd, Walter's university mentor and graduate school advisor, had recently died, and Newmark offered Walter the position of senior faculty member in the structural engineering section. "What a compliment," he recalled, "but we had recently hired Don Oglesby and Lee Dondanville. Our company was beginning to grow, and I have never regretted not accepting the University's offer."

Another engineer joining the Hanson staff at that time was John C. Casson, a graduate of the Massachusetts Institute of Technology. His prior work experience included mainly the design of municipal water systems. At Hanson, Collins & Rice, he became primarily responsible for structural and general civil engineering design and planning.

61

During the firm's first five years, Hanson, Rice & Collins contracted for fifty-one bridge projects in fifteen Illinois counties, either directly or by subcontract with other engineering firms. Five of the county and township structures were in Sangamon County, with more than fifteen bridges in neighboring Macoupin County.

In his first few years after leaving the position of state bridge engineer, Walter was reluctant to solicit contracts from the Illinois Division of Highways. "I believed it better not to leave the impression in anyone's mind that I had resigned with the knowledge that we would obtain future work from the state through friendships or political connections."

That situation changed in 1957, when Richard Schertz, engineer of design for the Division of Highways, contacted Walter about developing three twin-structure bridges between Collinsville and St. Louis. He enthusiastically agreed to do the work, "and our good professional relationship continues to this day with the now-named Illinois Department of Transportation."

During the presidency of Dwight D. Eisenhower in the 1950s, the federal government developed the Interstate Highway System, sometimes considered a national defense program. "One of our largest projects at the time evolved from that program," Walter explained, "the design of all the bridge structures on the new four-lane bypass highway around the east side of Springfield":

In the late 1950's the Hanson firm designed seven structures on Interstate 55 on the east side of Springfield. Shown above is a recent photograph of the structure that, in later years, connected I-72 to I-55.

They were designed to satisfy the new interstate standards regarding roadway widths and bridge clearances. Many of those bridges have since been widened to accommodate changes in traffic, but the basic structures, designed and built in the 1950s, still exist. That section of highway is now designated Interstate 55, and a portion of it carries both I-55 and I-72 traffic. It has been a personal privilege to have driven over and under these bridges for more than half a century.

When the Illinois Toll Road System was developed in the late 1950s, Hanson, Collins & Rice designed several bridges in the Des Plaines, area under a subcontract with Crawford, Murphy, & Tilly of Springfield. "I recall well the days that my good friend Pat Murphy and I spent in negotiation with the Toll Road Commission in Chicago. We were also consultants on problems encountered by other firms during the design and construction of some Toll Road projects."

Concurrent with their work on the Illinois toll roads, Hanson, Collins & Rice designed several bridges on the Edsel Ford Expressway in Detroit, Michigan, for Hazelet and Erdal, a Chicago consulting firm that held the prime contract.

Along with promoting their expertise in bridge design and construction, Walter and his partners began stressing proficiency in the geotechnical area. During the 1950s, the Illinois Department of Conservation implemented an extensive program of state dams, lakes, and park facilities. As bridge engineer earlier in the decade, Walter had become friends with Carl E. Thunman, chief engineer for the Department of Conservation.

Carl knew about our knowledge of Illinois geology and soil behavior, so beginning in 1956 we were employed by the state to perform soil and foundation reports for most of the dams in Illinois—twenty-two in the first five years of our firm. In several cases, we were assigned the design and preparation of plans for entire dam projects. Other times we were consultants only during construction.

The Department of Conservation (now the Department of Natural Resources) has remained a substantial client through the ensuing decades. I am confident in saying that our firm has been involved with the design and construction of more dams and lakes in Illinois than any other private engineering organization.

One project for the Department of Conservation was the design of a small dam near the restoration of the Mormon community at Nauvoo. The dam location presented difficult geological problems, which the engineers overcame by placement of impervious embankment materials against the abutments to prevent seepage. "The annual wine and cheese celebrations in Nauvoo," Walter said, "have made good use of the embankment as a stage and the field below the dam as a theater."

A unique Hanson, Collins & Rice project was completed for the University of Illinois Astronomy Department—planning and construction supervision for a radio telescope near Danville, Illinois. The fixed telescope rotated only as the earth moved, a design that in later years would be superseded by moveable antennas.

In 1956 and again in 1960 Hanson, Collins & Rice served clients in Illinois and Wisconsin, consulting on foundation problems on structures designed by the Frank Lloyd Wright architectural organization. The first occurred near Buffalo, Illinois, where the Michael Scully family had hired prominent builder Sam Lancaster to construct a farm home.

Excavating for the massive concrete foundation that would support a heavy fireplace and a sizable portion of the roof, workers discovered a deposit of soft peat. Upon examining the situation, Walter advised Lancaster either to continue excavating until he encountered better soil or to drive pilings that would provide the required support. The contractor decided on further excavation, "and the beautiful farm home still stands along Interstate 72, between Springfield and Decatur."

In Madison, Wisconsin, the city retained the Warzyne Engineering firm to review foundation plans proposed by the Wright firm for a large municipal building, to be constructed on fill material deposited on soft lake bottom formations. Warzyne engineers contacted Walter, who recommended that the building should be supported on piles driven to depths well below the soft material. "I believed that the Wright design would have resulted in excessive settlements throughout the structure. The building, known as Monona Terrace, was not constructed for another forty years, but it rests safely on several hundred piles."

One of the firm's largest building projects during the period was the structural design for an eleven-story addition to the Franklin Life Insurance Company headquarters in Springfield. A special feature was a deep basement, well below the water table, intended for document storage. "We started the project with a property survey and soil borings," Walter said, "then during construction installed a sump and associated special pumps. Hadley & Worthington of Springfield was the architectural firm on the building—the beginning of a long professional relationship between our two firms."

For construction of the Assembly Hall on the University of Illinois campus in 1959, Hanson engineers served as consultants on foundation issues to Ammann & Whitney, a renowned New York structural engineering firm. "It was a special privilege to be engaged on the Assembly Hall with them and the New York architect. A few years later we associated with Ammann & Whitney on several structures in Wisconsin for the Johnson complex of office and manufacturing buildings."

———————————•+◆+•———————————

During the mid-1950s, Walter made a temporary return to his educator role by assisting in the development of higher-education institutions in the state. In 1957 the Illinois General Assembly established the Commission of Higher Education to study the role and needs of colleges and universities and to make recommendations to the Governor and the legislature. Governor William G. Stratton, with endorsement by the Illinois Society of Professional Engineers, appointed Walter to the nine-member Commission:

At that time, the University of Illinois was in process of establishing a branch in Chicago that would include a college of engineering. Southern Illinois University was lobbying for a college of engineering at Carbondale, as well as a branch of the university at Edwardsville. Consequently, there was considerable friction between U of I President David Dodds Henry and SIU President Delyte Morris.

Since the state was also involved at that time in expansion of the community college system, there was a lot of activity and political discussion throughout the state dealing with higher education.

At the time of my appointment to the Commission, I was not aware that Governor Stratton had requested a feasibility study regarding an engineering college at Southern Illinois University. Because of my having been on the University of Illinois faculty, President Morris and his contingent immediately identified me as the "University of Illinois' member" of the Commission. There was no way in their minds that I would be a non-partisan member and would always be against an engineering school at Southern Illinois University.

Fortunately, I was a member of the Illinois Engineering Council, which represented societies dealing with all branches of engineering in Illinois. I also represented the Central Illinois Section of the American Society of Civil Engineers and the Illinois Society of Professional Engineers.

In November, 1957 the Commission of Higher Education chose Walter as chairman of its newly formed three-member Subcommittee on Engineering Education, to study and make recommendations for expanded engineering education in the state. The Illinois Engineering Council assisted the members with an advisory group of engineers from Chicago, Decatur, and Mount Vernon.

The Subcommittee compiled an "Engineering Education Questionnaire," mailed to high schools and colleges throughout the state and to more than fifty engineering colleges nationally. Subcommittee members also sent survey forms to the 5,500 members of the Illinois Manufacturers Association, requesting reports on their current and future utilization of engineers and engineering technicians. In addition, the Subcommittee held individual conferences with engineering college deans in Illinois and in other states that had more than one public engineering school.

At the conclusion of the year-long assessment, Walter reported the Subcommittee's recommendation advising that Southern Illinois University should establish an engineering school but that the immediate priority should be organization and expansion of the community college system throughout the state.[2] "Eventually, as expected," he recalled, "but after considerable heated debate and compromise, the Illinois General Assembly authorized an engineering college at Southern Illinois University."

During Walter's tenure on the Commission of Higher Education, the legislature approved the establishment in Springfield of both Sangamon State University and Lincoln Land Community College. "There was much pressure for the Springfield institution to become a branch of the University of Illinois at Champaign/Urbana, but a special committee of the Commission voted instead for Sangamon State University to be an upper-division institution governed by the Illinois Board of Regents." At that time, the Regents also governed Illinois State University, Northern Illinois University, and Eastern and Western Illinois universities. "The decision was based largely, in my opinion, on the fact that the Commission wanted to maintain a reasonable balance between the University of Illinois and Southern Illinois University." In 1995, Sangamon State did become a branch of the University of Illinois and was later expanded to a four-year institution—"a good decision," according to Walter.

The Commission of Higher Education completed its work in 1961. Governor Otto Kerner and the General Assembly approved the Commission's recommendation to create the permanent Illinois Board of Higher Education to help in the administration of Illinois' institutions of higher learning. "At my request, I was not appointed to the new Board," which continues today as the agency responsible for coordinating planning and programming at state universities.

———————————•••◆•••———————————

By 1960 the number of annual Hanson, Collins & Rice projects had increased to more than one hundred. Approximately one-third were either complete bridge designs or related bridge projects. Another third were soil and foundation reports, in the geotechnical area of expertise, and the remaining were miscellaneous civil engineering projects. Personnel in the firm, in addition to the original partners, had increased to ten, and plans were being made for a move to larger facilities.

By then, however, the three partners realized that they did not see the future through the same eyes. "Dean and Marc, who were outstanding structural engineers and expert bridge designers, were less inclined than I to diversify into other areas of civil engineering. I wanted to expand the geostructural area, which would mean increased work on retaining structures and underground structures associated with such construction as urban rail systems. I was also looking forward to our company serving as the prime contractor on more projects, rather than so often as subcontractor to a larger firm."

Regrettably, the partners also disagreed on some personnel matters and business decisions. Their solution was to divide the work in progress into thirds and create two separate engineering firms. The three men offered each of the employees a position in either company. "The day that we talked to all of our employees," Walter said, "was probably the most difficult in all of the days that I was in business."

Walter's partners formed the Collins and Rice engineering firm and in the ensuing years would work with him on joint ventures. Walter established as a sole proprietorship the Walter E. Hanson Company.

Endnotes

1   Cooney, "The Old Midland Trails and Its Shoal Creek (Illinois) 137 Year Old Bridge," Office of the Engineer, Clinton County, Illinois.

2   Record Group 555.000, "Illinois Commission of Higher Education," Illinois State Archives, Springfield.

Construction of AT&T's earth satellite station began in 1962 when Herb Burt, AT&T's chief engineer, and Walt Hanson inspected the site in Andover, Maine, and conducted a preliminary foundation investigation consisting of a geologic seismic survey. The antennas continue as part of a worldwide communications system.

TEN

Reorganization, Diversification, and Going National
1960-1974

Ever since the founding of the United States, leading civil engineers have been key in contributing to its progress. They have been involved in the creation and building of the nation's modern facilities, advanced engineering systems, and technological marvels. What civil engineers have done and continue to do adds value and makes every citizen's daily life more satisfying and productive. The products of an engineer's work are uplifting to the human spirit.

Richard G. Weingardt, *Engineering Legends*

Early in 1961 the new firm, Walter E. Hanson & Company, relocated to a new building at 1227 South Fifth Street. Hanson occupied one-third of the facility, with a materials laboratory in the basement. After a few years, Walter purchased the building and expanded into another third of the space.

Most of the Hanson, Collins & Rice personnel had chosen the new Hanson firm, including Lee Dondanville, who assumed management of the soil and foundation jobs. Jack Casson became responsible for bridges and other structure-related work. Robert Oglesby and Vince Schulte, both civil engineering graduates, had joined the company shortly before the reorganization.

The new firm's primary business involved the completion of projects initiated in previous years, including several county bridges and dams for the Illinois Department of Conservation. Within a few months, however, the number of new jobs began to increase rapidly.

A notable project in the first year of Walter E. Hanson & Company involved design work on the Red Mountain Expressway in Alabama. As subcontractor to Harry Hendon & Associates of Birmingham and Harlan Bartholomew & Associates of Memphis, Tennessee, Hanson engineers oversaw deep slope excavations of the road between Birmingham on the north side of Red Mountain and the communities of Homewood and Mountain View to the south. They also designed several grade separations and large retaining-wall structures along the Expressway near Birmingham.

"Of historical interest," Walter said, "is the fifty-five-foot cast iron statue of the Roman god of the forge, Vulcan. Known as the Iron Man of Birmingham, Vulcan represents the vision that built the city. The monument is second in size in the United States only to the Statue of Liberty."

Originally made for the 1904 World's Fair in St. Louis, Missouri, the Vulcan statue represented Birmingham and its iron foundries, then for years was displayed at the state fairgrounds in Birmingham. In 1935, with federal financial support, Works Progress Administration (WPA) employees restored the aging statue and placed it on a stone pedestal at the crest of Red Mountain.[1] "We were instructed by city officials," Walter recalled, "not to endanger Vulcan during construction of the Expressway."

Walter E. Hanson & Company engineers would return to Alabama several years later to design several interstate highway bridges near Montgomery, another joint project with Harlan Bartholomew & Associates.

In 1962, following Sue Hanson's father's retirement from the Midland Valley Railroad, her parents moved from Oklahoma to Springfield. For several years Earle Roling served as assistant office manager at Walter E. Hanson & Company, and then the couple relocated to Denison, Texas.

Also in 1962, engineers John M. "Jack" Healy and Eugene R. Wilkinson joined the Hanson firm, followed in 1963 by Richard W. "Dutch" Miller. All three had graduated from the University of Illinois, and all would have important roles in the company's growth and development. Healy and Miller, both geotechnical engineering majors, assisted Lee Dondanville. Wilkinson, who had been a student assistant in the civil engineering department, assisted Jack Casson in the steadily increasing areas of bridge and building design.

One of the firm's 1962 projects was a radar picket tower off the Georgia coast. Jack Healy was assigned with engineers from Raymond International to make borings in the Atlantic Ocean. Enroute to the construction site with seven other workers, about eight miles from Savannah Beach their 45-foot shrimp trawler took in water and sank in the predawn darkness.

From a distance, a pilot boat captain named George Henry saw a flare the men had made by setting ablaze a gasoline can, then was told that someone on another boat heard cries for help. Guiding his vessel to the area, he used searchlights in an attempt to locate survivors. One of Henry's crew "spotted the first man bobbing up and down in the choppy water," he later explained. "It was pitch dark over the water, the area was known for its monstrous sharks, a thunderstorm was approaching, and eight men were floundering helplessly in the sea."

Henry notified the Coast Guard, which dispatched three boats to the scene and rescued all eight workers. "The men who saved us were tremendous," Healy told a Savannah newspaper reporter. "Their procedure and the way they treated us was out of this world."[2]

AT&T Longlines

In the early 1960s, American Telephone and Telegraph Company began building microwave towers and underground coaxial transmission facilities connecting the entire United States, some projects directly, others indirectly, associated with national defense measures. University of Illinois Professor Ralph Peck, Walter's *Foundation Engineering* coauthor, recommended the Hanson firm as geotechnical consultant on the AT&T construction projects.

At the University in March, 1961, Peck, Dondanville, Walter, and several other engineers met with AT&T's chief engineer, Herb Burt. AT&T representatives later visited the Hanson office in Springfield, where the two firms signed an agreement that Walter E. Hanson & Company would assume geotechnical investigation responsibility for AT&T projects in all fifty states.

"That contract meant a great deal to our firm for years to come," Walter said. "The underground power-feed buildings were located approximately every hundred miles along the cable lines. Those buildings also served as bomb shelters, and our firm was responsible for recommending the safe soil pressure and seismic response that would resist the effects of a given-size bomb exploding a certain distance from the site, depending on the geological conditions at the site."

With the fear of a Soviet Union nuclear attack, the Distant Early Warning (DEW) Line across Canada was built in 1957, and the North American Air Defense Command (NORAD), headquartered at Ent Air Force Base in Colorado Springs, Colorado, was established. The NORAD facility controlled both American and Canadian air defense operations.

In the early 1960s the Department of Defense awarded contracts for a new NORAD Combat Operations Center, to be built within Cheyenne Mountain, south of Colorado Springs. The hidden complex would include fifteen buildings, housing the computers, communications equipment, and staff to watch for any pending attack. All of the buildings, some as tall as three stories, were designed to withstand the shock of earthquakes and nuclear explosion. The Hanson firm, as subcontractor to AT&T, received the contract to perform geotechnical work for the massive construction project.

"Our experience on the NORAD Combat Operations Center was memorable," Walter said. "The biggest problem was getting our rock-drilling rig to the top of Cheyenne Mountain, which we accomplished by helicopter. Our personnel, however, led by Lee Dondanville, had to climb the mountain by foot. Because of the terrain and altitude, the trek was both stressful and exhausting."

Construction began in May, 1961, and the $142.4 million facility attained full operational capabilities five years later, following transfer of the Ent Air Force operations to the Cheyenne Mountain complex.[3]

At East Branch, Utah, the Hanson firm provided the engineering services for an AT&T junction building near the "This is the Place" monument, honoring Mormon pioneers. "The AT&T site was on a bench of sand and gravel that had been deposited along the former shore of the Great Salt Lake," Walter recalled.

Behind the site and adjacent to the building was a steep slope of the Rocky Mountains, which required excavation to accommodate a portion of the building and the parking lot. I inspected the construction when the building was barely complete, and it appeared that the nature and extent of the excavation had created a dangerous instability of the mountain slope.

In order to get the attention of engineers in AT&T's Kansas City office, I reported that there was danger of losing the entire building from a mountain slide. After further inspections and deliberations, it was decided to reinforce the slope with rock bolts, providing additional safety for the building. Thus, I was able to again sleep at night, but I still worry about the building if a major earthquake were to occur near the site.

Another notable AT&T project, begun in 1961, was determining the subsoil and rock quality for the world's first earth-to-satellite station, at Andover, Maine. "We had just purchased a portable seismograph instrument in a small baggage case," Walter explained, "which also included a sledge hammer, and a steel plate about ten inches square. The new seismograph was not very effective at Andover because of the glacial boulders, but I have another lasting memory from that trip. My own bag, with a week's supply of clothes, was checked from Springfield to Portland, Maine, but was not on the airplane when I arrived. The bag was finally returned to Springfield several days after I was home—from working on this country's first commercial satellite station."

In 1962 the newly completed Andover Earth Station transmitted a live transatlantic television signal via the new TELSTAR satellite, launched aboard a Delta rocket from Cape Canaveral Air Force Station in Florida. Funded by AT&T and built at Bell Telephone Laboratories, TELSTAR became the first privately operated satellite to transmit not only television pictures but also telephone and high-speed data communications. Its success demonstrated the potential of today's worldwide commercial satellite communications system.

On subsequent AT&T projects, Hanson's portable seismograph equipment would create interest among fellow travelers. "At the San Francisco airport, where passengers waited for baggage at the bottom of a long conveyor, they watched as the seismograph gear slowly came down the belt. One man exclaimed, 'What the hell is that?' I doubt that we'd be permitted these days to carry such equipment on an airplane."

For a time in the 1960s, "AT&T carried us," Walter said. "One year our AT&T gross income was more than 40 percent of our total income. Our risks were reduced, however, because we had separate contracts for some of the projects." University of Illinois engineering professor Nathan Newmark served as a Hanson consultant on the AT&T work. An authority on seismic designs to resist earthquakes, Newmark was also a Cold War consultant to the federal government on bomb-resistant building designs.

The Hanson/AT&T affiliation would continue, involving approximately 1,800 projects during the next fifteen years.

Illinois Department of Conservation

In January of 1962, Walter received an emergency telephone call from Carl Thunman, Sr., chief engineer for the Department of Conservation. The new earth dam in the Washington County Conservation Area, south of Nashville, failed during initial filling of the reservoir. Several years earlier, the State of Illinois had purchased the large wooded tract, and Department staff made plans for construction of a 248-acre lake in the area between two small creeks. Hanson engineers prepared the soils and foundation report for the project, but had not been involved with final plans or construction specifications.

Thunman and Walter quickly drove the one hundred miles from Springfield to Washington County, to inspect the damaged dam and make recommendations for its repair. "After soil investigations of the embankment and foundation conditions," Walter reported that "the dam and spillway could be restored without risk of a recurring failure." Following his recommendations, contractors inserted needle beams through holes cut into the spillway riser and, after jacking the structure to its original position, they placed concrete grout beneath the base slab. Walter's report of the dam failure and repair procedures was later published in *The Military Engineer* magazine.[4]

In 1964 the Department of Conservation awarded Walter E. Hanson & Company the contract to design an earth dam on Big Branch Creek, in the Loud Thunder Forest

In 1962, a failure of the Washington County dam occurred during the initial filling of the lake. The repairs of the partial failures of the earthen dam and concrete spillway were supervised by Walt Hanson. The lake and park have served the public well for conservation and recreation since that time.

The beautiful Loud Thunder dam near Rock Island, Illinois, designed and supervised by Walter E. Hanson & Company, is unusual in two respects. The dam has no emergency spillway, and the primary spillway, designed to pass the maximum probable flood, was located on the earthen embankment. Staged construction was mandated to accommodate initial settlement of the embankment prior to construction of the concrete shute spillway.

Preserve in Rock Island County. Workers completed the 1,000-foot-long embankment, then, after about a year of settlement, constructed the concrete spillway and bridge, supported directly by the embankment. The impounded Big Branch Creek became the 167-acre Lake George. "The Loud Thunder construction was unusual," Walter recalled. "Because excavating through the high bluffs of the abutments was not feasible, the dam has no emergency spillway, and the primary spillway, which must pass the maximum probable flood, is located on the embankment."[5]

Company Reorganization

In 1964 Walter, Lee Dondanville, and Jack Casson agreed to incorporate the firm in the state of Delaware as a subchapter "S" corporation, to facilitate profit-sharing and distribution of ownership. Walter was elected president, with Dondanville and Casson as vice-presidents, and the three also served as the initial board of directors.

Still involved in cold-war defense construction, Hanson civil engineers Eugene Wilkinson, Robert Oglesby, and Norman Brown trained as "Certified Fallout Shelter Analysts" and designed civil-defense shelters for new buildings, especially schools. "By considering the need for shelter space early in the planning stage," they explained in

1964, "adequate protection can be provided by effective arrangement of the building layout and addition of mass to walls or roofs in locations that naturally lend themselves as protective spaces."[6]

In 1965 Hanson opened its first regional office, some seventy miles from Springfield in Peoria, Illinois. Wilkinson became director of company operations in the Peoria area, assisted by D. M Costello, a former Illinois Division of Highways district engineer. "The Peoria office was justified," Walter said, "by the amount of structural design that we were furnishing to the Peoria architectural firm of Phillips and Swager and Associates. That first branch office also served the county engineers in areas adjacent to Peoria."

In 1966 and 1967 the number of new jobs increased to more than two hundred annually, in addition to nearly the same number of AT&T projects. Major work included an addition to the University of Illinois Newmark Civil Engineering Laboratory, foundations for a sports complex in Puerto Rico, and construction of a Marriott Hotel in Massachusetts.

"Our first use of structural analysis by means of an electronic computer occurred in 1967," Walter said, "for a warehouse for Pabst Brewing Company in Peoria. The building was designed with a rather complicated frame":

> We contracted for access to the University of Illinois computer in the Civil Engineering Systems Laboratory, a room full of vacuum tubes. We had a direct line to their operators, engineers, and technicians, to help us analyze some of our projects and work out some of our problems. The University offered this service to engineers throughout the state. We had to pay a fee, which was expensive, but it was also a great learning experience.
>
> I talked about computer development with a young graduate student, Don Bartlett, who later came to work for us. I asked him to learn all he could about the subject, because I knew we would soon need to buy our own computers.
>
> Our first, in about 1974, was a "Prime" Computer, a 32-bit machine for scientific use; quite a number of engineering firms in those days purchased Primes. They were called minicomputers, not quite as large as the earlier ones with their huge vacuum tubes. We located our Prime in what we called the computer room, and each engineer had what was known as a dumb terminal at his desk, really just a monitor, connected to the Prime.

During most of the 1960s, the Hanson firm's only State of Illinois contract was for design of an underground parking garage in connection with restoration of the Old State Capitol in downtown Springfield. Using a system of hyperbolic paraboloids, Hanson engineers devised a unique structural roof for the two-level parking area. The three-year construction project was completed and dedicated in 1969.

75

The old Illinois State Capitol, built before Abraham Lincoln delivered his "House Divided" speech, was restored in the 1960's. The restoration project included a two-level underground garage below the building and surrounding yard and gardens for which Hanson Engineers devised a system of hyperbolic paraboloid slabs. The project received national recognition by the American Council of Consulting Engineers.

In the above photograph, from left to right, Walt Hanson, engineer, and Wally Henderson, architect, display the model to Springfield business leaders Franklin Schift and Al Myers. (© The State Journal-Register. Used with permission.)

"Our lack of state work was no doubt a blessing in disguise," according to Walter, "because it meant that we promoted and obtained most of our work from a more diversified clientele. At the same time, our projects for counties throughout Illinois kept growing, as did soil and foundation jobs for new clients across the country and even in Central America."

Hanson-Wilson, Inc.

Although their business continued to expand, Hanson officers realized that in order to design bridges for the State of Illinois and other states, the firm would need to assume responsibility for entire projects, including the road work. "In some cases," Walter recalled, "our bridge design was becoming only a small part of the entire project that the state was contracting to other private engineering firms."

Adjusting to the changing times, the Hanson officers in 1969 agreed to form a joint venture corporation with Wilson & Company in Salina. Thus, some fifteen years following the Kansas Turnpike work, the two companies combined the Hanson bridge-engineering capabilities with Wilson's surveying and transportation-engineering expertise. Hanson-Wilson, Inc. began receiving contracts from the Illinois Division of Highways and other clients for a number of sizable projects.

The Hanson-Wilson joint venture has continued through the years and today, from its headquarters in Kansas City, Missouri, is one of the largest providers of engineering services to the transportation industry.

The McCluggage bridge over the Illinois River at Peoria, Illinois was the first major project designed by the new Hanson-Wilson firm in the early 1970's. The complex traffic geometries were handled by Wilson & Company, while Hanson engineers designed the bridge structure, containing Illinois' first major curved steel-plate girders.

In 1968 Hanson furnished geotechnical services on a taconite (partially processed iron ore) storage facility for the Burlington Northern Railroad near Superior, Wisconsin. That began a relationship with the railroad on many projects, even after its merger with the Santa Fe line.

The year 1970 marked a significant expansion of Hanson and Hanson-Wilson projects. The firms received the contract for design of the McCluggage Bridge over the Illinois River at Peoria. Although Hanson engineers in the Peoria office were involved in the project, the truss designs were performed in the Springfield office, led by bridge engineer Nick Nicholson. He had joined the firm after retiring from the Illinois Division of Highways. "That was our first design of a curved steel-plate girder," Walter said, "as part of the approach to the bridge."

Another company first, in 1970, involved a section of the Washington, D.C. subway system, located under the Museum of the Arts. The Hanson firm was consultant to the contractor, Mergentime Corporation. "Charles Mergentime had formed the company following several years with Raymond International of New York, which had been our client on many jobs, including the AT&T towers and cable facilities. Our relationship with Mergentime's firm has continued through many years."

Hanson-Rodriguez, S.A.

Also in 1970, University of Illinois professor Don Deere suggested that Walter work with one of his former students, Augusto Rodriguez, to design hydroelectric projects in the Dominican Republic. Although the country was still struggling after years of dictatorship and several government transitions, the United States and other countries supported the new president, Joaquin Balaguer.

Meeting in Santo Domingo, Walter and Rodriguez agreed to form a joint venture under the name Hanson-Rodriguez. "I suggested Rodriguez-Hanson," Walter recalled, "but Augusto said there were too many Rodriguez surnames in the phone book, but there'd be only one Hanson."

Walter traveled to the Dominican Republic several times a month, and engineers from there, including Nelson Morales, came to Springfield for training and design work. He and Walter's secretary,

Left to right: José Betances, Augusto Rodriguez, Nelson Morales and Walt Hanson in the early days of the joint venture, Hanson-Rodriguez, in the Dominican Republic.

Claudie E. Daniels, met and eventually married. In the Dominican Republic, her bilingual skills became invaluable for translating project specifications into English and Spanish. Nelson Morales recently retired from his position as a senior hydraulic engineer and hydrologist with Hanson in Springfield. (Claudie's account of her involvement with the firm is included in the Appendix.)

Hanson-Rodriguez, S.A. designed several multi-million dollar projects, including the 175-foot high Rincon Dam, some sixty miles northwest of Santo Domingo. The concrete dam generates energy and furnishes irrigation water to a large agricultural area in the Cibao Valley. The firm also designed and constructed irrigation systems near Santiago, the country's second largest city, and in the Yaque del Norte River Valley, a major area for tobacco, sugar cane, banana, plantain, and rice crops. For those and other Dominican Republic projects, Hanson-Rodriguez, S.A. received financial assistance from the World Bank and the International Development Bank.

—————————————————

A significant job initiated in 1971 was geotechnical work for a new Central Illinois Light Company power plant at Duck Creek near Canton, Illinois. "In order to save considerable costs for a pile or concrete shaft foundation," Walter said, "we recommended mixing lime with the natural soil at the site, then compacting it to produce a sub-base similar to concrete. Apparently that first-of-a-kind power plant foundation has performed satisfactorily over the years."

Also in 1971 Hanson staff provided many engineering services for the Monterey Coal Company in Carlinville. That work was described in a paper entitled "Geotechnical Practice From the Coal Mine to the Ash Pond," which Walter coauthored for a session honoring Ralph Peck at the University of Illinois.[7]

Hanson Engineers, Incorporated

In 1972 Walter and the other officers agreed to change the company name from Walter E. Hanson & Company to Hanson Engineers, Inc. (HEI). They also changed the business structure to a regular corporation in order to further facilitate employee stock ownership. Planning for a new office building, the officers formed a separate employee-owned Hanson Engineers Building Corporation. After Jack Casson resigned that year to form his own company, Gene Wilkinson returned from Peoria to head the structural department at the home office. Don Fleming, who had joined the company several years earlier, assumed management of the Peoria branch.

During the 1960s, the publishers of *Foundation Engineering* had been requesting that Walter and his coauthors produce a second edition. "We agreed to write it," Walter explained, "even though all of us were occupied with numerous other activities. I made many trips to Urbana to meet with Ralph Peck and Thomas Thornburn as we developed the manuscript for the second edition. Rod Huffman of our staff prepared the design plates in his off-hours." The authors delivered the completed revision in early 1973, and the book was published in 1974. *Foundation Engineering*, Second Edition, was chosen that year as the McGraw-Hill Book Club selection for technical publications, even though it had been published by the Wiley company.

The second edition, like the first, was well received by civil engineers around the world. An example is the complimentary statement expressed by Professor Nainan of the Indian Institute of Technology, Madras, India in his book *Design of Foundation Systems*. Professor Nainan wrote that "particular mention must be made of the textbook *Foundation Engineering* (second edition)," which he considered "the single best book covering both soil mechanics and foundation engineering."

———•+•◆•+•———

Construction on the new Hanson building, at 1525 South Sixth Street in Springfield, began in 1973. Also that year, Hanson formed a transportation section within the company, managed by former Illinois Division of Highways engineer John Hine. He became a company vice-president, as did Wilkinson, Healy, and Miller, with Dondanville selected as executive vice president.

Professional Relationships

In addition to presiding over the company he founded, Walter continued active involvement in related organizations. He chaired the Illinois Association of Professions Committee on Legislation and was a member of the legislative committees of the Illinois Society of Professional Engineers, the Consulting Engineers Council of Illinois, and the Illinois Engineering Council. In an article, "Involvement in Legislation and Government," published in *The Illinois Engineer*, he encouraged greater public concern as a means of providing assistance to Illinois lawmakers.[8]

As chairman of the ISPE Legislative Committee in 1967, Walter led efforts for legislation regarding the selection of engineers by the Department of Public Works and Buildings:

> *At that time, the Division of Highways was located within the Department of Public Works and Buildings. Many of the ISPE members, including myself, felt that the selection of engineers for highway and other state projects was being made on the basis of political connections and contributions. Although we understood that it would be impossible to take this procedure completely out of politics, we felt there should be some method of selection that would give more emphasis to the qualifications of the engineering and architecture firms.*
>
> *The ISPE President at that time was J. Raymond Carroll, a professor of me-*

chanical engineering at the University of Illinois who supported a qualification-based selection procedure. Other ISPE members who were vitally interested in the issue were Len Crawford and Pat Murphy of Crawford, Murphy & Tilly, a Spring-field engineering firm.

Legislation was drafted during the 1967 spring session (House Bill 684), and ISPE members throughout the state were asked to contact their senators and repre-sentatives in support of the bill. But some ISPE members who had been active in politics—and accordingly received good consideration in the current selection proce-dure—offered resistance. There was resistance from other sources as well, and the bill was not widely accepted.

After considerable discussion within ISPE, as well as with members of ASCE and CECI, we decided to seek withdrawal of HB684. Although it was tabled in 1967, ISPE continued to work on the issue, and eventually the General Assembly passed a bill that established a qualification-based procedure. The Illinois law meets the requirements of the "Brooks Bill" passed by the U.S. Congress in 1972.

The process involves a selection committee that includes a non-engineering member as well as an engineer, appointed by the professional engineering societies, who must be disinterested in obtaining contracts. The state highway engineers, in-cluding the district engineer where the project is located, are also involved in the selection process. This procedure appears to work very well and has been introduced in other states. In 1983 I gave a paper on the subject to the National Bridge Confer-ence in Pittsburgh.[9]

In December, 1966, a Legislative Audit Commission report on alleged construc-tion irregularities at Eastern Illinois University led to considerable media coverage, par-ticularly in Chicago newspapers. In response, Governor Otto Kerner appointed a three-member committee to investigate the allegations. The Illinois Society of Professional Engineers recommended Walter as the committee's structural engineering member. The others were Chicago architect Philip Will, Jr., and Chicago contractor Leonard J. Graf.

During the course of their investigation, the men met with the university's presi-dent, architect, and contractor and inspected the buildings alleged to contain defects. In its formal report of May, 1967, the Committee indicated that the source of the allega-tions was probably a disgruntled former employee. Although they agreed that "some mistakes were made and that not all work was of good quality," the members found no evidence of negligence. "The result of the publicity," they noted, "has been a blow to the morale of the University and severe, unjustified damage to the reputation of the Board of Governors, the University administration, the architects and contractors. On hind-sight, it is most unfortunate that the original allegations were not dealt with early and responsibly by professionally qualified investigators."

After the Audit Commission presented the Committee report, Walter said, "We continued to receive criticisms about many items relative to the construction of build-ings at Eastern. One of the most prominent disagreements came from the editor of *Plant Engineering*, with whom I met later to discuss the issues."

In 1967, following Illinois General Assembly approval to establish Sangamon State University and Lincoln Land Community College in Springfield, Hanson Engineers, Inc., conducted location surveys for the new schools. "That was quite a controversial subject among local interests. The decision was based to some extent on the fact that the site should not be underlain by abandoned coal mines. A contiguous location south of the city was approved, and a civic committee was formed, of which I was a member, to raise funds for the purchase of the farm land where the two campuses are now located."

Later the Hanson firm would serve as the structural engineers and foundation consultants to the St. Louis architectural firm of Joseph Murphy and Associates, designers of Sangamon State University's Brookens Library. Named in honor of Board of Regents Chair Norris L. Brookens, the building includes classrooms and faculty offices. "Murphy and Associates also developed a future plan for the university, which has guided the development over the years of a beautiful campus. Over more than three decades, I have served on the University's Foundation board and taught classes at Lincoln Land, and our family has enjoyed the friendship of many faculty members and students at both schools."

An important and memorable family event occurred on September 2, 1967, when the Hansons' daughter, Karen, married Quentin Pletsch at Westminster Presbyterian Church in Springfield. "I think marriages of one's children are somewhat bittersweet events to their parents," Walter said. "At least, Karen's marriage was such to me."

The couple had been classmates at Knox College in Galesburg, Illinois, and upon graduation both obtained scholarships for graduate studies at Tulane University in New Orleans: Quentin in biochemistry and Karen in social work. They moved to a small second-story apartment on St. Charles Street, where her parents enjoyed visits during the next several years. Walt fondly recalled:

> My grandchildren, David, Amy, and Jonathan, were all born in the 1970s, after Karen and Quentin had received their degrees from Tulane. David came in Belleville, New Jersey, and Amy and Jonathan in Lexington, Kentucky.
>
> In 1973 Quentin decided to pursue an M.D. at the University of Kentucky. Amy was born in Vietnam and soon after her birth became a member of the Pletsch family. Jonathan arrived two years later. The family moved to Madison, Wisconsin, where Quentin completed his residency at the University. They then moved to Springfield. Needless to say, we were happy to have our enlarged family together.

Illinois Governor Richard Ogilvie in 1970 appointed Walter to the five-member Illinois Structural Engineers Examining Committee. In addition to composing both the written and oral examinations, the Committee corresponded with applicants for the structural engineer license and monitored pending legislation regarding the profession. In late 1972, Walter was elected chairman and reelected in 1975:

> *During my several years on the Committee, I frequently defended the selection of consulting engineers on the basis of professional qualifications rather than through a bidding process.*
>
> *The Committee had numerous discussions about making a requirement that the professional engineering license be obtained prior to receiving the structural engineering license. Within a few years of 1975, the General Assembly adopted a law requiring professional engineering registration before, or at least at the same time as, obtaining the structural engineering registration. The legislation also made possible licensing reciprocity with other states.*

Litigation and Arbitration

Walter's first experience as an expert witness, "and first exposure to the rigors of testimony and cross examination in a courtroom," involved a new Martin Oil Company gas station in Rantoul, Illinois. The facility had been built on the site of a demolished house, and the owner of the adjacent house alleged damages caused from the wrecking operations.

The case was tried in Urbana, and local attorney John Franklin, representing Martin Oil, requested that Walter appear as a defense witness:

> *I agreed, and visited the site, reviewed the soil and foundation report, and examined the drawings for the new filling station. There was no mention of instrumentation or protection of the adjacent house during construction, and no "before and after" photographs. That is, observational data was non-existent, except for the visible cracks in the house, which I concluded had not been caused by clearing of the next-door construction site.*
>
> *Mr. Franklin thought that the trial would be a battle of experts and he would depend heavily on my testimony. Although my ego was inflated, I suffered the nervousness of inexperience.*
>
> *The judge took the jury on an inspection of the house in question. He instructed no conversation during the inspection, but I overheard one juror whisper, "Lord, I sleep under worse cracks than these every night." Suddenly, my nervousness seemed to disappear.*

The opposing expert witness, an architect, was called first. I was allowed to listen to his testimony. Mr. Franklin's cross examination was not friendly, and I felt sorry for the architect, even though I had suggested some of the questions.

During the cross examination, the jury heard that the architect was not a structural engineer, that he had never done a soil and foundation investigation, that he had never seen a seismograph, that he didn't know the definition of damping and peak particle velocity. At the same time, the jury learned that walls frequently crack due to changes in weather and temperature.

By the time of my testimony, I think Mr. Franklin had already won the case. He must have had the same confidence, because he instructed me not to get carried away with theory in my statements. The opposing attorney showed me a photograph and asked, "Mr. Hanson this is Plaintiff's Exhibit Number 13. Do you recognize this round object?" "Yes sir, it is a wrecking ball, sometimes called a headache ball." "Mr. Hanson, how much would you say this wrecking ball weighs?" "I don't know." "You don't know? You have just testified that you have years of experience in construction." "Yes, but wrecking balls come in various sizes. If I knew the volume of the ball in cubic feet, the weight in pounds would be approximately 450 times the volume."

The lawyer changed the subject, and soon I was dismissed from the witness stand. Mr. Franklin called the following day to report that the jury had decided in our favor. I was pleased, because I believed the jurors had made a fair and just verdict.

In the mid-1960s, a jury in Rockford, Illinois found a structural engineer negligent in performance of his duties. The defendant had worked for Walter in the early 1950's when he was state bridge engineer. "It was apparent," Walter recalled, "that the jury had not understood the testimony of the structural engineer. It seemed to me that such cases could be more reasonably settled in arbitration or mediation rather than through formal court litigation."

He applied to become a panelist for the American Arbitration Association. His qualifications were accepted in 1967, and in subsequent years he listened to numerous disputes that were settled by arbitration. "I began each case by first reviewing the pros and cons and discussing the issue with Association officials. As a result, many of those cases were brought to a mediated settlement without further hearings."

One of Walter's most significant arbitration cases occurred in Ponce, Puerto Rico, involving a government agency against the contractor of a large shopping center. The contractor took a year to construct the drilled-pier foundation, instead of the sixty days he had originally estimated. Walter accepted the attorneys' request to serve as the arbitrator, under rules of the American Arbitration Association.

The testimony was presented and transcribed in both English and Spanish. The case required approximately two weeks of hearings, after which Walter wrote his findings in accordance with rules of the American Arbitration Association. "Because of the complex interrelationship of responsibilities and liabilities, no single party involved in such a controversy is really satisfied with the outcome. I'm not sure that I made a single friend in Puerto Rico, and I may have lost one or two, but my judgment in the case was not disputed."

Walter served as an expert witness in federal court in Chicago in a case involving David Novick, president of a consulting firm and a fellow member of the Structural Engineers Examining Committee. In making a series of foundation borings for a sewer in Chicago, Novick's company encountered considerable glacial till and other deposits containing boulders. The construction contractor filed suit against Novick, claiming that his borings data did not indicate the boulders to be as numerous as the workers encountered.

Walter testified that any contractor who had been involved with tunneling in the Chicago area—as this contractor had in the past—"should have known that the soil contained considerable amounts of large boulders. Therefore, there certainly was the possibility of finding them in random fashion. The federal judge, who had once been a candidate for Illinois governor and was later appointed to the federal bench, was apparently very much bored by the case. He was sound asleep during much of my testimony, so the prosecuting attorney's cross-examination was short, because he was reluctant to disturb the judge. The case ended with Novick being relieved of any malpractice."

University of Illinois

A staunch supporter of the University of Illinois, particularly the civil engineering department, Walter in 1964 was elected to the Board of Directors of the newly formed Civil Engineering Alumni Association. One of the organization's first issues was collective bargaining for professional and technical employees, including the civil engineering faculty. "It was often the case," Walter recalled, "that the ideas and resolutions of the CEAA Board were at odds with the thoughts and policies of the University President, Dr. David Henry."

When the Association established The Civil Engineering Trust, Walter served on the committee that administered the fund. In 1967, Nathan Newmark, head of the Civil Engineering department, asked the Civil Engineering Alumni Association to organize a Committee on Academic Relations. Walter served as the first chairman, emphasizing during his term the need for increased interdisciplinary emphasis within the curriculum. The following year the Committee was enlarged to include student officers of Chi Epsilon and the student chapter of the American Society of Civil Engineers. Walter chaired the expanded Committee until 1975.

Elected CEAA president in 1972, Walter mediated several disputes and differences of opinion between the Civil Engineering Department and the Office of the Dean. He also participated in the search for a successor when Professor Newmark retired as head of the Department of Civil Engineering.

After his presidency, Walter remained involved in Association activities, including helping organize a summer employment program for civil engineering students. In later years, he would continue to mentor students, some of whom came to the Springfield office of Hanson Engineers to learn about civil engineering consulting practice.

During the 1960s and 1970s Walter and other Hanson engineers participated in teaching two structural engineering courses at the University of Illinois. Their first course was structural systems design, followed by a senior course in structural engineering design:

> *I remember giving several lectures in the course dealing with bridge design. In particular, I lectured on the analysis of splice plates for girder bridges, pointing out what I considered to be an unreasonable procedure recommended by AASHO [American Association of State Highway Officials] specifications. Professor Narbey Khachaturian, in charge of the course, agreed with me.*
>
> *In the course we introduced a set of plans for a three-span girder bridge that had been designed by John Harms of our firm. Narbey told me that they continued to use those plans as an example in his structural design course.*

In 1977 Lee Dondanville of Hanson Engineers and Professor Chester Seiss, who succeeded Nathan Newmark as Chair of the Civil Engineering Department, initiated the annual Walter E. Hanson Graduate Study Award. Honoring its founder, the Hanson firm presents a certificate and monetary grant to an outstanding civil engineering senior who intends to pursue a graduate degree in a joint program of structural and geotechnical engineering.

In 1973 Walter received the College of Engineering Alumni Honor Award for Distinguished Service. His principal sponsor for the honor was Ven T. Chow, Professor of Hydrology and Hydraulics. Professor Chow had served as a consultant on several Hanson-Rodriguez dam projects in the Dominican Republic.

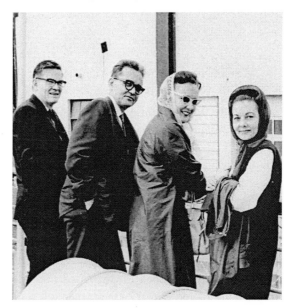

Ralph and Marjorie Peck join Walt and Sue Hanson for a Caribbean cruise prior to the 1973 national ASCE convention in Miami, Florida.

Endnotes

1 www.smithsonianmag.si.edu/smithsonian/issues04/mar04/poi.html

2 Savannah, Ga., *Evening Press*, Aug. 3, 1962.

3 www.fas.org/nuke/guide/usa

4 "Deformation Problems in Small Earth Dams," *The Military Engineer*, March-April, 1969, pp. 119-121.

5 In 1968, at a symposium in observance of the University of Illinois centennial, Walter Hanson, Leo Dondanville, and John Healy presented a paper on design and performance of the Loud Thunder Dam.

6 "Fallout Shelters in Your School Plans," Walter E. Hanson Company, 1964, p. 3.

7 "Geotechnical Practice from the Coal Mine to the Ash Pond," with Sergio A. Pecori, Donald D. Oglesby, and John M. Healy, *The Art and Science of Geotechnical Engineering, At the Dawn of the Twenty-first Century*, Englewood Cliffs, NJ: Prentice Hall, 1989.

8 *The Illinois Engineer*, Oct. 1968, p. 3.

9 "Selection Criteria for Bridge Consulting Engineers," *1st National Bridge Conference Proceedings*, Pittsburgh, Pa., 1983.

The 165-foot high Rincon concrete gravity dam was one of four dams designed by Hanson-Rodriguez in the Dominican Republic. The project provides irrigation, hydro-electric power, and potable water for several hundred thousand people.

ELEVEN

A New Building and Going International
1974-1981

We view our practice of engineering as much more than just tests, computations and the preparation of drawings; it includes the development and interchange of new ideas, new dimensions in thought, and the determination of new and better ways of doing things.

Walter E. Hanson

In summer of 1974, Walter and the other officers and employees of Hanson Engineers Incorporated relocated to their newly constructed headquarters. They hosted an Open House on the Thursday prior to Thanksgiving, which continues as an annual company tradition. "Every one of those events," Walter said, "has been well attended by engineers and architects and a wonderful cross-section of the Springfield business and education community."

The employee-owned Hanson Engineers Building Corporation did not prove to mirror the success of Hanson Engineers Incorporated. "I should have foreseen the problem," Walter explained. "The Building stockholders could profit only from the rent paid by HEI, but the high rent meant lower profit for HEI. Since the stockholders in the two companies were in differing proportions, some employees favored higher rent, others preferred lower rent. Our final solution, after considerable discussion and meetings, was to merge the building corporation into the engineering company by means of a stock exchange agreement. That proved to be a good decision, making much easier the financing of subsequent land and building additions during the next two decades."

HEI continued its growth in professional staff after the move to the new building. Sergio "Satch" Pecori, who would eventually become president, and Robert Cusick and Phil Borrowman, later to become vice-presidents, joined the firm during the period from 1974 to 1976. Pecori and Cusick worked from the Springfield headquarters, while

In 1974 the Hanson company moved to their new building at 1525 South Fifth Street, Springfield. The original building (shown above) has undergone three major additions, one of which is shown below, and several alterations until the complex presently covers two square blocks.

Borrowman joined the Peoria office.

Company growth also meant expansion of the accounting staff, and in 1974 Walter and vice-president Lee Dondanville began considering a library for the firm's diverse holdings of technical books, reports, conference proceedings, and other engineering literature. They wrote to librarians at other engineering firms, at local public libraries, and to national library associations seeking information regarding formation of a company library.

After a library consultant evaluated the collection and recommended methods of organization, a newly hired librarian began the task of organizing the Hanson holdings. A data processing consultant devised a library-card computer program that later became the basis for an online information storage and retrieval system. In 1976

90

the HEI Technical Library attained membership in the Rolling Prairie Libraries system and in the ensuing years has become a significant division of the company. "Nearly every day," Walter reports, "the library is visited electronically and in person by staff from Springfield as well as the branch offices." Hanson librarians participate in American Library Association programs and Rolling Prairie lending services.[1]

The use of computers for design and preparation of contract plans expanded and changed rapidly during the mid-1970s. Don Bartlett supervised the development of fifteen special-purpose programs for engineering calculations. "At the present time," he reported in fall of 1974,

> there are very few users manuals available due to the fact most of the programs were written in house and no one wrote a manual. However, there are people available who know how to use them if you should want to run a program.
>
> If you know of useful programs, would like to see about having a program developed for some calculation, or have questions on the programs, let me know.
>
> In addition, we have several special purpose programs still being developed. If you have a need for a program to do repetitive calculations, we may be able to develop it here in a short time.
>
> No knowledge of the terminal is needed to run the programs as most input data is given to Linda and she will run it for you.[2]

"Later came the personal computers, networks, the internet, and much more," Walter said. "I give considerable credit for our company's early development and use of computers to my experience with electronic communication in the Navy during World War II and to my good fortune in having been at the University of Illinois during the 'Newmark days' of research in the analysis of structures. On the other hand, I believe that often computers are used without an understanding of structural behavior and soil-structure interaction, and consequently errors sometimes occur."[3]

———— •+•◆•+•— ————

An important Hanson ownership and management change occurred in 1976, when Walter reduced his overall responsibilities and began to sell his stock to the company. Over a period of ten years, Hanson Engineers Incorporated would become an employee-owned company, owned proportionately by the employee stockholders, with an associated Employee Stock Ownership Trust (ESOT). The ESOT and more than 50 percent of the more than 350 employees own the company.

Within a few years, the increasing number of projects and staff necessitated an 8,400-square-foot, two-story addition, completed in 1978, to accommodate the firm's expansion. Changes in management also occurred, with Lee Dondanville becoming president in 1976 and Walter continuing as chief executive officer. Three years later Gene Wilkinson was named executive vice president, and Don Oglesby was elected to the board of directors.

Newly hired environmental engineer George Jamison established an environmental testing and consulting section in Springfield in 1976. Three years later, Dutch Miller transferred from the Springfield office to open a northern-Illinois branch in Rockford, after the Illinois Department of Transportation awarded Hanson-Wilson, Inc. (chartered in 1969) a construction engineering contract to supervise the construction of a section of Interstate 39 in Lee County. Phil Borrowman transferred from Peoria to head the structural design section in Rockford, and John Coombe joined the firm early in 1980, serving at both the Peoria and Rockford offices.

In 1976 Hanson Engineers, Inc. began a long relationship with Mergentime Corporation of Flemington, New Jersey, for structural and geotechnical engineering work relating to construction of mass transit systems in Washington, D.C., Atlanta, Philadelphia, Pittsburgh, Baltimore, and Boston.

In 1977 Hanson again worked as subcontractor to the Wilson Company in Salina, Kansas, for design of several bridges in Saudi Arabia. In connection with the projects, a group of Saudi engineers visited Springfield. "The real reason for their visit," said Walter, "was to observe the operations of the Illinois Department of Transportation. Nevertheless, it was also an opportunity for them to observe where some of their bridges were being designed and for us to better understand their problems. The leader of the Saudi Arabian group was a civil engineering graduate of Texas Tech, but he was very familiar with the engineering eminence of the University of Illinois."

For the Saudi Arabian Ministry of Communications, Hanson and Wilson engineers designed two delta-frame steel bridges for an expressway near the capital city of Riyadh. Both bridges were acknowledged as longer, wider, and higher than any previous bridge of the delta-frame design. "That work," Walter said, "was a good example of excellent cooperation and accomplishment between the Hanson and Wilson firms."

Foreign work also included several highway bridges in Haiti, financed by the World Bank. For that project, Hanson was a subcontractor to Sangamo Construction Company, headquartered in Springfield. A few years later, Hanson was again involved with Sangamo, on projects in Kuwait and the West Indies.

Among domestic projects were inspections of existing dams in Illinois and Missouri for the U.S. Army Corps of Engineers. The Corps initiated the Federal Dam Safety Inspection program to assess the condition of the dams regarding potential life and property hazards. Working under federal contracts, Hanson engineers inspected eighty Missouri dams for the Corps' St. Louis District and twenty-six Illinois dams for the Chicago District.

Another federal project during the 1970s was design of the Ruck-a-Chucky Bridge across the Sacramento River near Auburn, California. "The U.S. Bureau of Reclamation was in the process of designing a dam northeast of Sacramento as part of a flood control, power, and irrigation project," Walter said.

Model of the proposed Ruck-a-Chucky Bridge

The project included a new bridge over the upper reaches of the proposed new lake. We formed a joint venture with the T. Y. Lin firm in San Francisco, and Hanson-Lin was selected to design the bridge. Lin was primarily responsible for the superstructure, while we handled the foundations and all geotechnical aspects, including site location and characterization, slope stability, evaluation and anchor design.

The bridge, designed personally by T. Y. Lin, was a curved structure, supported by cables anchored into the mountains on both sides of the river. It was truly one of a kind, recognized as such throughout the civil engineering world. Unfortunately, due to environmental problems the project has not been built.

T. Y. was nominated as a Designer of the Year by Engineering News Record *magazine, and I attended the annual awards dinner in New York City. The banquet speaker, David McCullough, had just completed a biography of the engineers John Roebling and his son Washington, featuring their design and construction of the Brooklyn Bridge.*

Throughout the 1970s, Hanson-Rodriguez continued work on irrigation/hydropower projects in the Dominican Republic. Both the Sabaneta and the Rincon dams were completed, with the $80 million Hatillo Dam under construction. "The final one for which we were responsible was the Moncion Dam," Walter said, "in the northern area of the country." The $100 million project provides electricity and irrigation to 50,000 acres of cultivated land as well as flood control and potable water for several towns. "As time passed," he reported, "more and more of the engineering work on our Dominican Repub-

Ralph Peck and Walt Hanson confer with consultants and resident engineers at the Sabaneta Dam in the Dominican Republic.

lic projects was being accomplished by residents of the country, several of whom had obtained degrees in the United States."

<hr>

By 1979, its twenty-fifth anniversary, the Hanson firm had completed nearly seven thousand projects. More than one thousand of the jobs were located in Sangamon County; approximately three thousand were within Illinois, with the remaining three thousand spread throughout the fifty states and abroad. And while Hanson offered structural engineering as its principal consulting service since the founding year of 1954, the firm expanded by 1979 to offer complementary services of foundation engineering, materials testing, transportation engineering, hydrology/hydraulics, and environmental sampling and testing. All of the specialties were supported by in-house computer services.

As Hanson business and revenues continued expanding, price inflation and higher interest rates began creating adverse effects. "For example," Walter explained, "our gross income percentage dropped, and the decrease in net profits even more during that period. We needed to develop measures for coping with those recurring problems." (A detailed discussion of that situation is found in the following chapter.)

Professional Relationships

Walter continued his active involvement in engineering organizations, including an eleven-year tenure on the American Society of Civil Engineers Committee on Foundation and Excavation Standards. In 1978, at the national ASCE Convention in Chicago, he presented a paper on risk and liability in engineering practice. Three years later he served on a panel at the ASCE Convention in St. Louis, discussing design and construction of drilled piers and caissons.

He contributed the biographical chapter in the commemorative volume *Judgment in Geotechnical Engineering*,[4] honoring his friend and *Foundation Engineering* coauthor Ralph Peck and continued as an advisor to members of the ASCE student chapter at the University of Illinois. In 1981 he, along with University of Illinois professors Narbey Khachaturian and John Haltiwanger, decided to establish a fellowship fund in honor of Professor Thomas Clark Shedd. "We held meetings at ASCE conventions to discuss our plans, and eventually the Thomas C. Shedd Fund for Education in Civil Engineering Practice was born. The fund has continued to be popular, and I believe the Civil Engineering Department issues Shedd Fellowships of $5,000 whenever the interest from the principal is sufficient to justify the awards."

From 1975 to 1977 Walter served on the Structural Engineers Association of Illinois' Task Group on Continuing Education. The members' primary issue was mandatory requirements for renewal of professional engineering licenses. He also served on the Illinois Society of Professional Engineers' Task Group on Continuing Education. As chairman of the ad hoc Committee on Continuing Professional Development, he presented the members' final report, "Continuing Professional Development for Practice," published in the February, 1978 issue of *Illinois Engineer*.

In 1976 Walter became a member of the Sangamon State University Foundation in Springfield, serving on the board until 1991 and on various committees during his board tenure. He also served on the Structural/Foundation Subcommittee of the Illinois Department of Transportation Division of Water Resources, reviewing drafts of proposed "Rules for Construction and Maintenance of Dams" and presenting the final version for adoption in 1980.

In 1979 he chaired the University of Illinois College of Engineering Annual Fund Drive. "It was the first annual engineering fund drive that included the entire College of Engineering," he recalled. "Most of my work, however, involved contact with Civil Engineering alumni. It was a worthwhile national effort. Two years later, the University conducted an overall campaign for funds in which I participated as a member of the National Leadership Committee." The University also awarded him with membership in the President's Club, recognition of the Hanson firm's significant monetary contributions to his alma mater.

In addition, Walter in 1979 began an eight-year tenure on the Board of Natural Resources and Conservation, with oversight for the Illinois Water, Geology, and Natural History surveys within the Illinois Institute of Natural Resources. "My main contributions as a board member were helping convince Survey staff to use more computer programs in their scientific and administrative activities, encouraging the staff to attend Board meetings and become better acquainted with Board members, and promoting interdisciplinary approaches to research projects as well as to services for other departments and individuals in the state."

For his continuing involvement in professional activities, the Illinois Society of Professional Engineers honored Walter in 1980 with the Illinois

Walt Hanson receives the Illinois Award at the 1980 annual meeting of the Illinois Society of Professional Engineers in Quincy, Illinois.

Award, the organization's highest recognition. Thanking the Awards Committee at the ISPE annual meeting, he added, "My grandchildren think I'm a great engineer because, when they visit, I take them to some job site where there's lots of dirt, equipment and noise—and they can wear hard hats. This award will certainly reinforce my stature with them."[5]

In 1981 Walter received the Structural Engineers Association of Illinois' highest citation, the John F. Parmer Award.

Endnotes

[1]   Luanne Smith Kruse, "The Bibliophile's Vade Mecum: A Guide to the Library for the Users of Hanson Engineers, Inc. Technical Library," Feb. 1978, Hanson office files.

[2]   Don Bartlett, "Computer Programs Available" memorandum, Oct. 24, 1974, Hanson office files.

[3]   See Appendix for Hanson's speeches on computerization.

[4]   *Judgment in Geotechnical Engineering; The Professional Legacy of Ralph B. Peck,* New York: John Wiley & Sons, 1984, pp. 3-12.

[5]   Hanson, "Illinois Award Response," Hanson office files.

The Clark Bridge over the Mississippi River at Alton, Illinois, designed by Hanson Engineers in the late 1980's, was featured in a NOVA film, shown on PBS television.

TWELVE

Coping with a Depression, Recovery, and Retirement 1981-1986

Engineering is indeed a noble sport, and the legacy of good engineers is a better physical world for those who follow them.

Ralph B. Peck
Norwegian Geotechnical Institute Publication 207

For Hanson Engineers, Inc., the year 1981 commenced with a large project in Phila-delphia for the Mergentime Corporation. The two firms collaborated on construction plans and consultations for a metro tunnel beneath the street fronting the city's historic Masonic Temple. "Our primary concern was prevention of settlement that could dam-age the building," Walter recalled. "After inspecting the ongoing construction, one of our structural engineers advised Mergentime that the excavation, if continued, would cause a collapse. He stated that the workers might be on Walter Cronkite's 'Evening News,' because of the possible Temple damage. Needless to say, the construction details were altered. The project was completed safely, with minimum settlement of the Temple and surrounding buildings."

Another project with the Mergentime Corporation of considerable complexity was the underpinning for a nuclear reactor building at Consumers Power Plant in Midland, Michigan. "For a number of reasons," Walter said, "after the reactor superstructure had been built, the foundation was judged inadequate by federal regulatory officials. Hanson engineers had designed many special underpinning systems beneath structures, above, and adjacent to metro subways, but never to support a nuclear reactor. Nuclear energy was in much controversy at the time, and the building was eventually converted to a gas plant. Whether our underpinning will ever support a nuclear reactor is pure conjecture."

Work continued for the U.S. Corps of Engineers on dam inspections in Illinois and Missouri and for the Wilson Company on bridges in Saudi Arabia. The Saudi work included a review of a design-and-construction manual and a report on the effects of temperature changes on the construction of concrete bridges.

Another project, involving the University of Illinois' Memorial Stadium, commenced during a football game with Michigan State in September, 1982. Walter was not at the game but received a phone call the following day that the east balcony had vibrated badly during the game, causing considerable cracking of concrete and other damage:

I was asked to make an inspection of the stadium and participate in determining whether the games should be cancelled for the remainder of the season. The next game, against the University of Pittsburgh, was already a sellout, so millions of dollars were involved in the decision.

Following a thorough inspection with structural engineers from the civil engineering department, we agreed that if the damaged and loose concrete were removed and if the students would resist the temptation of stomping to the beat of the band, no resonance of the balcony would be created that would cause further damage. The President's office gave notice to fraternities, sororities, and other

During a game in the fall of 1982, vibrations of the east balcony of Memorial Stadium at the University of Illinois caused damage to concrete stands and columns. Walt Hanson served as a consultant and Hanson Engineers designed structural improvements that produced a safer stadium.

student organizations, and the band master was given instructions to choose and play his music carefully so as not to tempt the students into a resonance situation with the balcony. The remainder of the season was played without further damage.

The following year we received a contract to design stiffening trusses beneath the east main stands and modification to the balcony, which increased the natural frequency of Memorial Stadium and prevented any recurrence of intolerable behavior of the stands.

In 1983 work with the Mergentime Corporation included construction plans and consultations for an intercontinental ballistic missile silo in Arizona. Hanson was also consultant to the Pacific Gas & Electric Company on the failure of a penstock associated with a pump storage power plant in the Sahara Nevada Mountains.

Having commenced his bridge career in 1941 for Ash-Howard-Needles & Tammen with work on the Mississippi River bridge at Dubuque, Iowa, Walter always hoped that his own firm might be receive a similar assignment. The opportunity came in 1985, when the Illinois Department of Transportation awarded Hanson Engineers, Inc. the contract for structural, transportation, geotechnical, hydraulic engineering and technical support for a new $92 million Clark Bridge at Alton, Illinois, replacing the narrow through-truss structure built in 1928. The bridge is named for William Clark, who with Meriwether Lewis in 1803 crossed the Mississippi in the Alton vicinity on their "Corps of Discovery" expedition to the Pacific coast.

"Although I was in the throes of planning for retirement," Walter said, "I made several trips to the bridge site during the preliminary stages of the design, followed the development of the project, and attended the dedication in 1994." The four-lane cable-stayed Clark Bridge, spanning 4,620 feet across the Mississippi River, has received recognition in the engineering community, became the subject of a NOVA documentary, and is a tourist attraction for the city of Alton.

Projects in the environmental area continued, with a nationwide AT&T contract (known as the Spill Prevention and Countermeasures Plans). Hanson engineers inspected and designed remedial plans for buildings that use diesel oil to fuel motor generators for auxiliary power. Hanson also assisted the Central Illinois Public Service Company in instituting a cleanup program for abandoned gasification plants and worked for the Illinois Environmental Protection Agency on state and federal superfund projects. Because of the expanding environmental work, Hanson enlarged its hazard waste laboratory at the Springfield headquarters.

The firm's revenues in 1981 had increased more than three times from what it had been in 1976, when Walter announced his planned retirement for 1981. "However," he explained, "during that five-year period, double-digit inflation had reduced the percent of earnings available to fund Company programs, including 1) pension plans, 2) stock purchase plans, 3) dividends, 4) incentive compensation plans, and 5) retained earnings. (The percentage of earnings available for those programs continued to decline until 1984)":

In addition to the uncertain conditions at Hanson Engineers, the Koke Mill East Development in which I had a one-fourth interest, and had expected would be the main support of my retirement, was becoming an increasing liability. Fortunately, my bankers at the old Marine Bank had more confidence in the future than I possessed at the time. They had been close to our company since 1964, when I pur-

The 200-acre development in southwest Springfield, known as Koke Mill East, was commenced in 1977 but, due to inflation/depression, it was inactive for four years. Walt Hanson was one of four partners in this joint venture until 13 years beyond his retirement from Hanson Engineers in 1986.

chased our first building.

So, amidst inflation, recession, diminishing backlog of work and profitability, I decided to forego retirement for another five years as chief executive officer of the company.

During those final years, my billable time was largely devoted to the projects for the Mergentime Corporation and to bridges in Saudi Arabia for the Wilson Company. Management of the company was mainly in the hands of Lee Dondanville, president; Gene Wilkinson, executive vice president; Jack Healy, Dutch Miller, and John Hine as vice presidents; and Don Oglesby as vice president and secretary.

At the annual Hanson stockholders meeting on March 11, 1985, Walter reaffirmed his planned September retirement as Chairman of the Board. He indicated that although his involvement in the company's future would be limited, he would maintain a "continuing personal interest in watching the company's expansion and growth."[1]

President Dondanville, describing 1984 as "difficult," anticipated that 1985 would be "a year of continued challenges and transition." He and the other officers "engaged wise, talented outside advisors to help us map a program for future success. Our concentration was on management structure, long-term ownership, leadership transition, and growth. All efforts were focused on expanding services to existing clients, offering new services and developing new clients."

The officers also discussed additional study regarding funding for stock retirement, not only for present officers, but also to provide for younger stockholders at their retirement. "That may have been the beginning," Walter said, "of what has developed into an employee stock ownership and trust plan, for which I take no credit except to say that the company was in perfect shape in 1985 to become an outstanding employee-owned firm in all respects."

As of September, Walter retained 140 shares of Hanson company stock—about 10 percent of the total outstanding stock. In October he made his final report on a five-year "bottom line" study of the firm. His recommendations included 1) improving officers' billable time, and 2) holding a series of management sessions to discuss and implement improvements in efficiency, planning, administering, and monitoring work in progress.

The following January, he and the firm executed an agreement for the sale of his remaining stock holdings.

At the company's December meeting he outlined his plan for one-fourth involvement, "under a very flexible schedule. I will offer advice, when consulted, but will not be offended when my advice is not accepted, because I will not be making management decisions. My hourly rate for billable time will be the same as Don Oglesby's regular salary, so I hope that Don's financial situation improves next year."[2]

During his last meeting with the stockholders on February 28, 1986, he offered the following comments:

1. *In some respects, I suppose you'd say HEI has now become a "family" legacy. All of you are members of the "family." At this time it is up to you, not me, to*

select your management. This is because my interest in the "family" business will drop to zero at today's board meeting. I have mixed feelings about voting my stock for the last time.

2. If you elect me a director you recall that my term, by agreement, will end on July 14 this year.

3. Any further remarks would repeat what I already told you in December. But, once again, I do want to say thanks to all of you for your loyalty and support. If it hadn't been for your contributions there wouldn't be any "family" legacy.[3]

As grandfather Walt approached retirement, more time was spent with grandchildren David, Amy and Jonathan. Above, in 1978, they enjoy a ride in the trailer behind the lawn tractor.

Amy, David and Jonathan enjoy grandfather Walt's 70th birthday party in 1986.

Continued Professional Relationships

In the early 1980s the National Society of Professional Engineers formed an affiliated organization, the National Academy of Forensic Engineers. Since Walter had been involved with the American Arbitration Association and as an expert witness in court cases, he joined the new NAFE. He presented the paper "Foundation and Slope Failures" at a 1991 NAFE meeting in New Orleans. The organization granted him a life membership in the Academy in 1994.

Following his service on the Structural Engineers Examining Committee, the University of Illinois Extension Division in 1983 asked Walter to teach a refresher course covering foundation questions on the Structural Engineering examination. He conducted the class at the Illinois Department of Transportation building in Springfield, discussing many of the soil mechanics and foundation issues that had been included in previous examinations.

The following year he agreed to an Illinois Society of Professional Engineers request to serve on an examination review committee for the Illinois Department of Registration and Education. The other members were Ed Hoffman of Chicago and Narbey Khachaturian of the University of Illinois. "This committee was formed as a result of complaints from engineers who had taken the examination and probably failed. In other words, the Department was being criticized regarding the nature of the examination."

Meeting in Urbana, the committee members studied a proposed examination and submitted various comments and criticisms to the ISPE executive director. Later, they reviewed and rejected a proposed examination of the National Council of Engineering Examiners. "Our report," Walter explained, "was very negative concerning the adoption of the NCEE examinations in Illinois."

Having been involved in transportation projects in Washington, Atlanta, Pittsburgh and other cities, he accepted a 1982 invitation from the Illinois Associated General Contractors to participate in a seminar pertaining to construction disputes. His presentation, "Settlement of Construction Disputes," described his experience with mediation as an alternative to litigation procedures.

Walter continued on the Board of Natural Resources and Conservation, the supervisory entity over the state's water, geological, and natural history surveys. In 1984, when survey personnel promoted Illinois as the location for a proposed federal super-electron accelerator site, Walter monitored work on structural and geological aspects of the proposal.

He joined the newly formed Society for the Illinois Scientific Surveys, founded by conservation activist Gaylord Donnelley of Chicago to fund projects sponsored by the state surveys. Walter served as treasurer and board member of the nonprofit Society, which supports publications, exhibits and educational programs on science and the environment. During its formative years the organization, later known as The Nature of Illinois Foundation, was headquartered in the Hanson building.

In 1982, some eight years after his term as chairman of the University of Illinois Civil Engineering Alumni Association, the organization honored Walter with the CEAA

Distinguished Alumnus Award. He had received a similar award from the University of Illinois College of Engineering in 1973.

At a 1985 meeting of the West Branch of the Central Illinois Section of the American Society of Civil Engineers, he spoke on "Whatever Became of the Foundation Engineer?" He expressed his concern that foundation engineering "was being departmentalized into pure geotechnical engineering and pure structural engineering, with very little connection between the two. I felt that it was true in both the academic and practice worlds."

Also that year the American Society of Civil Engineers bestowed Walter with its Honorary Member Award at the annual convention in Detroit. That recognition was a "highlight of my professional career. In order to confer this national award, the ASCE must receive many petitions regarding the individual from ASCE sections across the country."

Other honors included Life Fellow Membership in the American Consulting Engineers Council (1973) and the Illinois Society of Professional Engineers Honorary Award (1984).

Among Walt Hanson's numerous awards is the Honorary Member in the American Society of Civil Engineers received at the annual convention in 1985. Few engineers receive this award, and Walt considers it a highlight of his career.

Endnotes

1   "Minutes of 1985 Meeting of Stockholders," March 11, 1985, Hanson office files.

2   Hanson, "Remarks at Company Meeting," Dec. 29, 1985, Hanson office files.

3   "Stockholders," Feb. 28, 1986, Hanson office files.

4   www.natureillinois.com

Walt works at his desk in the Walter E. Hanson Collection Room at Hanson Professional Services (formerly Hanson Engineers). The room, contiguous to the company's large technical library, contains most of Walt's publications, speeches, committee correspondence and many other personal files.

THIRTEEN

Active Retirement Years

Since the world is run by those who show up, civil engineers must show up as leaders on a regular basis—and become more involved and active in their communities—to have a consequential impact on the world around them. . . . Doing this will not only enhance the public's awareness and acceptance of civil engineers as community leaders, but will convince people that civil engineers care about more than engineering and construction projects— that they are serious about making their communities better places to work and live.

Jeffrey S. Russell, ed., *Perspectives in Civil Engineering*

Upon his formal retirement from Hanson Engineers, Inc., Walter moved to a small office in the headquarters building while continuing in a much reduced capacity on several ongoing projects. One such undertaking involved the Burlington Northern Railroad. For years, on miles of track south of Superior, Wisconsin, the railroad had been plagued with slope stability problems along the right-of-way and at bridge abutments. "Conditions continued to deteriorate," he explained, "even though remedial construction had been made in many locations, some of which Hanson engineers had designed several years before I retired."

Walter studied the problems with

The crack in the embankment parallel to the railroad track indicates imminent failure endangering operation of rail traffic.

Trenches were excavated in the embankment and filled with granular material to stablize the slope. The slickensided nature of the clay in the embankment is evident.

Dutch Miller, manager of Hanson's Rockford office. They agreed that the best solution would be relocating the track to better geological conditions on an abandoned right-of-way, thus eliminating the constant maintenance problems. Engineers in the Rockford office completed construction plans for the relocation, assisted by staff in Springfield. "That project, from beginning to end, involved interesting histories of ancient glacial lake deposits and the geotechnical characteristics of materials associated with such deposits."

By the time of Walter's retirement, all of the Hanson-Rodriguez projects in the Dominican Republic had been completed except the Moncion dam. He sold his ownership in the company to partner Augusto Rodriguez and agreed to return to the Dominican Republic to participate in a lecture series at the University NPHU, the largest private university in Santo Domingo:

Augusto and his wife, Helena, came to Springfield for my retirement receptions in 1986. At that time, he and I established the Hanson-Rodriguez Fund in the University of Illinois Foundation for the education of engineers from the Dominican Republic and other countries who desire to pursue graduate degrees in civil engineering. All that I received from selling my Hanson-Rodriguez stock was donated to the fund.

Upon completion of the dams in the Dominican Republic in 1986, Walter and Sue Hanson, and Augusto and Helena Rodriguez met with Springfield mayor William Telford. Mayor Telford presents a Lincoln memorabilia to Augusto to celebrate the success of the Hanson-Rodriguez joint venture.

In the fall of 1989, Walter was invited to participate in a University of Illinois symposium honoring his colleague and longtime friend Narbey Khachaturian. Walter and Hanson engineer John Harms prepared a paper, "The Old and New Clark Bridge" at Alton, Illinois, describing not only the structure being designed by Hanson engineers at that time but also a brief history of worldwide bridge engineering. In September, how-

Cofferdam leakage during gatehouse construction on the New Croton Water supply system for New York City. Walt Hanson served as a consultant to the Mergentime Corporation during the difficult construction conditions shown in the photograph.

ever, Walter struggled with angina problems that led to open heart surgery. In his absence, Harms presented the paper, with introductory remarks by company vice-president Gene Wilkinson.

For several years after retirement, Walter remained involved in Hanson metro projects with the Mergentime Corporation and the underpinning for the nuclear reactor building in Midland, Michigan. Then on November 11, 1990 he received a telephone call from Charlie Mergentime. "I'm in deep trouble," he told Walter, "on the construction of a new gate house on the water supply system for New York City; and I believe you are the only person that can keep me out of bankruptcy. (Charlie knew how to play to a person's ego.)"

Mergentime explained that his engineers were encountering dangerous problems caused by some unknown conditions totally different from those shown on the bidding plans. "Furthermore, he said that neither the City of New York engineers nor the engineering firm that had prepared the contract documents were willing to admit the presence of changed conditions":

> *I wasn't particularly interested in becoming involved in anything that would require a lot of time, but I agreed to review the contract documents and the other pertinent materials, such as photographs and job memos. After Charlie sent me a box of what he considered the relevant information, it became apparent that I would need help in handling this assignment, and we agreed that I could call on other Hanson engineers as needed. Chuck Burgert joined me on the project and did most of the research and analysis on the job.*
>
> *We found the history of the New York water system as interesting as the engineering aspects of Mergentime's construction difficulties. In fact, the two could hardly be separated. The history commenced in 1799 when the New York state legislature gave the newly created Manhattan Company the exclusive right to supply water to New York City. At that time former U.S. Senator from New York, Aaron Burr, headed the company, and there is reasonable conjecture that the politics of the New York water supply system may have contributed, along with many other political*

disagreements between Burr and Alexander Hamilton, to the tragic duel between the two men in 1804. We also learned that not until the 1820s did the city leaders began to investigate water sources outside the city limits.

From old records in a New York museum, we discovered that Mergentime's construction problems in 1992 were closely connected to the original Croton dam construction about 150 years earlier. The old dam had become submerged in the 1880s during the building of a new system, consisting of a higher dam and reservoir. The contract plans from which Mergentime was building the new gate house did not reveal the large stone spillway of the original dam. The stones were the source of Mergentime's problems during installation of steel pilings in the cellular coffer dam around the construction site. Mergentime managed to complete the job at greatly increased costs, for which he was eventually reimbursed.

In addition to Hanson projects, Walter spent considerable time on the rapidly developing 200-acre Koke Mill East Planned Unit Development. "For me," he recalled, "participating in management decisions of the Koke Mill project was an ideal retirement activity. I was able to contribute engineering expertise, while my partners were experts in other areas of real estate development. The Koke Mill Development became known as the best-planned multi-use addition to Springfield":

During the development of the Koke Mill properties, Walt Hanson reserved a lot for an office building for Hanson Information Systems of which his daughter, Karen, is president and CEO.

The development of the Koke Mill area of Springfield has presented another precious memory to Sue and me. After working for several years for two small companies that provided internet service, Karen and her partner, Raj Mohanty, decided to enter the service field as owners of a new company. In 1997 they were able to purchase the company Family Net, for whom they were employed. Sue and I owned 50 percent of the company at the time of purchase.

During the following two years, business of the new company grew, and in 2000 they moved into a new building on a lot in the Koke Mill area that my partners and I had previously developed. In fact, I had purchased my partners' share in the lot the previous year, in anticipation of the needs of the new company.

In order to benefit from the familiarity of the Hanson name, we incorporated as Hanson Information Systems, Inc. In 2004 the company purchased our stock and operates now as a minority-owned business.

Needless to say, to have helped found two highly respected companies gives me considerable pride of accomplishment.

In 1991 Walter presented "Working for an Engineering Firm in Private Practice" at the University of Illinois' First Annual Civil Engineering Issues Seminar. The student chapters of the American Society of Civil Engineers and Chi Epsilon, the Illinois Transportation Engineers, and Associated General Contractors sponsored the program.

Enjoying retirement activities, Walter and Sue joined her sister and brother-in-law, Edna and Truman Wester, on a European trip. The Hansons had traveled in Europe once previously. "In 1973 we had applied for passports to the Soviet Union and whatever else was required for travel to that country," Walter recalled, "to attend a meeting of the International Society of Soil Mechanics and Foundation Engineers. But the travel agent couldn't handle the red tape in time":

> *Sue and I decided that we would instead visit Europe. We went to England, the Netherlands, Germany, Austria, Italy, Switzerland, and France.*
>
> *In Italy I was interested in the aqueducts and bridges. As the Romans took over the world, their engineers went with the armies, building bridges for the armies to cross.*
>
> *On the later retirement trip with the Westers, we traveled to Spain and Portugal, where we viewed the structures of several prominent civilizations. For instance, Jews had founded Toledo, Spain before the time of Christ, but in the eighth century Muslim Moors from North Africa took over the area. Centuries later, during the Crusades, Christians captured a Muslim palace in Cordoba and added to it with a distinctly different architecture involving stone arches.*

Continuing his involvement in community projects, in 1988 Walter was elected to the Board of the Greater Springfield and Sangamon County Chamber of Commerce and served as chairman of its Transportation Committee. Members developed a priority listing of street and road projects within and around Springfield. "We worked with engineers in the Illinois Department of Transportation to establish a list of high-priority transportation projects. It is satisfying today to observe that nearly all of those projects, including Veterans Parkway around the north side of Springfield and the extension of Toronto Road to the University of Illinois at Springfield, have been completed. The one remaining project, an extension of 11th Street to the University, is currently under construction. I was pleased to receive the President's Award for this work," an annual recognition for significant Chamber involvement.

No doubt, Walter's most cherished honor was received in 2006, when he was elected

to the Illinois Engineering Hall of Fame. His citation reads: "As an educator, author, practicing engineer and business owner in Illinois, Walter E. Hanson has been instrumental in promoting and advancing the engineering profession, researching new techniques and theories, and completing important engineering and infrastructure projects in Illinois and around the world."

Ralph Peck and Professor William Hall, Head of Civil Engineering, meet with Walt Hanson during the establishment of the Hanson Engineers Professorship at the University of Illinois.

Throughout his civil engineering career in Springfield, Walter was active in the ministries and programs of Westminster Presbyterian Church, and after retirement in 1986 he continued that involvement. In addition, he increased his association with Springfield College in Illinois. Some highlights of his accomplishments in those areas are described in the following chapter.

Walt Hanson addresses employees of Hanson Professional Services, Inc., at a picnic celebrating the company's 50th anniversary in October, 2004.

112

Friends gather at the Springfield's Island Bay Yacht Club to celebrate Walt Hanson's 90th birthday. Standing behind Walt on the right is Dean Collins, one of Walt's partners in the formation of Hanson Engineers in 1954, who hosted the luncheon.

Retirement years allowed Walt Hanson to spend more time in Kansas visiting family and friends. He is shown at the left with sister Etta Hanson in 1990 at the annual "Mickelson Cousins Reunion" at Melvern Lake.

At the right, Walt and Sue Hanson admire and play with their first great-grandchild, Jessica Hanson Pletsch, born November 28, 1994.

113

Walt Hanson attends the Mickelson cousins reunion in 1994 at Melvern, Kansas.

Above, four generations gathered on September 14, 2005, to celebrate Walt and Sue's 65th wedding anniversary. From left to right are grandson David Pletsch, Walt, great grandson J.D. Pletsch, great-granddaughter Jessica Pletsch, Sue and daughter, Karen. During this event Karen announced the creation of the Hanson Family Fund, a charitable fund.

114

Westminster Presbyterian Church, Springfield, Illinois has been home to the Hanson family since they arrived in Springfield in 1951.

FOURTEEN

Integration of Church and Civil Engineering Practice

RECOLLECTIONS OF WALTER HANSON*

Have faith in the creative law of your own mind, in the goodness of God and in all things good, a joyous expectancy of the best, and a firm belief inscribed in your heart . . . Infinite Intelligence will lead you out of your difficulty and show you the way.

Joseph Murphy

Religion has undoubtedly influenced my practice of civil engineering, and I believe that most of the influences in later years originated during my "family days" as a youngster on the farm. My parents were members of the First Presbyterian Church of Lyndon, and, as a family, we attended Sunday school and church every Sunday except when roads to town were impassable.

I remember that I considered Sunday school generally interesting and always tolerable, but why did the preacher have to tell the sad stories in his sermons that caused my Mother to cry? I, together with my sister, Etta, memorized the Lord's Prayer, Ten Commandments, 23rd Psalm, and the Sermon on the Mount, and upon demonstrating our accomplishment before an elder, became members of the church.

In addition to the good influences provided through the church, of greater importance were the examples set by my parents. Both were unpretentious and of the highest integrity. I often heard such comments as "You must be stretching the truth," "You're not abiding by the golden rule," and "Remember, actions speak louder than words." One of Mother's frequent admonitions was, "Walter, you're getting too big for your britches."

This essay, distinct from the chronological biography of the previous chapters, presents Walter Hanson's thoughts on the importance of faith and education throughout his life and career.

Walter Hanson was baptized and became a member of the First Presbyterian Church of Lyndon, Kansas in 1925. The church eventually closed on December 31, 2000, having served the congregation since 1876. (Photo courtesy of Arlo Bell, local historian, Lyndon.)

My wife Sue's parents and family were dedicated members of the First Methodist Church of Durant, Oklahoma and usually attended church services twice a week. Sue tells of their walking many blocks at night to attend midweek prayer meetings, in addition to the Sunday services. I will always remember Mr. Roling's insistence that someone return thanks before every dinner. That was often my responsibility.

Following our marriage, Sue and I maintained memberships in our childhood churches in Kansas and Oklahoma, and it was not until we were settled in Urbana, Illinois after World War II that we became active members of a congregation.

When our daughter, Karen, was old enough to attend kindergarten class, Sue and I became members of the First Presbyterian Church in Urbana. I recall teaching a Sunday school class of junior high students, whom I found a great deal more challenging than any class of engineers at the University.

Sue participated in a women's circle, where she met Karon Bone, wife of Dr. Robert "Bob" Bone. Bob had gained honors as a parachutist during World War II and after the war became head of the department responsible for the University's veteran programs. When we moved to Springfield, the Bones recommended that we visit Westminster Presbyterian Church, where they had grown up together. (Bob and I met in later years at several meetings of the Illinois Commission of Higher Education, after he had become president of Illinois State University at Bloomington/Normal.)

When we joined Westminster in 1952, less than a year after moving to Springfield from Urbana, the church leaders were beginning to plan for a major building expansion. The pastor, Dr. Edward W. Ziegler, and his wife, Gladys, had given high priority to welcoming and integrating the war veterans and their families into church activities. Membership was increasing much faster than could be accommodated in the existing building.

Sue and I became active in the church's programs. I taught a class of high school students and was soon elected to the Board of Deacons. Sue joined the Women's Association circles, and Karen attended a class for second- and third-graders from various Springfield schools. Sue and I were founding members of Paridoffs, a group of young married couples that met monthly for Christian fellowship.

During 1953, the needs of Westminster were studied, alternate plans were drawn up, and many special hearings were conducted. In May, 1954, at a congregational meeting, the church officers received unanimous authority to conduct a campaign to raise $220,000, the estimated cost of the building expansion. Seventy-two percent of the congregation pledged to the campaign, and ground-breaking for the "Church-School Addition" occurred in December, 1954. W. E. Hanson & Associates had been created three months previously, and I was busy with the Kansas Turnpike bridges in Kansas. The remodeled building and new addition were occupied in 1955 and dedicated in 1956.

In the following three decades, members of our family would become involved in many Westminster projects.

Dr. Ziegler retired in 1969. Sue, who had previously become an Elder and member of Session, was chosen to head the nominating committee for a new pastor. The committee chose James S. Barge, who had previously served as associate pastor for four

The beautiful organ and choir balcony in the sanctuary of Westminster Presbyterian Church, Springfield, Illinois. Walt and Sue Hanson were active on the committees that planned, designed and constructed the addition to the church.

years, and almost concurrently, James A. Fry was chosen to be Associate Pastor. "The two Jims, as they were affectionately nicknamed, carry the heavy mantle of 135 years of pastoral heritage and they carry it lightly and with aplomb."[1]

One of the Westminster undertakings that the Hanson family remembers best is the organ and balcony project. Sue was a member of the Music Committee that chose the new Schlicker organ, and Hanson Engineers designed the structural aspects of the balcony. The architect, Bryant Hadley, and the builders, Fred Blythe and Jack Jones, were all Westminster members and, within the next two years, would design and build the new Hanson Engineers office building. The Westminster organ and balcony were completed in 1972 and dedicated in honor of Dr. and Mrs. Ziegler.

In addition to the various Westminster building and maintenance projects, one other activity stands out in my memory. In the early 1980s, church groups and United States citizens as a whole were giving much thought to the buildup of the arms race between the United States and the Soviet Union. I accepted the chairmanship of a Peace Committee, appointed by Rev. Barge to arrange programs on peace and national defense. At a morning service on February 22, 1982, I gave the "Concern of the Church," stating, among other comments:

> Sometimes we are inclined to feel that if we openly express our true feelings for disarmament and peace, we may be singled out as being against strong national defense. Actually, any dichotomy of disarmament and peace on one hand, and strong defense and patriotism on the other hand, may be more imagined than real.

In 1981, Karen and her family had returned to settle in Springfield. She became active in the work of Westminster and was elected a deacon and later an elder and president of the Westminster Women's Association, Following my retirement from Hanson Engineers in 1986, I continued to serve on Session committees responsible for the church's repair and maintenance programs.

———————•◆•———————

My first acquaintance with Springfield College in Illinois occurred while it was still known as Springfield Junior College. Rodney Baxter, an engineer friend, was teaching a course in geology and invited me to lecture on the subject as it related to geotechnical engineering. I was impressed by the students, faculty, and small-college surroundings.

After Lincoln Land Community College came into being in 1967, student enrollment at Springfield College dropped, and for several years the trustees could not afford adequate maintenance of the buildings. James "Pat" Murphy, partner in the engineering firm of Crawford, Murphy and Tilley, and I made a survey of the structures and recommended a maintenance program to the Trustees, chaired by Willard "Bunch" Bunn, CEO of the old Springfield Marine Bank. Shortly thereafter, Mr. Bunn asked me to make a structural inspection of the Brinkerhoff Home, built in 1869, which housed the president's and others offices of the school.

After my study, I reported to the Trustees that the Home was in sound condition and that with appropriate roof repairs and other restorations, it would be attractive and usable at much less cost than a replacement. I gave them three reasons for the restoration: 1) If the building was needed for the College to function properly, the project would be good from that standpoint; 2) Not another structure in Springfield could tie into the civic community as this one would; and 3) Many people would appreciate the historic significance of the restoration.[2]

Thus commenced a decade and more of satisfying involvement with Springfield College in Illinois. After a

Historic Brinkerhoff Home, on the campus of Springfield College in Illinois.

term on the Board of Trustees, I was elected Chairman in 1977. That year we established Brinkerhoff Home, Inc. as a separate not-for-profit organization, and with the outstanding leadership of Doris Bucari, we organized events and obtained grants to help fund the restoration work. I particularly enjoyed my association with Sister Francis Marie Thrailkill, O.S.U., who was the SCI president during my tenure as Chairman. In 1993 the Trustees awarded me an Honorary Doctorate of Humane Letters.

———•◆•———

Professional ethics are not necessarily learned at church services nor in formal classes of an academic curriculum dealing with public affairs, although such exposures are usually worthwhile. As previously discussed, more than anything, the quality of personal ethics stems from the mother and father within the family relationship at an early age. For example, what

Sue and Walt Hanson help dedicate the new Multi-Media Room in Dawson Hall at Springfield College in Illinois, made possible by Sue's gift. Jack Healy, vice president of Hanson Engineers and chairman of the SCI Board, assists in the official ribbon-cutting.

121

is the effect on a youngster who hears his/her father boast about making money on a stock transaction resulting from inside knowledge? Or, that the father obtained an engineering contract by paying a percentage of his fee to someone with good connections to the governor? These are only two of the many gray areas of professional conduct that may or may not be legal and under certain parameters be unethical.

Shortly after I retired in 1986, there was much publicity about ethics in Washington, D.C. House Speaker, James Wright, Jr., was charged with unethical practices in connection with his book royalties, speaking fees, and employment of his wife. Edwin Meese III, President Reagan's Attorney General, became involved in the so-called Iran/Contra matters and was accused of ethical violations. Michael Milken, a partner in a Wall Street brokerage firm, was charged with securities violations and became one of the principals in a book written by James Stewart, who won the Pulitzer Prize for reporting in 1988.

This media turbulence prompted me to give a speech to the Springfield Cracker Barrel Club entitled "The Gray Area of Ethics and Money" (see Appendix). A post script should be added to that speech: former Speaker Wright is now a professor at Texas Christian University; Edwin Meese is a fellow at the Heritage Foundation; and Michael Milken heads several prominent philanthropic foundations, including the Prostate Cancer Foundation. Criteria for judging the quality of lives are not easily stated.

A recent interesting, enlightening, and somewhat frightening book dealing with engineering ethics on a worldwide scale is *Confessions of an Economic Hit Man*, by John Perkins.[3] I would emphasize that his case histories of crime and corruption, although no doubt true, was not the modus operandi of Hanson-Rodriquez in the Dominican Republic. See Appendix entitled "Hanson-Rodriquez: From Springfield to the Dominican Republic," by Claudie Morales.

Endnotes

[1]   Frances Fowler Allen, *The Story of Westminster*, 1975.

[2]   Alice Rosa Lacey, *The Story of Brinkerhoff Home*, 1995, pp. 59-60.

[3]   John Perkins, San Francisco, CA: Koehler Publishers, Inc., 2004.

An aerial view (2007) of the campuses of the University of Illinois at Springfield (formerly Sangamon State University) and Lincoln Land Community College. Walt Hanson served on several state and local commissions and committees during the establishment of the colleges. In the following years, the Hanson firm furnished engineering services on various phases of campus development. Walt served on the University Foundation Board and other committees, and taught a class on materials testing at LLCC. (Photograph by Roger Williams, Springfield)

APPENDIX

Textbooks

Foundation Engineering, with Ralph B. Peck and Thomas H. Thornburn, New York: John Wiley & Sons, 1953.

Foundation Engineering, Second edition, with Ralph B. Peck and Thomas Thornburn, New York: John Wiley & Sons, 1974.

Published Papers (* indicates reprinted in this Appendix)

"Secondary Stresses in Bridge Members Due to Their Own Weight," ASCE *Civil Engineering,* March, 1944.

"Shearing Stress Distribution in Box Girders with Multiple Webs," with John E. Goldberg and J. G. Clark, Discussion, ASCE *Transactions,* Vol. 114, 1949.

"Successive Approximations for Beams on an Elastic Foundation," Discussion, ASCE *Transactions,* Vol. 116, 1951.

"Footings on Typical Sandy and Clayed Soils," with Ralph B. Peck and Thomas H. Thornburn, *Progressive Architecture,* Dec. 1953.

* "Constant Segment Method for Analysis of Nonuniform Members," with Wallace F. Wiley, *ASCE Transactions,* Vol. 121, 1956.

* "A Consulting Engineer's Views on Continuing Education," ASCE Central Illinois Section, *Proceedings of 1964 Annual Meeting and Technical Conference,* University of Illinois Bulletin, Aug. 1965.

"Professional Practice of Structural Engineering for Buildings," with John E. Rinne, Nomer Gray, James O. Power, and Clarence E. Rinne, ASCE *Manual #45B,* 1966.

* "Involvement in Legislation and Government, *Illinois Engineer*, Oct. 1968.

"Problems in Earth Work Construction and Lessons Learned, "ASCE Cincinnati Section, *Proceedings, Soils Symposium VI*, 1968.

* "Use and Performance of Quaternary Materials in the Loud Thunder Dam," Illinois State Geological Survey and University of Illinois Department of Civil Engineering, *Proceedings, Symposium on the Quaternary of Illinois*, 1968.

* "Deformation Problems in Small Earth Dams," *The Military Engineer*, March/April 1969.

"Small Dams: Particular Problems and Considerations," with David E. Daniels, University of Louisville Department of Civil Engineering, *Proceedings, Eighth Ohio River Valley Soils Seminar*, 1977.

"Risks and Liability in Engineering Practice," with John P. Gnaedinger and Narbey Khachaturian, ASCE *Issues in Engineering*, Oct. 1979.

"Selection Criteria for Bridge Consulting Engineers," 1st *National Bridge Conference Proceedings*, Pittsburgh, Pa., 1983.

"Drilled Shaft Design; A Structural Engineering Perspective," *ASCE Convention Proceedings*, 1984.

"The Life and Achievements of Ralph B. Peck," *Judgment in Geotechnical Engineering*, New York: John Wiley & Sons, 1984.

* "Geotechnical Practice from the Coal Mine to the Ash Pond," with Sergio A. Pecori, Donald D. Oglesby, and John M. Healy, *The Art and Science of Geotechnical Engineering, At the Dawn of the Twenty-first Century*, Englewood Cliffs, NJ: Prentice Hall, 1989.

* "The Old and New Clark Bridge," with John E. Harms, *Frontiers in Structural Engineering, Proceedings of a Symposium Honoring Narbey Khachaturian*, University of Illinois, July 1992.

"Uncertainties in the Geologic Environment," with Tien H. Wu, Discussion, *Journal of Geotechnical and Geoenvironmental Engineering*, Nov. 1997.

"LRFD and ASD in Foundation Engineering: It's Not an Either-Or Matter," *GeoStrata*, April 2003.

"Foundation Engineering; Judicious Use of LRFD and ASD in Foundation Design," *Structural Engineer*, May 2003.

Presentations [reprinted in this Appendix]

"County Highway Bridges—Engineering Requirements and Types of Construction," American Road Builders Association Annual Highway Conference, Springfield, 1962.

"Theory, Practice and Assumptions," ASCE Central Illinois Section and Bradley University Student Engineers Club, 1963.

"Education for Professional Practice: Perspective of Analysis and Design," World Congress for Engineering Education, Illinois Institute of Technology, 1965.

"What are the Assumptions?," University of Illinois ASCE Student Chapter, 1967.

"Civil Significance," University of Illinois Chi Epsilon Initiation Banquet, 1972.

"Settlement of Construction Disputes," Illinois Associated General Contractors, 1982.

"Cross-Cultural Aspects of Engineering Practice (With Emphasis on Work in the Dominican Republic)," University of Illinois, CE 295, 1982.

"Assumptions and Judgments 100: A Prerequisite for Computer Science 101," Adlai E. Stevenson Lecture Series, Panel on High Technology and Higher Education, 1984.

"Engineers: Changing Ideas into Reality," Southern Illinois University, 1985.

"Civil Engineers, Lawyers, and Other People," University of Illinois ASCE Student Chapter and Alumni Dinner, 1985.

"Whatever Became of the Foundation Engineer?," ASCE Central Illinois Section, 1985.

"From Research to Practice, or Vice Versa?," Illinois State Water Survey, 1988.

"The Gray Area of Ethics and Money," Cracker Barrel Club, Springfield, 1989.

AMERICAN SOCIETY OF CIVIL ENGINEERS

33 WEST 39TH STREET, NEW YORK, N. Y.

Constant-Segment Method for Analysis of Nonuniform Members

BY

WALTER E. HANSON, M. ASCE, AND
WALLACE F. WILEY

WITH DISCUSSION BY

Messrs. THOMAS F. HICKERSON; EUGENE J. VAYDA;
JARO J. POLIVKA; and WALTER E. HANSON
and WALLACE F. WILEY

Paper No. 2842

Reprinted from TRANSACTIONS, Vol. 121, 1956, p. 1317

AMERICAN SOCIETY OF CIVIL ENGINEERS

Founded November 5, 1852

TRANSACTIONS

Paper No. 2842

CONSTANT-SEGMENT METHOD FOR ANALYSIS OF NONUNIFORM MEMBERS

By Walter E. Hanson,[1] M. ASCE, and Wallace F. Wiley[2]

With Discussion by Messrs. Thomas F. Hickerson; Eugene J. Vayda; Jaro J. Polivka; and Walter E. Hanson and Wallace F. Wiley

Synopsis

There are several general methods of analysis for beams having variable moments of inertia. Although precise, these methods are time-consuming and subject to numerical errors. Even the combination of column analogy and moment distribution sometimes becomes quite laborious.

A method is presented herein which requires comparatively little computation and which is simple in concept and use. The method is based on the division of a flexural member into a number of segments of equal length, each segment being assumed to have a constant cross section and modulus of elasticity. In this respect the method may be considered an approximation; however, the accuracy afforded is very high, and even with slide-rule computations it is entirely sufficient for all design purposes.

The material presented herein covers only the computation of stiffness, carry-over factors, fixed-end moments, and dead-load deflections; however, the method is applicable to similar problems.

Basic Concepts

The behavior of a flexural member acted on by any combination of transverse loads and end moments is dependent on the angle changes produced along the beam. These angle changes can be computed from the properties of the $(M/E\,I)$-diagram; M is the applied bending moment, E represents the modulus of elasticity, and I is the moment of inertia.

Note.—Published, essentially as printed here, in March, 1955, as *Proceedings-Separate No. 649*. Positions and titles given are those in effect when the paper or discussion was approved for publication in *Transactions*.

[1] Cons. Engr., Hanson, Collins & Rice, Springfield, Ill.

[2] Senior Bridge Designer, Illinois Div. of Highways, Springfield, Ill.

1317

For any nonuniform beam the shape of the $(M/E\,I)$-diagram is irregular and may present difficulties in the computation of slopes and deflections. Such difficulties can be overcome by using the principle of superposition; the total slope or deflection at any one particular point is the summation of the slopes or deflections at that point produced by all segments of the $(M/E\,I)$-diagram, each segment acting individually. While one segment is being considered, all other segments of the beam are assumed at that time to have an infinite value

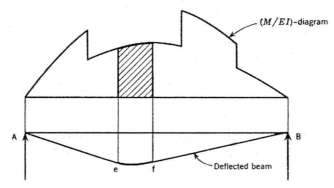

FIG. 1.—ACTION OF ONE FLEXURAL SEGMENT

of $E\,I$. Fig. 1 shows the behavior of a beam in which only the segment e f is assumed to be active.

If each segment may be considered to have a constant value of $E\,I$ throughout its length, numerical computations can be greatly simplified by the use of predetermined coefficients. These coefficients represent the effects of a segment of the moment diagram if this segment of the beam has a unit value of $E\,I$. In use, the coefficient for each segment is divided by the actual value of

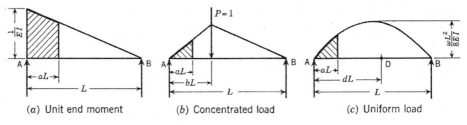

FIG. 2.—$(M/E\,I)$-DIAGRAMS

$E\,I$ for that segment, and the results are summed across the beam to obtain the total effect.

For purposes of computation, it is convenient to divide all beams into the same number of equal segments; the ten-segment scheme has been chosen for use herein. Each of the segments in this scheme is considered to have a constant value of $E\,I$ throughout its length. If the value of $E\,I$ changes within the segment, the weighted average value of $1/E\,I$ in the segment is used.

No sign convention is followed herein. The solution of any one of the equations will result in a positive quantity; the proper sign is applied according to the problem.

End Slopes Produced by Unit End Moments.—The slope at the end of a beam is numerically equal to the reaction of the $(M/E\,I)$-diagram at that end. If a unit moment is applied to end A of the beam AB which has a constant value of $E\,I$, the $(M/E\,I)$-diagram is as shown in Fig. 2 (a). If only the shaded segment is then assumed to have a finite value of $E\,I$, the end slopes caused by this segment are the reaction of the segment of the $(M/E\,I)$-diagram—that is,

$$\theta^A{}_A = \frac{L}{E\,I}\left(a - a^2 + \frac{a^3}{3}\right) \dots\dots\dots\dots\dots (1)$$

and

$$\theta^A{}_B = \frac{L}{E\,I}\left(\frac{a^2}{2} - \frac{a^3}{3}\right) \dots\dots\dots\dots\dots (2)$$

Similarly, for a unit moment applied at B,

$$\theta^B{}_B = \frac{L}{E\,I}\left(\frac{a^3}{3}\right) \dots\dots\dots\dots\dots\dots (3)$$

and

$$\theta^B{}_A = \frac{L}{E\,I}\left(\frac{a^2}{2} - \frac{a^3}{3}\right) \dots\dots\dots\dots\dots (4)$$

In Eqs. 1 through 4, $\theta^A{}_A$ is the slope at A caused by a unit moment applied at A, $\theta^A{}_B$ denotes the slope at B caused by a unit moment applied at A, $\theta^B{}_B$ is the slope at B caused by a unit moment applied at B, $\theta^B{}_A$ represents the slope at A caused by a unit moment applied at B, L is the span length, and a denotes the ratio of a distance measured from the left support A to the span length.

It should be noted that Eqs. 2 and 4 are equal and by the law of reciprocal relations this is true for any beam, no matter how the value of $E\,I$ varies; that is,

$$\theta^A{}_B = \theta^B{}_A \dots\dots\dots\dots\dots\dots\dots (5)$$

The quantities in parentheses in Eqs. 1 through 4 are coefficients of end slopes produced by a unit moment applied to the end of a beam having a constant value of $E\,I$. They represent, however, the slopes caused only by that segment of the $(M/E\,I)$-diagram extending a distance $a\,L$ along the beam—that is, all of the beam except this segment is considered to have an infinite value of $E\,I$.

The value of a coefficient for a segment extending from $a_1\,L$ to $a_2\,L$ is the difference between the values obtained by substituting successively for a the values of a_1 and a_2 in the factor in parentheses. Values of these coefficients for ten segments of equal length are presented in Table 1 (a).

When the value of $E\,I$ is not constant throughout the length of the beam, the true value of an end slope is obtained by summation, thus:

$$\theta^A{}_A = L\left(\frac{C_1}{E\,I_1} + \frac{C_2}{E\,I_2} + \cdots + \frac{C_{10}}{E\,I_{10}}\right) \dots\dots\dots\dots (6)$$

in which C_1 through C_{10} are segmental coefficients for end slopes or deflections given in Tables 1 through 3. Because E is generally a constant it can be placed outside the parentheses. Also, for convenience of computation, if some value, I_0 of the moment of inertia is taken as a reference value,

$$\theta^A{}_A = \frac{L}{E\,I_0}\left(C_1 \frac{I_0}{I_1} + \frac{C_2\,I_0}{I_2} + \cdots + C_{10}\frac{I_0}{I_{10}} \right) \dots\dots\dots (7)$$

Eq. 7 represents the general procedure used herein to evaluate the properties and behavior of beams that have nonuniform sections.

TABLE 1.—COEFFICIENTS FOR END SLOPES

Segment	(a) End Moments			(b) Uniform Load	
	$\theta^A{}_A$	$\theta^B{}_B$	$\theta^A{}_B = \theta^B{}_A$	$\theta^w{}_A$	$\theta^w{}_B$
1	0.090333	0.000333	0.004667	0.00217917	0.00015417
2	0.072333	0.002333	0.012667	0.00535417	0.00097917
3	0.056333	0.006333	0.018667	0.00697917	0.00235417
4	0.042333	0.012333	0.022667	0.00735417	0.00397917
5	0.030333	0.020333	0.024667	0.00677917	0.00555417
6	0.020333	0.030333	0.024667	0.00555417	0.00677917
7	0.012333	0.042333	0.022667	0.00397917	0.00735417
8	0.006333	0.056333	0.018667	0.00235417	0.00697917
9	0.002333	0.072333	0.012667	0.00097917	0.00535417
10	0.000333	0.090333	0.004667	0.00015417	0.00217917

Carry-Over and Stiffness Factors.—The moment carry-over factor from end A to end B of a beam is defined as the moment produced at the fixed end B by a unit moment applied at A. It can be shown that

$$C_{AB} = \frac{\theta^A{}_B}{\theta^B{}_B} \dots\dots\dots\dots\dots (8a)$$

and

$$C_{BA} = \frac{\theta^B{}_A}{\theta^A{}_A} \dots\dots\dots\dots\dots (8b)$$

in which C_{AB} is the moment carry-over factor from end A to end B and C_{BA} is the moment carry-over factor from end B to end A.

Because the stiffness factor K at the end of a beam is defined as the moment required to rotate that end through a unit angle, it follows that when end B is simply supported

$$K_{AB} = \frac{1}{\theta^A_A} \dots\dots\dots\dots\dots\dots\dots (9)$$

and when end B is fixed

$$K'_{AB} = \frac{\theta^B_B}{\theta^A_A \theta^B_B - \theta^A_B \theta^B_A} \dots\dots\dots\dots (10)$$

in which K_{AB} is the stiffness factor at end A if end B is simply supported and K'_{AB} denotes the stiffness factor at end A if end B is fixed. When end A is simply supported,

$$K_{BA} = \frac{1}{\theta^B_B} \dots\dots\dots\dots\dots\dots\dots (11)$$

and when A is fixed

$$K'_{BA} = \frac{\theta^A_A}{\theta^A_A \theta^B_B - \theta^A_B \theta^B_A} \dots\dots\dots\dots (12)$$

in which K_{BA} is the stiffness factor at end B when end A is simply supported and K'_{BA} represents the stiffness factor at end B when end A is fixed.

Thus, it is evident that, after the values of the end slopes have been determined, the carry-over factor and stiffness factor may be found by using Eqs. 8 to 12. Also, it should be noted that the units of Eqs. 9 to 12 are such that the stiffness factors vary directly as the moment of inertia times the modulus of elasticity and inversely as the length of the beam.

Fixed-End Moments.—Fig. 2(b) shows the $(M/E\,I)$-diagram for a simple beam having a constant value of $E\,I$ and acted on by a unit concentrated load. For any segment extending a distance $a\,L$ along the beam from the left support A, when $a < b$,

$$\theta^P_A = \frac{L^2}{E\,I}\left[\left(\frac{a^2}{2} - \frac{a^3}{3}\right)(1 - b)\right] \dots\dots\dots\dots (13)$$

and

$$\theta^P_B = \frac{L^2}{E\,I}\left[\frac{a^3}{3}(1 - b)\right] \dots\dots\dots\dots\dots (14)$$

in which b is the ratio of the distance measured from the left support to the point of application of load P to the span length, θ^P_A denotes the slope at end A caused by a unit concentrated load, and θ^P_B is the slope at end B caused by a unit concentrated load.

When $a > b$,

$$\theta^P_A = \frac{L^2}{E\,I}\left[b\left(a - a^2 + \frac{a^3}{3}\right) - \frac{b^2}{2} + \frac{b^3}{6}\right] \dots\dots\dots\dots (15)$$

and

$$\theta^P_B = \frac{L^2}{E\,I}\left[b\left(\frac{a^2}{2} - \frac{a^3}{3}\right) - \frac{b^3}{6}\right] \dots\dots\dots\dots (16)$$

The quantities in brackets in Eqs. 13 through 16 are coefficients for end slopes produced by a segment of the $(M/E\,I)$-diagram extending a distance $a\,L$ from end A. Coefficients for ten equal segments have been evaluated from these equations and are given in Table 2. By the use of these coefficients the total

TABLE 2.—COEFFICIENTS FOR END SLOPES PRODUCED BY A CONCENTRATED LOAD

$$\theta^P_A = 0.009067\,\frac{L^2}{EI} \qquad \theta^P_B = 0.004933\,\frac{L^2}{EI}$$

For θ^P_A (VALUES OF b read as 0.9, 0.8, 0.7, 0.6, 0.5, 0.4, 0.3, 0.2, 0.1 with Segment 10…1)

For θ^P_B (VALUES OF b read as 0.1, 0.2, 0.3, 0.4, 0.5, 0.6, 0.7, 0.8, 0.9 with Segment 1…10)

Segment	0.1	0.2	0.3	0.4	0.5	0.6	0.7	0.8	0.9
1	0.004200	0.003733	0.003267	0.002800	0.002333	0.001867	0.001400	0.000933	0.000467
2	0.007233	0.010133	0.008867	0.007600	0.006333	0.005067	0.003800	0.002533	0.001267
3	0.005633	0.011267	0.013067	0.011200	0.009333	0.007467	0.005600	0.003733	0.001867
4	0.004233	0.008467	0.012700	0.013600	0.011333	0.009067	0.006800	0.004533	0.002267
5	0.003033	0.006067	0.009100	0.012133	0.012333	0.009867	0.007400	0.004933	0.002467
6	0.002033	0.004067	0.006100	0.008133	0.010167	0.009867	0.007400	0.004933	0.002467
7	0.001233	0.002467	0.003700	0.004933	0.006167	0.007400	0.006800	0.004533	0.002267
8	0.000633	0.001267	0.001900	0.002533	0.003167	0.003800	0.004433	0.003733	0.001867
9	0.000233	0.000467	0.000700	0.000933	0.001167	0.001400	0.001633	0.001867	0.001267
10	0.000033	0.000067	0.000100	0.000133	0.000167	0.000200	0.000233	0.000267	0.000300

values of end slopes for beams with variable moments of inertia may be found by a summation process similar to that indicated by Eq. 7.

For a unit uniform load w (Fig. 2(c)),

$$\theta^w{}_A = \frac{L^3}{E\,I}\left(\frac{a^2}{4} - \frac{a^3}{3} + \frac{a^4}{8}\right) \dots \dots \dots \dots \dots (17)$$

and

$$\theta^w{}_B = \frac{L^3}{E\,I}\left(\frac{a^3}{6} - \frac{a^4}{8}\right) \dots \dots \dots \dots \dots (18)$$

in which $\theta^w{}_A$ is the slope at end A caused by a unit uniformly distributed load and $\theta^w{}_B$ is the slope at end B caused by a unit uniformly distributed load. The coefficients of these slopes for ten equal segments are given in Table 1(b).

With the end slopes evaluated, equations can be used to determine the fixed-end moments; for a concentrated load P, when both ends of the beam are fixed,

$$M^F{}_A = P\,(\theta^P{}_A\,K'{}_{AB} - \theta^P{}_B\,C_{BA}\,K'{}_{BA}) \dots \dots \dots \dots (19)$$

and

$$M^F{}_B = P\,(\theta^P{}_B\,K'{}_{BA} - \theta^P{}_A\,C_{AB}\,K'{}_{AB}) \dots \dots \dots \dots (20)$$

in which $M^F{}_A$ is the fixed-end moment at end A of span AB and $M^F{}_B$ is the fixed-moment at end B.

For uniform loads when both ends of the beam are fixed,

$$M^F{}_A = w\,(\theta^w{}_A\,K'{}_{AB} - \theta^w{}_B\,C_{BA}\,K'{}_{BA}) \dots \dots \dots \dots (21)$$

and

$$M^F{}_B = w\,(\theta^w{}_B\,K'{}_{BA} - \theta^w{}_A\,C_{AB}\,K'{}_{AB}) \dots \dots \dots \dots (22)$$

For concentrated loads when end A is simply supported,

$$M^F{}_B = P\,(\theta^P{}_B\,K_{BA}) \dots \dots \dots \dots \dots (23)$$

For uniform loads when end A is simply supported,

$$M^F{}_B = w\,(\theta^w{}_B\,K_{BA}) \dots \dots \dots \dots \dots (24)$$

It should be noted that the units of the terms in parentheses in Eqs. 19, 20, and 23 are such that the moments are the product of load and length. Similarly, the moments from Eqs. 21, 22, and 24 reduce to the form of load per unit length times length squared.

Dead-Load Deflections.—The dead-load deflection at any point on a beam can also be computed by the method of constant $(E\,I)$-segments. In this case, however, the quantities used are the moments of the segments of the $(M/E\,I)$-diagram rather than the reactions.

In order to compute the dead-load deflections of both simple and continuous beams, parabolic, triangular, and rectangular moment diagrams may be considered. The parabolic diagram is used to compute the simple-beam deflections; the triangular and rectangular diagrams serve for computing the deflections caused by end moments.

Fig. 2 (c) shows a beam having a constant value of $E I$ subjected to a parabolic $(M/E I)$-diagram resulting from a uniformly distributed load of w per unit length. The deflection Δ_D at point D (which is a distance d from A) caused by that segment of the $(M/E I)$-diagram extending a distance $a L$ along the beam from the left support A can be expressed, when $a < d$, as

$$\Delta_D = \frac{w L^4}{E I}\left[\tfrac{1}{2}\,(1 - d)\left(\frac{a^3}{3} - \frac{a^4}{4}\right)\right] \quad\text{(25)}$$

When $a > d$,

$$\Delta_D = \frac{w L^4}{E I}\left[\frac{d}{2}\left(\frac{a^2}{2} - \frac{2\,a^3}{3} + \frac{a^4}{4}\right) - \frac{d}{2}\left(\frac{d^2}{6} - \frac{d^3}{12}\right)\right] \quad\text{(26)}$$

Similarly, for a moment M_T applied at end B, when $a < d$,

$$\Delta_D = \frac{M_T L^2}{E I}\left[(1 - d)\,\frac{a^3}{3}\right] \quad\text{(27)}$$

When $a > d$,

$$\Delta_D = \frac{M_T L^2}{E I}\left[d\left(\frac{a^2}{2} - \frac{a^3}{3}\right) - \frac{d^3}{6}\right] \quad\text{(28)}$$

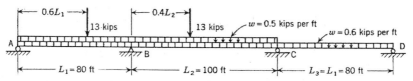

FIG. 3.—THREE-SPAN CONTINUOUS BEAM AND LOADINGS

For a rectangular moment diagram with equal moments applied at ends A and B when $a < d$,

$$\Delta_D = \frac{M_R L^2}{E I}\left[(1 - d)\,\frac{a^2}{2}\right] \quad\text{(29)}$$

When $a > d$,

$$\Delta_D = \frac{M_R L^2}{E I}\left[a\,d\left(1 - \frac{a}{2}\right) - \frac{d^2}{2}\right] \quad\text{(30)}$$

In Eqs. 25 through 30 the quantities in brackets are coefficients of the deflection of point D on a beam having a constant value of $E I$. These quantities are due only to the segment $a L$ of the $(M/E I)$-diagram. Coefficients are evaluated for ten equal segments in Table 3 for values of d of $\tfrac{1}{4}$, $\tfrac{1}{2}$, and $\tfrac{3}{4}$.

For beams of nonuniform section the deflections are computed by the same process of summation as that indicated by Eq. 7 for end slopes.

EXAMPLES OF APPLICATION

Fig. 3 shows a three-span continuous beam and loading; there will be determined the negative moments at supports B and C and the deflection at the $\tfrac{1}{2}$ point of span AB due to the uniform dead load of 0.6 kip per ft.

TABLE 3.—COEFFICIENTS FOR DEFLECTIONS

(a) PARABOLIC MOMENT DIAGRAM

(b) TRIANGULAR MOMENT DIAGRAM

(c) RECTANGULAR MOMENT DIAGRAM

VALUES OF d

Segment	(a) Parabolic 1/4	(a) Parabolic 1/2	(a) Parabolic 3/4	(b) Triangular 1/4	(b) Triangular 1/2	(b) Triangular 3/4	(c) Rectangular 1/4	(c) Rectangular 1/2	(c) Rectangular 3/4
1	0.0001156250	0.0000770833	0.0000385417	0.00025000	0.00016667	0.00008333	0.003750	0.002500	0.001250
2	0.0007343750	0.0004895833	0.0002447917	0.00175000	0.00116667	0.00058333	0.011250	0.007500	0.003750
3	0.0016388021	0.0011770833	0.0005885417	0.00439583	0.00316667	0.00158333	0.017500	0.012500	0.006250
4	0.0018385417	0.0019895833	0.0009947917	0.00566667	0.00616667	0.00308333	0.016250	0.017500	0.008750
5	0.0016947917	0.0027770833	0.0013885417	0.00616667	0.01016667	0.00508333	0.013750	0.022500	0.011250
6	0.0013885417	0.0027770833	0.0016947917	0.00566667	0.01233333	0.00758333	0.011250	0.022500	0.013750
7	0.0009947917	0.0019895833	0.0018385417	0.00466667	0.01133333	0.01058333	0.008750	0.017500	0.016250
8	0.0005885417	0.0011770833	0.0016388021	0.00316667	0.00933333	0.01310417	0.006250	0.012500	0.017500
9	0.0002447917	0.0004895833	0.0007343750	0.00166667	0.00633333	0.00950000	0.003750	0.007500	0.011250
10	0.0000385417	0.0000770833	0.0001156250	0.00116667	0.00233333	0.00350000	0.001250	0.002500	0.003750

Moment diagram reference values:
(a) $M = \dfrac{L^2}{8}$, $\Delta_{0.5} = 0.0019896 \dfrac{L^4}{EI}$
(b) $M = 1$, $\Delta_{0.5} = 0.0061667 \dfrac{L^2}{EI}$
(c) $M = 1$, $\Delta_{0.5} = 0.01750 \dfrac{L^2}{EI}$

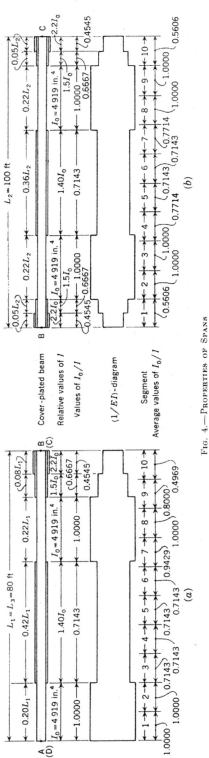

FIG. 4.—PROPERTIES OF SPANS

TABLE 4.—COMPUTATIONS FOR BEAM IN FIG. 4

(a) SPAN AB

Segment	For θB_B		For θP_B		For θw_B	
	Table 1(a)	θB_B	Table 2	θP_B	Table 1(b)	θw_B
1	0.00033	0.0003	0.00013	0.00013	0.00015	0.00015
2	0.00233	0.0023	0.00093	0.00093	0.00098	0.00098
3	0.00633	0.0045	0.00253	0.00181	0.00235	0.00168
4	0.01233	0.0088	0.00493	0.00352	0.00398	0.00284
5	0.02033	0.0145	0.00813	0.00581	0.00555	0.00396
6	0.03033	0.0217	0.01213	0.00867	0.00678	0.00484
7	0.04233	0.0399	0.01360	0.01283	0.00735	0.00693
8	0.05633	0.0563	0.01120	0.01120	0.00698	0.00698
9	0.07233	0.0579	0.00750	0.00608	0.00535	0.00428
10	0.09033	0.0449	0.00380	0.00139	0.00218	0.00108
Total		0.2511		0.05237		0.03372

(b) SPAN BC

Segment	For $\theta B_B = \theta C_C$	For $\theta B_C = \theta C_B$		For θP_B		For θP_C		For $\theta w_B = \theta w_C$	
	$\theta B_B = \theta C_C$	Table 1(a)	$\theta B_C = \theta C_B$	Table 2	θP_B	Table 2	θP_C	Table 1(b)	$\theta w_B = \theta w_C$
1	0.0506	0.00467	0.0026	0.00280	0.00157	0.00020	0.00011	0.00218	0.00122
2	0.0723	0.01267	0.0127	0.00760	0.00760	0.00140	0.00140	0.00535	0.00535
3	0.0563	0.01867	0.0187	0.01120	0.01120	0.00380	0.00380	0.00698	0.00698
4	0.0326	0.02467	0.0175	0.01360	0.01050	0.00740	0.00571	0.00735	0.00567
5	0.0217	0.02467	0.0176	0.01213	0.00867	0.00987	0.00705	0.00678	0.00484
6	0.0145	0.02467	0.0176	0.00813	0.00581	0.00987	0.00705	0.00555	0.00396
7	0.0095	0.02267	0.0175	0.00493	0.00380	0.00907	0.00700	0.00398	0.00307
8	0.0063	0.01867	0.0187	0.00253	0.00253	0.00747	0.00747	0.00235	0.00235
9	0.0023	0.01267	0.0127	0.00093	0.00093	0.00507	0.00507	0.00098	0.00098
10	0.0002	0.00467	0.0026	0.00013	0.00007	0.00187	0.00105	0.00015	0.00008
Total	0.2663		0.1382		0.05268		0.04571		0.03450

The variation in the moment of inertia and values of I_0/I for the end spans and center span are given in Fig. 4. The average values of I_0/I for each of the 10 equal segments in each span are also shown in this illustration.

In Table 4 there is shown a typical form of the computations for determining the end slopes at end B of span AB and at both ends B and C of span BC. The values of I_0/I are obtained from Fig. 4, and the values of the coefficients are taken from Tables 1 and 2. The value of the coefficient for each segment is multiplied by the value of I_0/I for that segment, and the product is entered in the adjoining column. The columns are then totaled; the values of these column totals, when multiplied by the ratio $L/E\,I_0$, yield the end slopes.

Carry-Over Factors and Stiffness Factors.—Span AB is simply supported at A; therefore, the stiffness is found by Eq. 11—

$$K_{BA} = \frac{1}{0.2511} = 3.98 \frac{E\,I_0}{L_1}.$$

The beam is continuous over supports B and C; therefore, carry-over factors and stiffness factors for span BC are computed from Eqs. 8, 10, and 12:

$$C_{BC} = C_{CB} = \frac{0.1382}{0.2663} = 0.519$$

$$K'_{BC} = K'_{CB} = \frac{0.2663}{(0.2663)^2 - (0.1382)^2} = 5.14 \frac{E\,I_0}{L_2}.$$

It should be noted that, when the coefficients in Table 1(a) are used for the analysis of span BC, end A becomes B and end B becomes C. Because of symmetry the computations for span BC are reduced considerably, and the stiffness determined for span AB also applies to span CD.

Fixed-End Moments.—The fixed-end moment at support B is for the concentrated load, from Eq. 23,

$$M^F{}_B = 13.0\ (80)\ (0.05237 \times 3.98) = 217 \text{ ft-kips}$$

and for the uniform load, from Eq. 24,

$$M^F{}_B = 1.1\ (80)^2\ (0.03372 \times 3.98) = 944 \text{ ft-kips}$$

which results in a total $M^F{}_B$ of 1,161 ft-kips.

The coefficients for the end slope at B are obtained from Tables 2 and 1(b). After the end slopes at B resulting from the concentrated and uniform loads have been determined, the respective fixed-end moments are computed from Eqs. 23 and 24.

In a similar manner, the fixed-end moments are obtained at supports B and C for the loads in span BC. Because the span is fixed at both ends, the moments are found from Eqs. 19, 20, 21, and 22—

For the concentrated load, from Eq. 19,

$$M^F{}_B = 13.0\ (100)\ [(0.05268 \times 5.14) - (0.04571$$
$$\times\ 0.519 \times 5.14)] = 194 \text{ ft-kips}.$$

For the uniform load, from Eq. 21,

$$M^F{}_B = 1.1 \ (100)^2 \left[(0.03450 \times 5.14) - (0.03450 \right.$$
$$\left. \times 0.519 \times 5.14) \right] = 939 \text{ ft-kips.}$$

These result in a total $M^F{}_B$ of 1,133 ft-kips. For the concentrated load, from Eq. 20,

$$M^F{}_C = 13.0 \ (100) \left[(0.04571 \times 5.14) - (0.05268 \right.$$
$$\left. \times 0.519 \times 5.14) \right] = 123 \text{ ft-kips.}$$

For the uniform load, from Eq. 22,

$$M^F{}_C = M^F{}_B = 939 \text{ ft-kips.}$$

These result in a total $M^F{}_C$ of 1,062 ft-kips.

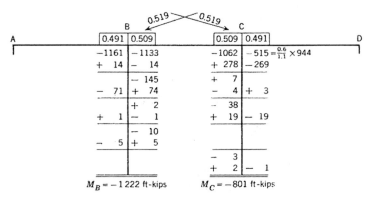

(a) Moments due to dead load plus live load

(b) Moments due to dead load

FIG. 5.—MOMENT-DISTRIBUTION COMPUTATIONS

It should be noted that these computations are reduced because of symmetry of the uniform load and of the properties of the beam.

No computations for the fixed-end moment in span CD have been made because the moment may be determined by a ratio after the computations for the uniform load in span AB have been made.

Moment Distribution.—The actual moments at supports B and C due to the total loading on the three-span continuous unit are computed in Fig. 5(a); the dead-load moments are determined in Fig. 5(b). The stiffnesses are

$$K_{BA} = \frac{3.98}{80} = 0.0497$$

and

$$K'_{BC} = \frac{5.14}{100} = \frac{0.0514}{0.1011}.$$

The distribution factors are

$$BA = CD = \frac{0.0497}{0.1011} = 0.491$$

and

$$BC = CB = \frac{0.0514}{0.1011} = 0.509.$$

These computations are self-explanatory. It is important to note that the computations for relative stiffness and distribution factors take into account the differences in span lengths. Because the same reference value of I_0 was used in determining the values of relative I in all spans and because E is constant, these values need not be included in the computations for the relative stiffnesses.

TABLE 5.—DEAD–LOAD DEFLECTION AT MIDPOINT OF AB

Segment	I_0/I	For Uniform Load		For Moment at B	
		Table 3(a)	$\Delta_{\frac{1}{2}}$	Table 3(b)	$\Delta_{\frac{1}{2}}$
1	1.0000	0.0000771	0.000077	0.0001667	0.000167
2	1.0000	0.0004896	0.000490	0.0011667	0.001167
3	0.7143	0.0011771	0.000840	0.0031667	0.002260
4	0.7143	0.0019896	0.001416	0.0061667	0.004400
5	0.7143	0.0027771	0.001976	0.0101667	0.007250
6	0.7143	0.0027771	0.001976	0.0123333	0.008790
7	0.9429	0.0019896	0.001873	0.0113333	0.010690
8	1.0000	0.0011771	0.001177	0.0093333	0.009333
9	0.8000	0.0004896	0.000392	0.0063333	0.005060
10	0.4969	0.0000771	0.000038	0.0023333	0.001160
Total			0.010255		0.050277

Deflection.—The dead-load deflection at the $\frac{1}{2}$ point of span AB is computed in Table 5 using the coefficients from Table 3. It should be noted that this deflection is made up of two parts. The deflection resulting from the simple beam, parabolic moment diagram is downward, whereas the deflection due to the triangular variation in negative moment, Fig. 5(b), is upward:

$$\Delta_{\frac{1}{2}} \downarrow = \frac{0.010255 \times 0.6 \times 80^4}{30,000 \times 4,919} = 0.001710 \times (12)^3 = 2.95 \text{ in.} \downarrow$$

$$\Delta_{\frac{1}{2}} \uparrow = \frac{0.050277 \times 514 \times 80^2}{30,000 \times 4,919} = 0.001121 \times (12)^3 = \frac{1.94 \text{ in.} \uparrow}{1.01 \text{ in.} \downarrow} = \Delta_{\frac{1}{2}}.$$

CONCLUSIONS

The example contained herein demonstrates the constant-segment method of analysis and the usefulness of predetermined constants. Tables 4 and 5 represent much less labor than that required by any other method of analysis. The method and constants presented herein have been used to obtain a direct solution for moments and deflections but they are also useful in the development of influence lines.

It should be noted that one of the distinct advantages of the use of the constants given in Tables 1, 2, and 3 is the ease with which computations such as those given in Tables 4 and 5 may be developed by single settings of the values of I_0/I on the slide-rule or computing machine.

DISCUSSION

Thomas F. Hickerson,[3] M. ASCE.—Although not specifically stated by the authors, this work is based on the conjugate-beam method. In the belief that this principle offers the best approach to structural analysis and particularly to beam slopes and deflections, it has been used exclusively in a similar work.[4]

Comparing Fig. 6(a) and Fig. 6(b), it is obvious Eq. 5 is correct without citing Maxwell's law of reciprocal relations.

At the bottoms of Tables 1 through 3, the totals could have been given to advantage. Thus, in Table 1(a), from left to right, the totals would be 0.33333, 0.33333, and 0.16667, indicating that, as a limiting condition, when I is constant throughout the member,

$$\theta^A{}_A = \frac{1}{3}\frac{L}{E\,I} \quad\dots\dots\dots\dots\dots\dots\dots\dots (31)$$

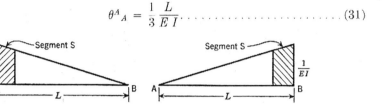

Fig. 6.—$(M/E\,I)$—Diagrams for Span AB

and

$$\theta^B{}_A = \frac{1}{6}\frac{L}{E\,I} \quad\dots\dots\dots\dots\dots\dots\dots\dots (32)$$

for a unit moment at A.

Also, in Table 2 for $b = 0.4$, the total is 0.064. Hence, if I is constant,

$$\theta^P{}_A = 0.064\frac{P\,L^2}{E\,I} \quad\dots\dots\dots\dots\dots\dots\dots (33)$$

The stiffness, carry-over, and distribution factors are based on the assumption that the other end of the member is fixed—a condition that usually does not exist. Hence, distribution and carry-over must take place through a few cycles in order to obtain the final correct result.

The inclusion of coefficients for deflections produced by a concentrated load would have added to the completeness of the paper. Perhaps Messrs. Hanson and Wiley wished to avoid dealing with absolute maximum deflections. However, the midspan-deflection coefficients are closely representative of the maximum deflections.

The neatness, clarity, and accuracy of the paper is commendable. However, one may doubt whether it presents the simplest and shortest procedure for obtaining slopes, deflections, or moments when I is variable.

[3] Formerly Prof. of Civ. Eng., Univ. of North Carolina, Chapel Hill, N. C.
[4] "Statically Indeterminate Frameworks: Beam Deflection When I Is Constant or Variable," by Thomas F. Hickerson, University Press, Chapel Hill, N. C., 1949.

EUGENE J. VAYDA,[5] M. ASCE.—The interpretation and presentation of this subject by Messrs. Hanson and Wiley are to be commended. To illustrate this method of analysis, the fixed-end moment at the top of a haunched column that is bent by an offset force and hinged at the bottom, as shown in Fig. 7(a), shall be determined.

The elastic line of the simply supported beam AB, bent by a moment M (in which $M = P e$), will have a slope with the horizontal of θ_P at point B (Fig. 7(b)). The moment of inertia is computed at the center of gravity of each division (Fig. 7(c)). After finding M_P and M_P/I at the center of gravity of each division, the reaction of the conjugate beam, loaded with the (M_P/I)-diagram, is R_P at point B (Fig. 7(d)) and

$$E\,\theta_P = R_P \dots\dots\dots\dots\dots\dots\dots (34)$$

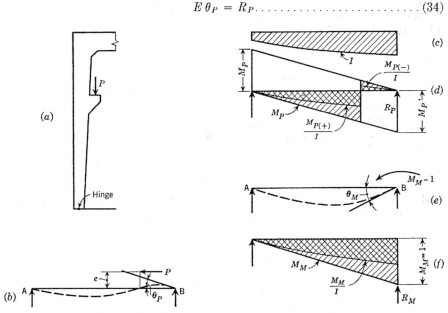

FIG. 7.—HAUNCHED COLUMN SUBJECTED TO OFFSET LOAD

The slope with the horizontal of the elastic line at point B when the same simply supported beam is bent by a moment of unity is θ_M (Fig. 7(e)). After finding M_M and M_M/I at the center of gravity of each division, the reaction at point B, of the conjugate beam, loaded with the (M_M/I)-diagram, is R_M (Fig. 7(f)). Therefore,

$$E\,\theta_M = R_M \dots\dots\dots\dots\dots\dots\dots (35)$$

and if the total slope of the elastic line at the fixed end B is θ_B,

$$E\,\theta_B = E\,(\theta_P + \theta_M) = R_P + R_M\,M_M = 0 \dots\dots\dots (36)$$

from which

$$M_M = -\frac{R_P}{R_M} \dots\dots\dots\dots\dots\dots\dots (37)$$

[5] Designer, Tippetts-Abbett-McCarthy-Stratton, Engrs., New York, N. Y.

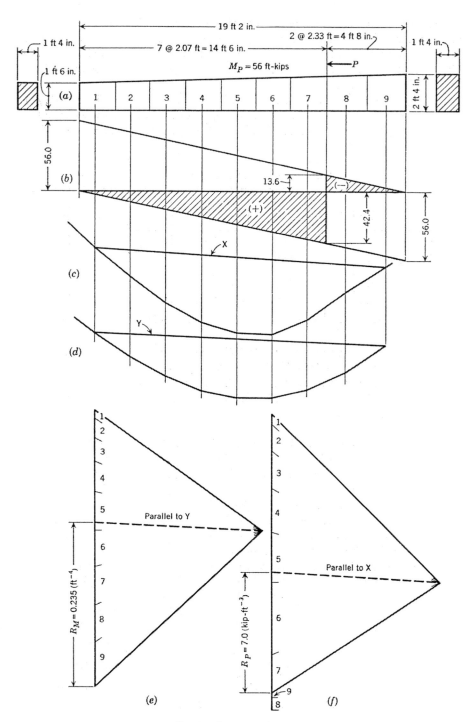

FIG. 8.—GRAPHICAL ANALYSIS

Graphical analysis offers a fast solution of the problem in which a crane runway is attached to the vertical member of a rigid frame. It is assumed that a bending moment of 56 ft-kips is created (Fig. 8(a)) and that the column is hinged at the 1 ft-6 in. end and fixed at the 2 ft-4 in. end; the computations have been made in Table 6.

In Fig. 8(b), M_P is determined for each division point. With the (M_P/I)-force polygon (Fig. 8(f)) the funicular polygon of Fig. 8(c) is drawn; the line drawn in Fig. 8(f) parallel to the line X of Fig. 8(c) cuts of the reaction of the conjugate beam, R_P.

TABLE 6.—COMPUTATIONS FOR FIG. 8

Segment	Value of I, in ft⁴	Value of M_P, in foot-kips	Value of M_P/I	Value of M_M for unit moment at B	Value of M_M/I
1	5.00	3.03	0.61	0.054	0.0108
2	5.92	9.08	1.53	0.162	0.0273
3	6.94	15.13	2.18	0.270	0.0390
4	8.20	21.18	2.58	0.378	0.0460
5	9.30	27.73	2.94	0.486	0.0521
6	10.70	33.28	3.11	0.594	0.0555
7	12.10	39.33	3.25	0.702	0.0580
8	13.90	−10.20	−0.735	0.815	0.0585
9	15.90	− 3.40	−0.214	0.950	0.0600

From the force polygon (Fig. 8(e)) the funicular polygon of Fig. 8(d) is drawn. The line in the (M_M/I)-force polygon (Fig. 8(e)) parallel to the line Y of Fig. 8(d) cuts off the reaction R_M of the conjugate beam.

The fixed-end moment M_F at the large end is the quotient of the two conjugate-beam reactions.

JARO J. POLIVKA,[6] M. ASCE.—In the "Synopsis" it is noted that there are other methods of analysis for beams having variable moments of inertia but these are said to be more time-consuming and subject to numerical errors. One method which proves to be very simple and permits checking during various steps of the computations is the method of constant centers of elastic rotations or fixed points.[7, 8, 9] This method is advantageous in that a great part of the computations can be applied to any type of loading. The continuous beam analyzed as an example by Messrs. Hanson and Wiley needs only two fixed points to be determined because of symmetry, and the resulting bending moments for any type of loading can be found directly, with any accuracy required, without using a series of approximations characteristic of the method of moment distribution. The fixed points are determined by slopes θ^A_A, θ^B_B, and θ^A_B computed either by the method presented by the

---

[6] Cons. Engr., Berkeley, Calif., and Lecturer, Stanford Univ. Stanford, Calif.

[7] "Graphical Methods of Analyzing Statically Indeterminate Structures," by J. J. Polivka, *Mimeographed Lectures*, Univ. of California, Berkeley, Calif., 1940, and 2d Ed., 1942.

[8] "Frames and Bents in Reinforced Concrete," by J. J. Polivka, *Revue du Béton Armé*, Vols. 9 and 10, Brussels, 1920.

[9] "Continuous Arches on Elastic Supports," by J. J. Polivka, *Der Brueckenbau*, Vols. 4, 5, and 6, Heidelberg, 1920.

authors, or, more accurately, by the same moment-area method, but applied to actual segments having different moments of inertia; there is practically no difference in the results of both methods. For example, Table 4(b) indicates the values $\theta^B{}_B = 0.2663$ and $\theta^B{}_C = 0.1382$, and the writer computed the corresponding values to be $\theta^B{}_B = 0.263996$ and $\theta^B{}_C = 0.140636$, their sum being 0.404632 as compared with the authors' sum of 0.4045.

Every such analysis should be checked for final results. A simple method consists in computing the final slopes under any given loading at supports B and C for both adjacent spans, and these slopes must be numerically equal. It is suggested that one perform this checking for any of the assumed types of loading.

WALTER E. HANSON,[10] M. ASCE, AND WALLACE F. WILEY[11].—The discussions that have been presented are most interesting and have contributed to the understanding of the method and its application; the comments have been constructive in nature and clearly presented. The writers appreciate these discussions as well as the many favorable comments from engineers who have recognized the time-saving features of the method in the analysis of indeterminate highway bridge girders having variable moments of inertia.

The writers agree with Mr. Hickerson that the paper is based on the conjugate-beam method. However, many other methods could be listed as bases for the work—among these are moment area, elastic weights, and angle changes. It is preferred to group all these methods under the general classification of geometry of small angle changes.

Mr. Hickerson states that "the stiffness, carry-over, and distribution factors are based on the assumption that the other end of the member is fixed—a condition that usually does not exist." Apparently, Eqs. 9 and 11 were overlooked; these give the stiffness factors, and Eqs. 23 and 24 give the fixed-end moments when one end of the span is simply supported.

Messrs. Vayda and Polivka both discussed interesting and expeditious methods of analysis involving some graphics. It is agreed that graphical procedures often expedite the solutions of many structural problems.

During the development of the paper the writers were primarily concerned with its application to the analysis of continuous highway bridges. The example used is easily recognized as a typical three-span beam with cover plates subjected to the uniform and roving concentrated live loads given in the specifications of the American Association of State Highway Officials (AASHO). Moreover, the method was extended to computations for dead-load deflections which are commonly shown on bridge plans to facilitate the construction of forms to proper elevations and dimensions to compensate for deflections caused by dead weight.

Subsequent to the publication of the paper, the writers have used the method in the analysis of several welded, haunched, highway bridge girders.

---

[10] Cons. Engr., Hanson, Collins & Rice, Springfield, Ill.
[11] Senior Bridge Designer, Illinois Div. of Highways, Springfield, Ill.

In these designs the H-S truck loading given in the AASHO specifications[12] has governed the positive moment values at the center of the spans. Unless the span length is exactly 140 ft, the concentrated wheel loads of this specified truck do not coincide with the $\frac{1}{10}$ points of the span. The writers have concluded that for this condition of loading it is sufficiently accurate, for purposes of design, to compute equivalent simple-beam reactions at the $\frac{1}{10}$ points and to use these reactions as the loads applied to the girder. In this way, Table 2 can be readily utilized in the analysis of this type of loading.

[12] "Standard Specifications for Highway Bridges," A.A.S.H.O., 6th Ed., 1953, p. 162.

A Consulting Engineer's View on Continuing Education

Walter E. Hanson
Consulting Engineer
W. E. Hanson and Associates
Springfield, Illinois

Introduction

The reasons for continuing education of personnel in consulting engineering firms in private practice are essentially the same as for engineers in other categories of employment. There is, however, one reason why engineers in private practice may consider the need for continuing education in a slightly different light. This difference is a natural reflection of the private enterprise and business aspects associated with private practice. There is competition in our business, and the natural instinct of survival compels us to plan ahead. We cannot at any time become apathetic about our qualifications because they represent our security. In other words, continuing education is one important way to improve our chances of being selected for the job. Needless to say, after the agreement is signed, we do a better job in the performance of our services for the client.

There is another closely related point about which I feel very strongly. No private practitioner is entitled or should be allowed to offer his services as a consulting engineer unless he possesses technical competence. Technical competence means up-to-date knowledge. Registration laws have helped immeasurably to protect the public in this regard, but they are obviously only a part of what is required to maintain and build the profession of engineering. Continuing education is so important to us in private practice because it renews, not our legal, but our ethical right to offer our services.

I am a member of three major engineering societies that appear to be actively engaged at present in the promotion of continuing education. These are NSPE and CEC in addition to ASCE. It seems to me that the recent increased interest in this subject merely reflects the fact that more and more engineers have come to realize that technical competence and professionalism are inseparable. Many of us have felt strongly concerning this relationship for many years. This is why we have always belonged to and participated in the proceedings of technical societies in addition to the professional groups. So, we are happy to see the increased emphasis being placed on continuing education, but we also believe that a lot of rather nebulous ideas need to be brought into the focus.

In the first outline of this talk, I intended to devote considerable time to "reasons why continuing education is necessary." I also intended to discuss "who needs continuing education." Even though we must understand "why" and "who" before a program can be developed, I believe that these questions have perhaps received adequate discussion elsewhere, if not at this meeting. Suffice it to say here that needs do exist, and that all engineers, from those in administrative positions to the engineering technicians, possess various types of needs and desires for continuing education.

I prefer in this limited time to discuss three responsibilities in connection with continuing education: (1) individual, (2) company, and (3) institutions of higher education. Moreover, I shall withhold my own ideas on implementation of programs until the discussion period.

The Responsibility of the Individual

This is where we start. Here we are dealing with special interests, motivations, ambitions, and the willingness (or lack of it) to subject oneself to personal disciplines, and for that matter, an occasional sacrifice. The tendency to pass individual responsibility on to either the company or to the universities occurs too frequently.

I am inclined to believe that the greatest responsibility for continuing education should rest with the individual. By this statement, I mean that more than one-half of the new knowledge that an individual gains should be learned by self study. Indeed, are we entitled to call ourselves professional unless we accept such a responsibility?

So, let us not carry continuing education to the point of reduction in individual responsibility and the great sense of satisfaction that comes with achievement by and for one's self. Continuing education by other than the individual method should only be enough to guide, stimulate and complement individual efforts.

Every once in a while, in our continuing education, we should read and study outside our specialized technical interests. I have learned considerably during the past year from a correspondence course in "The Economics of National Defense." Also, during the recent campaign, a book entitled "The Heart of Man" by the eminent psychiatrist, Dr. Erich Fromm, proved very enlightening. I gained a deeper impression that neither of the candidates possessed a very good understanding of the subject. You will recall that the English scholar, T. R. Glover, pointed out the dangers of just a little sound knowledge. Then, there is also the danger of knowing too much about too little—completely removed from the whole concept and context.

The Responsibility of the Company

The management policies of a company create the attitudes and atmosphere, either favorable or unfavorable, to continuing education. Interests of management in personal aspirations are important. Let me say that an attitude of complacency on the part of management induces absolutely no individual motivation. Actually, such a company attitude retards individual motivation and before long, vacancies occur which have to be filled by others soon to become disenchanted.

Within limits determined by profits and budgets, a company can respond to its responsibilities. It can grant educational leaves with pay, or a least some subsidizer. It can pay for the time and expenses of employees in attendance at meetings of technical societies. It can pay tuitions for night courses which benefit the student as well as the over-all qualifications and capabilities of the company. It can provide time occasionally during working hours for special lectures, films, and other meetings in the realm of continuing education. But these possibilities must be considered only complementary to individual efforts.

It must be realized that the returns from company investments in continuing education are, to a great extent, intangible quantities. There exists an indefinite optimum which is influenced by many factors, not the least of which is the amount of individual effort expended. Under any given set of circumstances, there is a point of diminishing return when measured from a profit standpoint. That is to say, a company can conceivably spend so much time becoming educated that it does not have time to complete the work for which it is being paid. In fact, this sort of thing happens whenever a company undertakes an engineering project for which it is poorly qualified. I think that, at the best, you can call this continued education at the expense of the client; at the worst, it is education leading to bankruptcy. Here, I find myself back to my introductory remarks concerning competency and professionalism.

The Responsibility of the Institution of Higher Education

I think it is clear at this point that I do not believe that we in private practice look to the engineering colleges for solutions to all of our continuing education needs. The universities are responsible for only a small part, and only then on a cooperative and mutually beneficial basis. But it is an essential and very important responsibility.

We look to the university faculties and facilities for guidance and stimulation. We need to learn from them the latest developments in theory and the results of research in their laboratories and on projects in the field with which they have been associated. Although refresher courses, short courses and conferences are still needed, I believe that the time has come to shift some of our emphasis to "new knowledge." It would appear that programs will have to vary from those which provide a mere introduction to new knowledge to the longer detailed courses.

My advice to you who are members of university faculties is: remain patient and composed, because future requests for continued education will be many. Of course, you will continue to be exasperated by our notorious insistence that everything we learn from you must have an immediate practical application to our current projects. You may want to use some of the aspects of responsibility that I have mentioned as criteria in your evaluation and consideration of proposed programs. I am sympathetic, because I know from experience some of the problems that you face. Some requests are bound to sound unclear and even unreasonable to you.

About 100 years ago, Rankine condemned the idea that theory and practice should be "contrasted and placed in opposition, as denoting two conflicting and mutually inconsistent ideas." He criticized the "lack of communication between men of science and men of practice," and he endeavored to further the liaison between science and engineering.

The job ahead in continuing education is a huge one. It is imperative that we face it in a spirit of cooperation and a dedicated willingness to accept our rightful share of responsibility. There is no alternative if we expect to move ahead.

Involvement In Legislation And Government

By
Walter E. Hanson, P.E.

Chairman, Committee on Legislation
Illinois Association of Professions
And
Member, Legislative Committees
Illinois Society of Professional Engineers
Consulting Engineers Council of Illinois
Illinois Engineering Council

The Situation

Bills, bills, bills—in excess of 4000—stacked a yard high. This was the picture on each legislator's desk in the Illinois House and Senate during the month of June, 1967. Since that time, the 75th General Assembly has reconvened three times. Once in September, 1967, and again in March and July, 1968. In January, 1969, only a few months from now, the 76th General Assembly will convene, and the number of bills will no doubt be greater.

The members of the 75th General Assembly deserve our commendation for their consideration, deliberations and final judgments on more than 4000 bills, and for their attention to many other related matters of public concern. They also merit much more help from the general public than they have ever received in the past.

Greater public concern and assistance are imperative if we are to achieve success in the solutions of our current and future problems. These problems involve many disciplines, and they become more complex every day. Interprofessional action is required, and this means greater interprofessional involvement in legislation and government.

Why Your Help is Needed

Too many of us are inclined only to vote for the candidates of our choice; some do not become involved even to this extent. Whether we vote or not, we expect our legislators and other elected officials to go to Springfield possessed with all the wisdom necessary to introduce, consider and pass intelligently upon many thousands of bills, and to administer all previous laws. To anticipate so much without our help is clearly unreasonable. Members of the General Assembly do not have at their disposal the time, necessary staff, and physical facilities to research every bill. The only alternative is for each of us to lend a willing and constructive hand in the legislative process and in government.

Many different types of action are needed to accomplish the necessary overall involvement. These vary from a frequent letter of advice and appreciation to your legislator or other public official to becoming a candidate yourself. In between these limits of involvement is work to be done on the campaign committee of a candidate of your choice, the legislative committee of your professional society, or some special commission of government.

Since political campaigns require finances, it should be recognized that monetary contributions to the campaigns of candidates of your choice are important. Such contributions must be made with prudence, but they should be made. If a candidate is worthy of your support, he will prefer 1000 contributions of five dollars to 10 of five hundred dollars, or to a single contribution of five thousand dollars. There is probably no one thing that would have more beneficial influence on government than a greater number of small contributions which would equal and exceed, in total amount, the present larger contributions made by fewer contributors. The political action program of your professional society also needs your support so that it can contribute prudently to the campaigns of qualified candidates of both political parties.

Conclusion

Whatever the nature of involvement in legislative and government affairs, it should originate voluntarily with the individual. But, apathy and complacency too often deter voluntary participation. A special interest is usually required before "volunteers" appear on the scene. Although special interests cannot and, indeed, should not be eliminated, it must be recognized that good legislation and good government per se are the special interests of everyone. When, and only when, these paramount special interests, intangible as they seem to be, are deeply believed, will we achieve the necessary optimum involvement.

In other words, government of the people and for the people can be accomplished only by the people. And people working together in an interprofessional involvement in legislation and government can contribute much. What do you plan to do?

Use and Performance of Quaternary Materials in the Loud Thunder Dam

Walter E. Hanson, John M. Healy, and Leo J. Dondanville, Jr.
Walter E. Hanson Co., Springfield, Illinois

Abstract

The Loud Thunder Dam, located in the Loud Thunder Forest Preserve, Rock Island County, Illinois, was built during 1964 and 1965 by the Illinois Department of Conservation.

Quaternary materials used in the embankment consist of alluvium, loess, and glacial till. Sorting of materials and zoning of the embankment were required because of the engineering properties and availability of the different materials.

Observations on settlement platforms and other reference stations were made during construction and subsequent to the completion of the dam. These data provided the basis for engineering decisions, particularly concerning the construction of the chute type primary spillway, which was located on the embankment slope. Piezometers were installed near the downstream toe of the dam to observe pore water pressures in the filter blanket during the initial impoundment of the reservoir.

Introduction

Loud Thunder Dam is on Big Branch Creek near its confluence with the Mississippi, approximately 15 miles west of Rock Island, Illinois, in the Loud Thunder Forest Preserve (fig. 1). Responsibility for the development and operation of the dam and lake rests with the Illinois Department of Conservation. The County of Rock Island is responsible for the maintenance of the high-

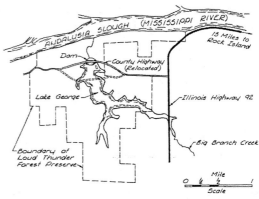

Figure 1 – Vicinity map, Loud Thunder Dam.

155

way that crosses the dam.

Subsequent to the subsurface and borrow investigations by our firm, detailed plans and specifications were prepared by the Beling Engineering Consultants of Moline, Illinois. Construction was accomplished by the Pautler Brothers Construction Company of Chester, Illinois.

Construction of the dam was started during the summer of 1964, and most of the embankment section was completed by the end of the year. After approximately one year, during which time the settlement of the embankment was observed and found to diminish to an acceptable rate, the construction of the spillway was started. The concrete spillway and bridge structure are supported directly by the embankment, and this portion of the project was accomplished during the fall of 1965 and the spring of 1966.

The impoundment of Lake George behind the dam started in October 1966. At the present time (January 1968), the reservoir is essentially full, and discharge over the spillway is expected momentarily. The lake is approximately 170 acres in area, extends approximately 2 miles in length, and has a maximum width of about a half mile. Favorable topographic characteristics of the valley are such that a major portion of the lake will exceed 50 feet in depth.

Loud Thunder Dam is a rather large earth structure in comparison with other dams constructed by the Illinois Department of Conservation. The length of the embankment is approximately 1000 feet, and its height across most of the valley is between 70 and 75 feet. However, it was necessary to remove and replace a portion of the soft valley alluvium beneath the original ground surface, and to also extend a cut-off trench into the underlying shale bedrock. These operations resulted in a maximum over-all height of compacted embankment of about 85 to 90 feet.

The detailed soil and foundation engineering investigation began with a geological appraisal of the site. It continued with a program of test borings and laboratory testing, which provided the basis for an engineering evaluation of seepage, stability, and consolidation. An initial foundation engineering report gave recommendations for the design cross section and for the construction of the embankment. Thereafter, the entire cycle of design and construction was monitored in order to ascertain that the design parameters evaluated in the site investigation and engineering analysis would, in fact, be obtained in the construction of the dam.

Site Geology

A generalized cross section through the valley and abutments of the dam is presented as figure 2.

Both the valley and the adjacent uplands are underlain by gray shale of Pennsylvanian age. This shale is present at depths of 10 to 15 feet across the valley and at similar depths below the soil overburden on the valley slopes. Thicker soil deposits overlie the shale bedrock in the upland areas. The Pennsylvanian age shale is horizontally bedded, essentially impermeable to seepage, and practically incompressible under the weight of

156

the embankment. Therefore, the major geologic and engineering considerations in the development of this project involved the Quaternary soil materials in the valley and on the upland. The shale bedrock on the upland is mantled with glacial till and windblown silt (loess). The surface material is loess, which

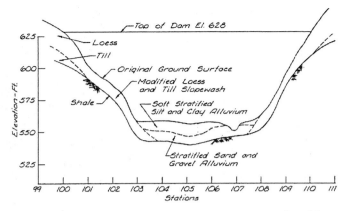

Figure 2 – Generalized and cross section of valley, Loud Thunder Dam.

ranges from 20 to 30 feet in thickness and which, in its unweathered state, is essentially a very fine-grained sandy silt with little or no cohesion. The top 5 or 6 feet of the loess is generally weathered to a somewhat more cohesive state. Unfortunately, however, even the weathered loess possesses a rather low clay content. The glacial till beneath the thick upland loess mantle contains more clay and is an ideal embankment material. In general, though, it was uneconomical to use glacial till in more than a minor portion of the embankment because the till was covered by too much loess.

The valley alluvium above shale bedrock was found to be only 10 to 15 feet thick. The lower half consisted essentially of sand and gravel. These sediments are quite permeable, and it was considered necessary to block the seepage path they afforded beneath the completed embankment. The upper portion of the valley alluvium is a fine-grained silty and clayey soil derived from slope wash combined with slack-water deposition during periods of floods on the adjacent Mississippi. These fine-grained alluvial materials are quite soft and compressible, and were, therefore, a source of concern from the standpoints of embankment stability and settlement. It was decided that they would have to be removed from beneath the embankment to improve the compressibility and stability performance of the completed dam.

The soil materials on the slopes and in irregular low areas along the valley walls consist of mixed slope wash of loessial and glacial origins. These deposits are well graded and contain a higher percentage of clay than does the upland loess. They were used as a principal source of borrow material for the embankment.

Embankment Design

During the design of the embankment cross section and the consideration of its factors of safety for various conditions, it was evident that the low strength of the upper valley alluvium, if not removed, would require very flat slopes on the dam. It was realized also at this stage of the design that a concrete chute spillway and bridge structure

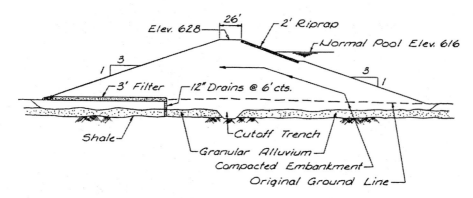

Figure 3 – Embankment cross section, Loud Thunder Dam.

probably would be located on the embankment and that, for this reason, total and differential settlements should be reduced to feasible and economical minimums. After due consideration was given to factors of safety, effects of settlement, and comparative costs, it was decided that the upper portion of soft valley alluvium should be removed. Other factors considered in the selection of side slopes on the embankment were the erosion potential of the available borrow and the probable increased cost of maintenance of steeper slopes. The final cross section utilized 3 to 1 slopes was analyzed by means of published stability factor curves and embankment strength parameters determined from laboratory tests.

The seepage characteristics of the valley alluvium and compacted embankment were evaluated during the design of an embankment cross section. It had been previously concluded that the upper, soft, fine-grained valley alluvium should be removed due to stability and settlement considerations. However, it was decided that the lower granular alluvium could remain in place, provided the seepage through this stratum were blocked by a cut-off trench carried into the underlying shale. These design features, used in combination with a filter blanket with relief wells along its upper extremity, completed the requirements for draw-down of the phreatic line from the reservoir, as well as cut-off, interception, and pressure relief for any sources of potential seepage. The final design cross section of the embankment is shown in figure 3.

During the investigative and design stages for this project, it became apparent that there would be significant advantages resulting from the use of a single chute spillway if it could be located on the compacted embankment. Estimates were made of the consolidation that would occur within the granular alluvium and compacted embankment if a spillway were built on the embankment. These estimates were based mainly upon past laboratory and field experience with similar borrow materials utilized in other earth dams and highway embankments. From these studies, it was estimated that approximately 9 inches of embankment settlement would occur, and that about 50 percent of this total would take place during the construction period. It was further estimated that the settlement of the crest of the dam during the first year would be between 2 and 3 inches, and that about an equal amount would occur thereafter.

Because both the magnitude and rate of settlement were critical to the feasibility and construction scheduling of the spillway, a system of instrumentation was devised to measure the amount and rate of settlement at various points within the interior of the cross section and on the surface of the completed embankment. The settlement

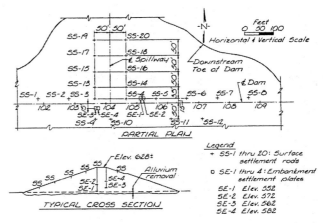

Figure 4 – Location of settlement platforms and surface reference points, Loud Thunder Dam.

data showed the diminishing nature of the consolidation and proved extremely useful in determining the time at which construction of the spillway could safely proceed. The locations of settlement platforms and surface reference points are shown as figure 4.

Observations and Performance

At most locations in northwestern Illinois, the availability of good borrow materials is a critical consideration in the design and construction of earth dams. The site of the Loud Thunder Dam is no exception. Initially, it was assumed that the upstream portion of the embankment would be zoned to receive the more clayey borrow material and that the less cohesive material would be zoned in the downstream portion. However, it was possible to construct approximately two-thirds of the height of the embankment by blending the silty, nonplastic loessial soils with the more clayey glacial tills, weathered loess, and shales, resulting in a relatively cohesive and impermeable embankment. The success of this mixing operation and the location of the quantity of clayey material to make it successful were the results of more detailed experimentation and borrow investigations during the construction stage of the project.

As the contractor planned his operations and as the borrow pits were developed, it became apparent that the use of the more clayey borrow materials would have to be broadened to a maximum extent to satisfy the seepage and stability design criteria. It also became apparent that the softer shale in some of the borrow pits could be excavated, broken down, and blended within the fill almost as easily as some of the clayey glacial till materials. However, laboratory tests on compacted samples of the shale revealed undesirable volume change characteristics, and the use of shale in the embankment was restricted to very small quantities. Through experimentation in the field and laboratory, it was determined that the required strength and impermeability of the embankment could be achieved by controlled mixing of all available materials. As previously mentioned, about two-thirds of the height of embankment was constructed in this manner as a relatively homogeneous cross section.

As construction progressed, however, the diminishing availability of clayey borrow materials became more critical, and in the final 20 to 25 feet of the embankment, clayey materials were used only in the outer surfaces. In this upper portion of the dam, the nonplastic loessial materials, which possess less desirable characteristics with respect to seepage and surface erosion, were placed in the interior of the embankment.

Figure 5 shows time-settlement plots representing the results of observations on the four settlement platforms located within the embankment. Settlements observed along the top of the dam at various dates after completion are plotted on figure 6. The vertical and horizontal displacements of two lines of surface reference points adjacent to the chute spillway are shown on figure 7.

The data given in figure 5, 6, 7 were invaluable in determining the time that the surface of the embankment was stable enough to permit work to commence on the spillway. It should be noted, also, that the magnitudes of settlements were somewhat larger than those predicted during the design phase. However, the predictions were based

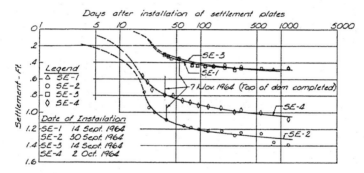

Figure 5 – Settlement plate readings, Loud Thunder Dam.

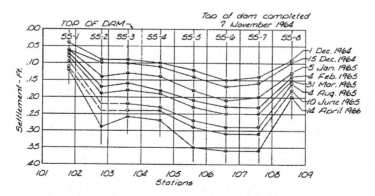

Figure 6 – Vertical crest settlement, Loud Thunder Dam.

160

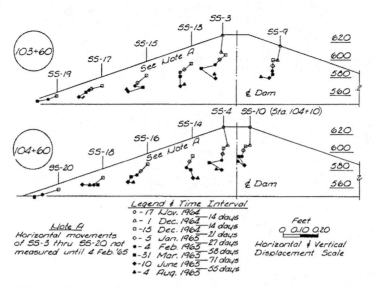

Figure 7 - Surface displacements, Loud Thunder Dam.

on a number of theoretical and empirical procedures, which cannot always be considered a satisfactory substitute for field observations.

During the development of the borrow sources adjacent to the valley walls, some of the slopes that were cut became quite steep. As a result, one slide of quite significant proportions developed. However, this occurred several hundred feet from the embankment and did not affect the stability of the dam. Nevertheless, special treatment of the slide itself, and of area above the slide, was required to assure long term stability of the shoreline under operational conditions of the lake.

Conclusions

Although it is early in the life of Loud Thunder Dam, all indications are that the Quaternary materials were used successfully from the standpoints of economy, safety, and performance. The use of geological information concerning the origin of materials, when combined with an accurate determination of their engineering properties, has proven valuable in the development of this project. Only through such an approach were the investigation, design, and construction coordinated so that an optimum facility could be obtained with safety and economy.

The use of instrumentation and observations in the evaluation of the performance of the embankment was of particular value in proving the feasibility of supporting the spillway structure on the embankment and in determining the time at which its construction could be safely started. This experience indicates the feasibility of similar designs for future projects. However, it also indicates the need for instrumentation, observations, and analyses of field data.

161

Deformation Problems
in Small Earth Dams

By Walter E. Hanson

Many more small earth dams are constructed each year than large ones. Although the design methods and performance records of large earth dams often have been reported, there are some problems especially associated with the smaller earth structures which should be studied.

The deformation of an earth dam and the relation of the deformation to time are important factors to be considered whenever a concrete spillway is to be supported on the embankment. The underlying materials may, in some cases, contribute more to the total deformations that the embankment. Sometimes, the construction of the spillway must be delayed until the magnitude and rate of the deformations have diminished to acceptable values. This reduces the extent of interaction between the concrete and the earth and thereby lessens the likelihood of intolerable distress occurring in the spillway structure.

The factor of safety of an earth dam is commonly estimated by stability analyses of cross sections at right angles to the center line of the dam. The factor of safety of any given cross section above the potential surface of failure is defined as the shearing strength of the embankment and underlying subsoil divided by the corresponding stresses computed for the potential surface of failure. In such analyses, the ultimate shear strengths of the materials are used, irrespective of the different strains (deformations) necessary for the development of the stresses (strengths).

An earth dam may be considered as a massive "beam" spanning a valley. Sometimes the abutments of the dam represent rigid supports, and the valley materials provide a more or less elastic-plastic foundation beneath the beam. The magnitude of the shears, moments, stresses, and deformations are functions of the stress-strain and strength properties of the beam. But stresses and deformations are functions also of the same properties of the materials in the underlying valley. Thus interaction does occur, and whether or not such behavior might lead to failure is determined by the deformation-strength characteristics of the beam as well as its supports.

Loud Thunder Dam

The Loud Thunder Conservation Dam across Big Branch Creek near its confluence with the Mississippi, approximately 15 miles west of Rock Island, Illinois, is an example of such a small dam (Figure 1). The embankment is approximately 1,000 feet long, and its height across most of the valley is between 70 and 75 feet. It was necessary to remove and replace part of the soft valley alluvium beneath the original ground surface, and to extend a cut-off trench into the underlying shale. These operations resulted in a maximum over-all height of compacted embankment of 85 to 90 feet.

Construction was started in the summer of 1964, and most of the embankment was completed by the end of the year. After about one year, during which the settlement of the embankment was found to diminish to an acceptable rate, the construction of the spillway was started. The concrete spillway and bridge structure (Figure 2) were supported directly by the embankment. This part of the project was completed during the fall of 1965 and spring of 1966. The impoundment of the reservoir behind the dam began in the fall of that year, and the first discharge over the spillway occurred in the spring of 1968. The area of the lake is some 170 acres, extending about 2 miles in length and about a half mile in width. Topographic features of the valley are such that the depth of a major part of the lake will exceed 50 feet.

Figure 1. Loud Thunder Dam and Lake

Figure 2. Concrete Chute Spillway and Bridge

Subsoil Conditions.—The detailed soil and foundation investigation began with a geological appraisal of the site, and continued with test borings and laboratory tests which provided the basis for an engineering evaluation of seepage, stability, and consolidation. The entire cycle of design and construction was monitored so that the design parameters evaluated in the site studies would be obtained during the construction of the dam.

A generalized cross section through the valley and abutments of the dam is shown in Figure 3. On the upland, the shale bedrock is mantled with glacial and wind-blown soils. The surface material is loess which varies from 20 to 30 feet in thickness and which, in its unweathered state, is a very fine sandy silt with little or no cohesion. The top 5 or 6 feet of this loess is generally modified by weathering to a somewhat more cohesive state. The glacial till beneath the thick upland loess contains more clay and is an ideal embankment material. But it became uneconomical to use the glacial soil to any extent in the embankment because of its depth below the surface.

163

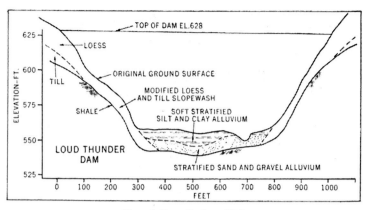

Figure 3. Cross Section of Valley

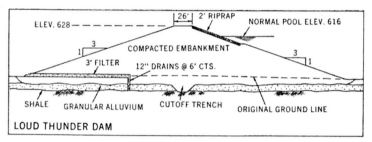

Figure 4. Embankment Cross Section

The soil materials on the slopes and in irregular low-lying areas along the valley walls consist of mixed slope wash of loessial and glacial origins. These deposits are well graded and contain a higher percentage of clay than the upland loess. Thus, together with the upland loess, they proved to be a principal source of borrow for the embankment.

The valley alluvium above the bedrock was found to be only 10 to 15 feet thick. The upper part of the alluvium consisted of soft and compressible silts and clays derived from slope wash combined with slack water deposition during periods of floods on the adjacent Mississippi River. The lower alluvium consisted of permeable sands and gravels.

Embankment.—During the design of the embankment cross section (Figure 4) and consideration of its factors of safety for various conditions, it was evident that the low strength of the upper valley alluvium, if not removed, would require very flat slopes on the dam. Since a concrete chute spillway and bridge structure were probably to be located on the embankment, total and differential settlements would have to be reduced to feasible and economical minimums. After due consideration of factors of safety, the probable amount and effects of settlement, and costs, it was decided that the upper portion of soft valley alluvium should be removed. Other factors considered in the selection of side slopes on the embankment were the possible erosion of the loess borrow and the cost of maintenance of steeper slopes. The final cross section with 3-to-1 slopes was analyzed by means of published stability factor curves and strength parameters determined from laboratory tests.

Evaluation of the seepage characteristics of the compacted embankment and granular alluvium indicated that the alluvium could remain in place, provided the seepage through this stratum were blocked by a cutoff trench carried to the underlying shale. These features used in combination with a filter blanket with relief wells along its upper extremity provided cutoff, interception, and pressure relief for any sources of potential seepage.

Since the amount and rate of settlement were critical to the feasibility and construction schedule of the spillway, a system of instruments was devised to take these measurements at various points within the interior of the cross section and on the surface of the completed embankment.

Observations and Performance.—Time-settlement plots of observations on four internal settlement platforms were made. The greatest settlement (approximately 1.3 feet) was noted at a platform located at about the lower one-third elevation of the embankment. The results appeared to confirm that the amount of settlement at any point within a fill depends upon the depth of underlying compressible material (including the natural subsoil) as well as the weight of the compacted earth above the elevation in question.

Settlements observed along the top of the dam at various dates after completion were plotted. The maximum settlement of the surface was less than 0.4 foot—less than the least of the internal settlements. This indicates that the consolidation of the embankment and underlying natural soil occurred rather rapidly.

Vertical and horizontal displacements adjacent to the concrete spillway were plotted and, as expected, the deformations changed from vertical near the center line of the dam to almost horizontal near the toe.

The use of instruments, observations, and plotted curves was of special value in proving the feasibility of supporting the spillway structure on the embankment and in scheduling the spillway construction. The contribution of the underlying subsoil to the deformations that occurred was relatively small.

Washington County Dam

The Washington County Conservation Dam is another small earth dam included for study. The site is a narrow point of the natural valley of a tributary to Locust Creek about 5 miles south of Nashville, Illinois (Figure 5). The embankment is approximately 600 feet long and its height above the valley is between 30 and 35 feet. Construction started in 1960 and was completed in 1961.

Failure.—The dam failed in January 1962 (Figure 6) when the lake level was still a few feet below spillway crest. The failure, although not centered on the spillway, involved considerable damage to that structure. The stilling basin at the downstream end of the spillway conduit is shown at the lower left in Figure 6. Almost all of the anti-seep collars on the 6-foot square conduit were destroyed. The riser barrel and entrance to the

Figure 5. Washington County Dam

Figure 6. Breach in Washington County Dam

spillway are shown near the middle of the picture. In Figure 6, vertical, and even slightly negative slopes of the embankment along the sides of the breach are noted. These steep slopes reflect the excellent strength of the compacted embankment which consisted of well-graded till available in abundant quantities at the site. Closure of the dam had been made at this point because low water flow during construction was discharged through a dewatering pipe connected to the spillway conduit.

In Figure 7, showing a cross section of the valley and an elevation of the dam, the approximate location of the failure is indicated. The depth to bedrock along the right side of the breach is only a few feet, while along the left side the depth increases to some 40 feet. The natural valley alluvium between the bottom of the embankment and bedrock is a rather soft compressible deposit of interbedded sands, silts, and clays.

The principal cause of failure was attributed to erosion through cracks which probably formed in the embankment as

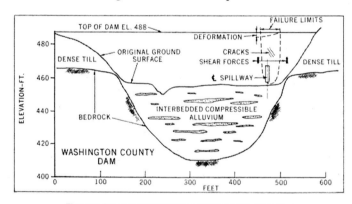

Figure 7. Cross Section of Valley and Elements of the Dam

the result of the large shear forces indicated in Figure 7, which, in turn, were the result of a relatively unyielding abutment on the right side and compressible support beneath the embankment to the left of the breach. The lack of pliability of the strong, compacted embankment meant that it could not adjust to the large differential settlement without cracking. After cracks formed, erosion began when the lake level rose above the cracks.

The original closure of the dam had been made near the region of failure, and may have contributed in some degree to the conditions that resulted in failure.

Repairs.—When the breach occurred, the dewatering facilities were opened immediately, and an upstream earth dike was promptly constructed around the spillway riser to prevent further erosion through the breach in case the dewatering pipe could not handle the total stream discharge. Within a few days an emergency spillway was excavated around the dam to provide further protection in case of floods.

Figure 8. Partly Restored Embankment, Washington County Dam

Following soil investigations of the embankment and foundation conditions, it was concluded that the dam and spillway could be restored without risk of a recurring failure. Needle beams were inserted through holes cut in the spillway riser and, after the structure was raised to its original position by jacking, concrete grout was placed beneath the base slab. After this, repairs were made to the spillway conduit, including the replacement of the anti-seep collars.

In the restoration of embankment material (Figure 8) the embankment slopes adjacent to the breach were cut back flat enough to accommodate compacting equipment. Readings on settlement platforms, the spillway structure, and piezometers were obtained and analyzed for construction control.

Conclusions

Experience with the earth dams described appears to justify the following conclusions:

1. Under favorable conditions, spillways for earth dams can be supported on the embankment. Observations and analysis of field data are imperative for success and safety.
2. Lateral deformations should not be overlooked. The recorded horizontal movement at the toe of the Loud Thunder Dam was about 2 inches, but much more unrecorded deformation must have occurred during construction.
3. The stress-strain characteristics of an embankment must be able to adjust to the deformations of the underlying foundation materials.
4. In the case of the Washington County Dam, strength of the embankment should have been sacrificed to obtain greater pliability.
5. When possible, spillway structures should be located outside regions of large differential settlements, and these same regions should be avoided for closures of earth dams.

Geotechnical Practice from the Coal Mine to the Ash Pond

by WALTER E. HANSON, SERGIO A. PECORI, DONALD D. OGLESBY, and JOHN M. HEALY*

Introduction

The mining and firing of coal for electrical energy produces vast quantities of waste materials which must be disposed of (or utilized as a resource) in a geotechnically and environmentally acceptable manner. Approximately 200,000,000 tons of soil and rock wastes are produced annually in the United States as a result of coal mining and coal preparation operations (1), and the firing of coal for electrical generation produces an annual accumulation of approximately 65,400,000 tons of fly ash, bottom ash and slag (2). Additionally, flue gas desulfurization (FGD) equipment using lime or limestone to reduce sulfur oxide stack emissions at coal firing plants produces significant additional volumes of solid wastes (scrubber sludge) containing water, dissolved solids and suspended solids (predominately calcium sulfite and calcium sulfate).

The geotechnical properties of these waste materials are important data for their proper handling and disposal or for their reuse in the marketplace. Hanson Engineers, Inc. (HEI), has served the coal and electric power industries for many years in their waste management practices, determining the properties of many of these waste materials and applying principles of geotechnical engineering to guide disposal prac-

* Special Consultant and Former Chairman, Hanson Engineers, Inc., Partner, Hanson Engineers, Inc., Senior Partner, Hanson Engineers, Inc, and Senior Partner, Hanson Engineers, Inc., respectively

168

tices or to determine their suitability as construction materials. The subject of this paper is three case histories which describe the practice of geotechnical engineering as it applies to coal mining/coal firing wastes and the value of these wastes as construction materials.

The first case history presents the evolution of disposal practices at a midwestern coal mine as influenced by field observations of early refuse storage areas and subsequent adoption of geotechnical design and construction techniques similar to those used for dams. The second case history is concerned with the use of fly ash in containment dike construction as an economical alternative to the more conventional approach of utilizing off-site soil borrow. The final case history describes the geotechnical properties of fixed FGD sludge and its successful use for railroad embankment construction.

Refuse Disposal at Midwestern Coal Mine

Background

Coal preparation (cleaning) at the mine produces both coarse refuse (treatment of coal > 0.5 mm size) and fine refuse (treatment of coal < 0.5 mm size). The coarse refuse is transported by truck from the preparation plant to an on-site disposal area where it is used to construct impounding embankments to store and contain the fine coal refuse. The fine refuse is pumped as a slurry from the preparation plant and discharged into the impoundment for settling of the slurry solids and clarification of the transporting water. Four refuse and slurry areas have been developed and subsequently closed since the mine opened in the early 1970s. The currently operating fifth area (designated as Pond No. 5) initially accepted slurry pumpage in 1978 and is designed to meet the storage demands of the mine until 1992. Figure 6.1 is a plan view of the mine property showing the currently operating No. 5 impoundment and past refuse disposal areas. The currently operating No. 5 area consists of a high-level southeast pond and a lower-level northwest pond interconnected by a sloping drain pipe passing through the separating haul road. Some of the refuse embankment sections approach 100 ft in height and are comparable in size to some of the highest dams constructed in Illinois.

Construction of Early Refuse and Slurry Areas

The mine was first operational in 1970, and early planning and design for refuse disposal was not strictly guided by geotechnical considerations. Initial disposal practices at the mine were developed prior to the catastrophic 1972 failure of the refuse disposal facility at Buffalo Creek in West Virginia which directed national attention to these types of facilities and ultimately led to the present-day regulations governing design and construction.

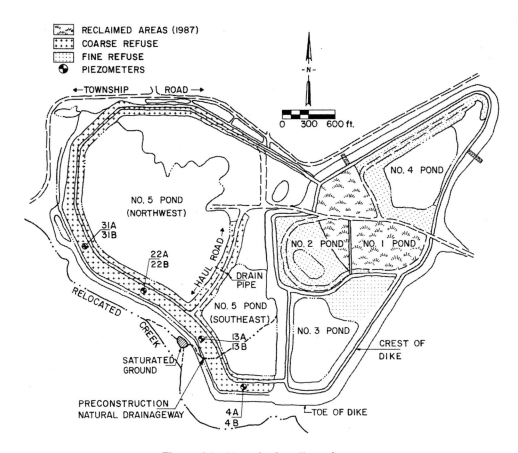

Figure 6.1 Plan of refuse disposal area

Design

Early design features which are typical of the first three disposal areas are illustrated in Figure 6.2 (Pond No. 4 is impounded by conventional clay dikes). The embankment section is a homogeneous mass of coarse refuse with a thin downstream clay cover to support vegetative growth as part of reclamation planning. The embankment construction and slurry placement were concurrent operations requiring careful allocation and planning for the refuse materials being produced. The foundation subsoils and rock strata supporting the embankments posed no special stability or settlement problems, and foundation treatment was limited to stripping of all vegetation and organic topsoil.

Embankment Construction

The placement procedure used for the coarse refuse consisted of: (1) dumping 6 ft to 8 ft high piles from haul trucks, (2) leveling the piles with a bulldozer (dragging an I-beam) to a maximum height of 4 ft to 6 ft, and (3) compacting the leveled refuse

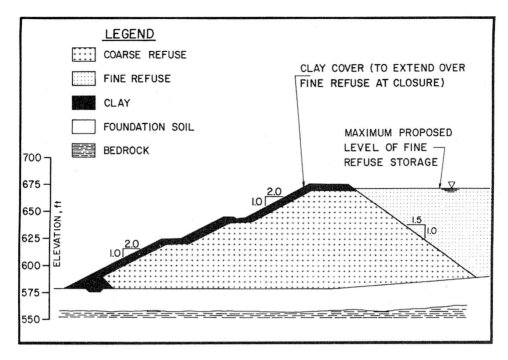

Figure 6.2 Typical embankment construction for Ponds No. 1, No. 2, and No. 3

under haul traffic. The compaction of coarse refuse dumped in areas adjacent to the stored slurry required special attention because of equipment operating near the inside embankment slopes.

The clay cover construction along the outside embankment slopes was scheduled slightly ahead of the coarse refuse placement. The clay borrow was brought in by scraper equipment, spread in 8 in. to 12 in. loose layers, and compacted by haul traffic. Generally, the outside clay cover was placed in a width compatible with the scraper equipment used (that is, 15 ft minimum width).

Embankment Distress

Refuse and slurry areas No. 1 and No. 2 attained final planned configurations without incident other than the development of some minor seepage and shallow surface slumps along the face of the outside clay cover. However, the embankment construction for Pond No. 3 was interrupted during three different periods by development of embankment distress. In October 1975 when the embankments had attained approximately one half of their design height, significant longitudinal cracking and water discharge were discovered in the clay cover on the outer slopes of the west and south embankments. No measurable slide movements occurred, and the quantity of water discharging from the cover eventually diminished to tolerable levels. In June 1977, a large slide developed along the still partially completed south embankment as shown in Figure 6.3. A study of this failure revealed that the sliding mass involved only the outside clay cover and that the slide movement was attributable to seepage

171

Figure 6.3 Clay cover slide at Pond No. 3

of impounded water through the coarse refuse and the subsequent buildup of water pressures behind the more impermeable clay along the outside slope. The remedial solution developed was the placement of a pressure relief drain behind the reconstructed clay cover as shown in Figure 6.4. In June 1978, a second large slide (approximately 400 ft long) developed along the south end of the west embankment. This slide occurred just as the embankments had attained their final design elevations and the impounded water and slurry were at their highest levels. Analysis of the failure again revealed that the main body of coarse refuse was not involved in the slide and that the movement could be attributed to the buildup of seepage water pressures behind the clay cover. Since the failure was limited to an area that would be enclosed by the newly planned No. 5 Pond, remedial action was limited to lowering of the No. 3 impoundment by several feet accompanied by some minor regrading of the slumped embankment slope. Seepage and flows of water from the distressed embankment area were able to be confined to the mine property.

Discussion

The coal company's planning of the early refuse and slurry areas occurred at a time when geotechnical engineering principles were not commonly applied to coal mine disposal practices, and the transfer of available technology from earth fill dams was still in its early stages. The embankment design as illustrated in Figure 6.2 does not satisfy many criteria now recognized as being essential to the safety and stability of an earth fill dam. Apparent deficiencies include: (1) relatively steep outside slopes

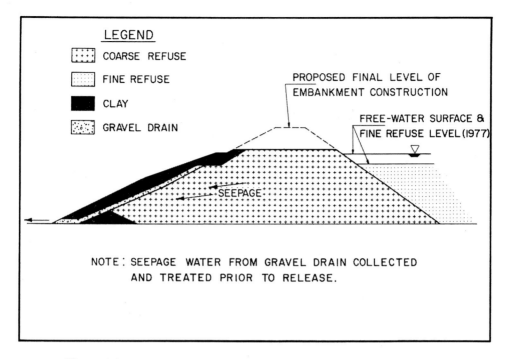

Figure 6.4 Remedial construction for clay cover slide at Pond No. 3 (1977)

for a homogeneous type embankment, (2) uncontrolled seepage flow through the embankment, (3) inadequate placement and compaction methods for the embankment construction, and (4) placement of a zone of reduced permeability along the outer slope. Despite these apparent deficiencies, the refuse embankments have fulfilled their intended function without major releases of the impounded water or fine refuse and without environmental damage.

Stabilizing factors which have contributed to the avoidance of major problems in the early refuse disposal areas and which are not present for most earth fill dam projects include: (1) exceptionally long construction periods (measured in years) which permit significant dissipation of pore pressures in the foundation and embankment, and (2) limited depths of free-water in direct contact with the embankment section (that is, embankments store fine refuse and do not impound great depths of free-water). In regard to the latter, the permeability of the stored fine refuse is most likely lower than that of the poorly compacted coarse refuse in the embankment. Free-water attempting to seep from the impoundment must first pass through the less pervious fine refuse, creating the effect of a zoned dam, and thereby depressing the phreatic line (and reducing seepage flows) in the outslope embankment sections. A common observation of the slides that occurred at Pond No. 3 was that the intensity of flows decreased with time following the initial slip of the clay cover, suggesting the probability that no distress would have resulted had seepage drainage been provided through the clay cover.

173

Geotechnical Properties of Embankment Materials

The October 1975 distress that developed in the clay cover at Pond No. 3 raised concerns among mine management that unchanged disposal practices could conceivably result in similar distress in the clay cover for future impoundments. Also, new federal rules and regulations (3) promulgated in September 1975 by the Mining Enforcement and Safety Administration (later to become the Mine Safety and Health Administration) stipulated that the design of all future refuse impoundments would be subject to engineering analysis to establish their stability. Included in the federal regulations (and a necessary part of the stability analysis) was a requirement to determine the "physical and engineering properties of the materials to be used in constructing each zone or stage of the impounding structure." In April 1976, mine management authorized the retainment of Hanson Engineers, Inc., to prepare a report for the newly planned Pond No. 5 addressing the technical requirements of the new federal regulations including determinations of the engineering properties of all refuse/foundation materials and recommended design for the coarse refuse embankment sections. The following paragraphs summarize field and laboratory studies carried out by HEI for the design of Pond No. 5. Comparisons are made between the coarse refuse properties determined by HEI and those obtained from a subsequent 1981 study of several midwest mines sponsored by the U.S. Department of Energy (4).

N-Values, Moisture, and Density. In 1972 and 1974, test borings were made through the completed coarse refuse embankments for Ponds No. 1 and No. 2 to provide data for preliminary performance evaluations. N-values (ASTM D 1586) and water content (ASTM D 2216) data obtained from these borings are shown plotted in Figure 6.5. Also shown in Figure 6.5 are corresponding data collected from two 1984 test borings made through the outslope areas of the coarse refuse embankments at Pond No. 5. Significantly lower water contents are noted for the coarse refuse at Pond No. 5. These lower moisture contents can be at least partially attributed to the presence of a seepage barrier in the embankment construction for Pond No. 5 (discussed in later paragraphs). The relatively poorly compacted embankments at Ponds No. 1 and No. 2 have apparently permitted the outward movement of water from the impoundments and increased the degree of saturation of the refuse construction.

In situ wet and dry densities for the Ponds No. 1 and No. 2 embankments were also obtained from the 1972 and 1974 test borings. These densities were calculated from weight measurements and moisture content determinations on coarse refuse specimens obtained by thin-walled tube sampling (ASTM D 1587). Wet densities ranged from 102 pcf to 129 pcf, and dry densities ranged from 85 pcf to 110 pcf. These wide ranges in density reflect the relatively uncontrolled compaction practices utilized for the embankment construction. The U.S.D.O.E. study reported a mean dry density for coarse refuse of 92.1 pcf with a standard deviation of 11.9 pcf.

Grain Size Distribution. Particle size analyses (ASTM D 422) were performed on a limited number of coarse refuse samples obtained from the constructed embankments at Ponds No. 1 and No. 2. Figure 6.6 shows the grain size distributions

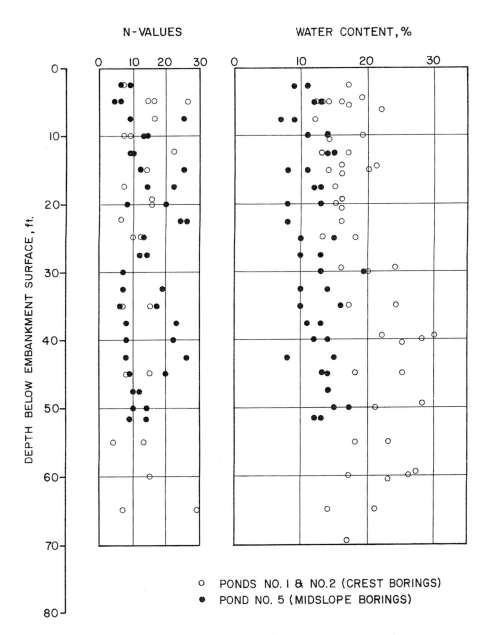

Figure 6.5 In situ data for coarse refuse embankment construction

for the coarse refuse samples as obtained by both dry-sieved and wet-sieved methods of testing. Also shown is the increased percentage of fines obtained by washing the dry-sieved samples through the No. 200 sieve.

The wet-sieved method reveals the high fines content of the coarse refuse and suggests that this material could be highly impermeable if placed and compacted under controlled conditions. The U.S.D.O.E. study confirms the fines contents for the coarse refuse at this mine (ranging from 19 percent to 67 percent), and reports permeability (hydraulic conductivity) coefficients in the range of 2.1 × 10⁸ to 4.5

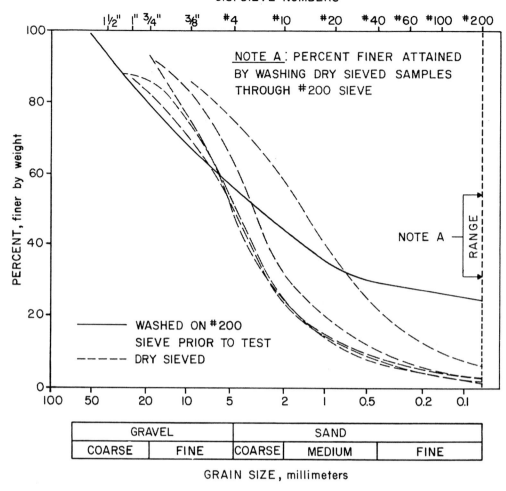

Figure 6.6 Grain size distribution for coarse refuse

$\times$ 10⁹ cm/sec for laboratory samples compacted to 95 percent standard Proctor densities.

Moisture-Density Relationships. Proctor tests (ASTM D 698) were performed on coarse refuse samples obtained from stockpiled areas at the mine where the refuse had been dumped but not yet spread and compacted by operating equipment. The results of this testing are shown in Figure 6.7 and summarized in Table 6.1. Oven-dried moisture contents were determined in accordance with ASTM D 2216.

Triaxial Tests. Isotropically consolidated triaxial compression tests were performed on coarse refuse specimens obtained by thin-walled tube sampling (ASTM D 1587) of the Pond No. 2 embankments. The samples were sheared under drained conditions at a slow enough rate to permit dissipation of pore water pressures. The failure envelope obtained for the in situ coarse refuse is shown in Figure 6.8. Also shown are the failure envelopes obtained by the U.S.D.O.E. study of the coarse

176

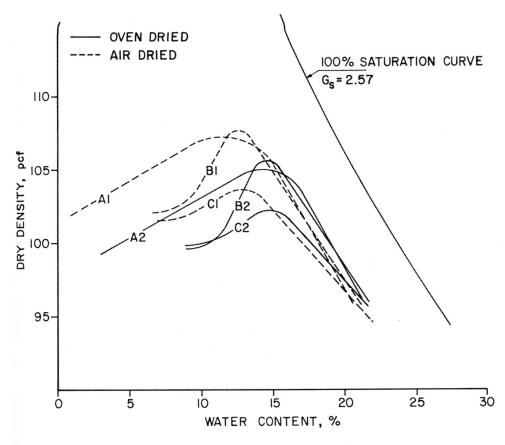

Figure 6.7 Proctor curves for coarse refuse

refuse at several midwestern mines. These envelopes are based on isotropically consolidated triaxial compression tests performed on both in situ and compacted (ASTM D 698) coarse refuse samples sheared under undrained conditions. The effective shear strength parameters calculated from the envelopes are tabulated in Figure 6.8.

Foundations and Borrow Materials. The index and engineering properties of the foundation subsoils and clay borrow were investigated and defined in response

TABLE 6.1 Results of Proctor Tests on Coarse Refuse

Stockpile Location	Oven Dried		Air Dried	
	Maximum Density in lbs/ft³	Optimum Moisture as a %	Maximum Density in lbs/ft³	Optimum Moisture as a %
1	105.5	14.5	107.7	12.5
2	102.2	15.0	103.6	13.0
3	105.0	15.0	107.1	12.0

Note: ASTM Standard Method D 2216

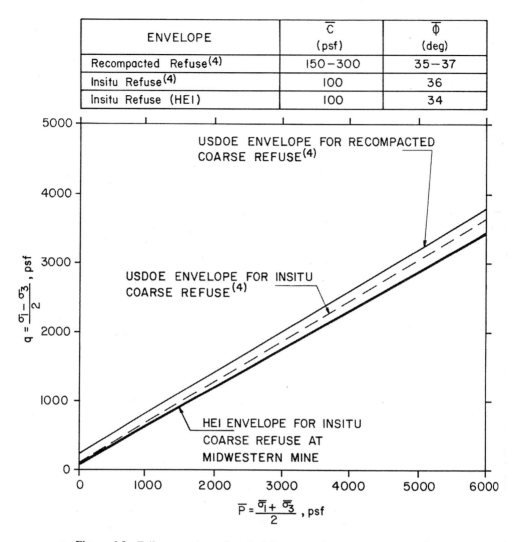

ENVELOPE	$\overline{C}$ (psf)	$\overline{\phi}$ (deg)
Recompacted Refuse[4]	150−300	35−37
Insitu Refuse [4]	100	36
Insitu Refuse (HEI)	100	34

Figure 6.8 Failure envelopes for triaxial compression tests on coarse refuse

to the regulatory requirements. The use of clay borrow was restricted by the coal company to the outslope cover construction for the first three impoundments. The design of the No. 5 impoundment also utilized clay borrow within the main embankment sections as a seepage barrier.

HEI's design for Pond No. 5 incorporates an upstream clay zone to provide an engineered seepage barrier between the impounded slurry and coarse refuse portions of the embankment. The clay barrier concept satisfied current regulatory requirements for embankment seepage control while also providing an economical design through use of readily available on-site soil borrow. Initial placement of the clay zone and coarse refuse began in 1978, and the conditions of construction in 1987 are shown in Figure 6.9. The embankment construction is essentially completed (with the exception of the outer slope clay cover), and slurry pumpage will continue until the fine refuse attains its final design level in 1992. Figure 6.9 shows that the final 8.0

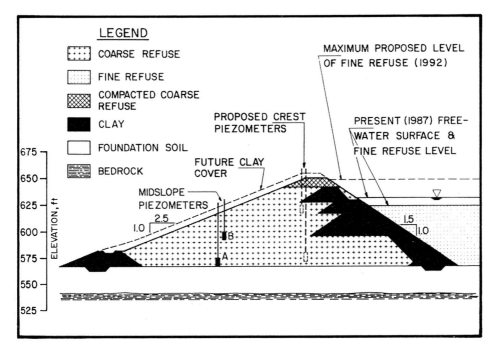

Figure 6.9 Embankment construction for Pond No. 5

ft of the engineered seepage barrier is constructed of compacted coarse refuse rather than compacted clay. This design feature permitted use of surplus amounts of coarse refuse that existed in the latter phase of embankment construction in lieu of the relatively more expensive clay borrow. The suitability of the coarse refuse for the upper barrier construction was based upon its grain size characteristics and field compaction studies on test sections.

Stability Analyses and Monitoring Requirements. Preconstruction stability calculations for the embankment design were submitted to the regulatory agency in May 1976 utilizing the measured engineering properties of the refuse/borrow/foundation materials and applying standard methods of effective stress analysis. The results of the stability analyses are tabulated in Table 6.2 and compared with regulatory requirements. A basic condition of the stability analyses was the assumption of a low phreatic surface within the coarse refuse portion of the embankment. This assumption placed reliance on the clay zone and fine refuse to effectively mitigate movement of water into the coarse refuse during the operational life of the disposal area (approximately 14 years). No internal seepage control features (such as vertical drains, drainage blankets, and toe drains) were incorporated into the embankment design. Their decisions were based upon (1) engineering judgment questioning their practical need, and (2) the major costs and construction difficulties that would have been involved.

The regulatory agency accepted the embankment design as submitted but stipulated that the coarse refuse portions of the embankment be monitored for evidence

179

TABLE 6.2 Factors of Safety for Pond No. 5
Embankments

Method of Analysis	Computed		Regulatory	
	Static	Earthquake	Static	Earthquake
Circular Arc Failure	1.71	1.17		
			1.5	1.2
Wedge Failure	1.75	1.22		

Note: Maximum Pool with Steady State Seepage

of seepage and embankment saturation. In response to the agency's directive, eight midslope piezometers were installed in June through August 1984 at the locations shown in Figures 6.1 and 6.9. The eight crest piezometers shown in Figure 6.9 are scheduled for installation during the middle to latter part of 1987.

Embankment Construction.   The procedures for placement of coarse refuse in the No. 5 embankments were varied from earlier practices to improve compaction. After initial dumping from trucks in 6 ft high piles, the coarse refuse was spread with a D7 dozer to a maximum thickness of 3 ft and compacted by five passes (minimum) of a self-propelled sheepsfoot roller (Caterpillar 825C). The placement criterion was the attainment of a 2 ft (maximum) thickness following compacting with no specific density requirements or field measurements.

Use of coarse refuse within the upper portion of the seepage barrier shown in Figure 6.9 required more strict compaction criteria to be observed. After initial dumping in 6 ft high piles, the coarse refuse was spread with a D7 dozer to a maximum thickness of no more than 9 in. The refuse was then compacted to a maximum thickness of 6 in. utilizing a minimum of five passes of the identical sheepsfoot equipment used for the outslope areas. Field density checks were routinely conducted to ascertain that the compaction specification (97 percent Standard Proctor density) was being satisfied by the field procedures. Figure 6.10 presents a summary plot of the field density data that have been collected as compared to laboratory compaction data represented by Proctor Curve B2 of Figure 6.7.

The field data of Figure 6.10 show that placement densities more than satisfy the specification requirements, and that placement moisture contents are generally dry of optimum. Water contents of less than 10 percent to 12 percent are most likely the result of prolonged drying periods between the initial dumping of the coarse refuse and subsequent spreading and compaction. The general practice was not to add water to the refuse during placement operations.

The major portion of the seepage barrier was constructed utilizing on-site clay borrow placed under controlled conditions of compaction. The clay borrow was

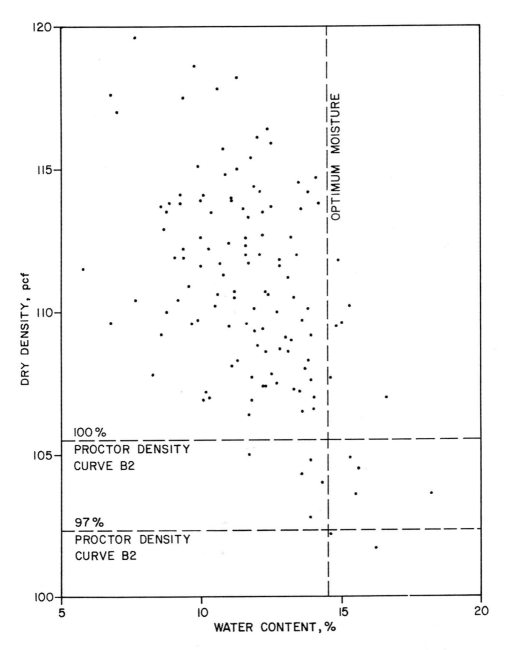

Figure 6.10 Field density test results for compacted coarse refuse seepage barrier

transported by scrapers, spread in 12 in loose lifts, and compacted with a self-propelled sheepsfoot roller (Caterpillar 815). The compaction specifications required moisture contents within three percentage points wet or dry of the Standard Proctor optimum value, and in-place unit weights no lower than 95 percent of the Standard Proctor maximum density. Since several different soil types suitable for the core construction were present in the borrow areas, the "family" of Standard Proctor curves shown in Figure 6.11 were developed for the field compaction control.

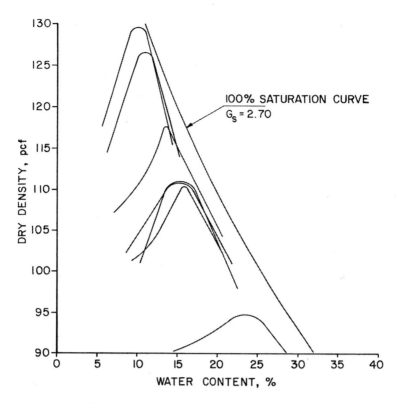

Figure 6.11 Proctor curves for clay borrow

Piezometer Data. The conditions of installation for the midslope piezometers are summarized in Table 6.3. The piezometers are of the open standpipe type with the plastic slotted tips and surrounding gravel packs sealed from down-hole infiltration by bentonite clay. All piezometer tips are situated entirely within the coarse refuse with the exceptions of deep piezometers 4A and 13A which have shallow penetrations into the natural underlying subsoils (2.1 ft and 0.7 ft respectively).

Figure 6.12 is a plot of the water levels observed within the piezometer standpipes

TABLE 6.3 Piezometer Installations for Pond No. 5 Embankments

Piezometer	El. Y1	El. Y2	Schematic
4A	622.53	570.3	
13A	621.65	570.2	
22A	618.47	564.5	
31A	622.35	569.6	
4B	622.40	589.9	
13B	621.66	590.2	
22B	618.05	584.9	
31B	622.14	590.1	

Note: 4A & 13A Penetrate Natural Subsoils

182

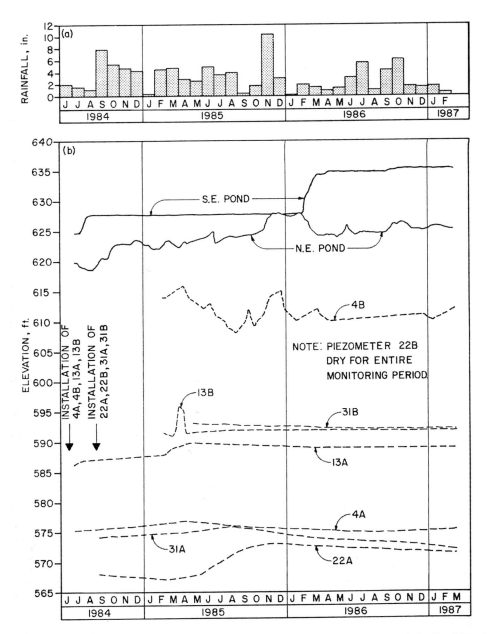

Figure 6.12 Precipitation data and water level data (free-water and piezometers) for Pond No. 5

from initial installations in June and August 1984 to February 1987. Also plotted in Figure 6.12 for the same time period are the monthly precipitation values and the free-water levels for both the northwest and southeast portions of the No. 5 Pond.

The bore holes for all B-series piezometers were dry at the time of initial installations. The bore holes for the deep A-series piezometers encountered water at depths ranging from 45 ft to 49 ft, and collection of water level data from the A-series piezometers was possible shortly after installation. However, as shown in Figure 6.12(b), water levels were not found in piezometers 4B, 13B, and 31B until the first and second quarters of 1985, and piezometer 22B has remained dry for the entire monitoring period.

No obvious correlations exist between the water level trends in the shallow depth (B-series) piezometers and the pond level fluctuations shown in Figure 6.12(b). The water levels for 13B and 31B have remained essentially constant since the initial measurements in early 1985. The water levels recorded within these piezometers are only a little more than 1.0 ft above the bottom of the porous tips and are judged to represent seepage water trapped at the bottom of the piezometer units rather than true piezometric surfaces within the embankment. The source of the seepage water is from heavy precipitation falling (and in some instances ponding) on the exposed refuse surfaces and infiltrating down to the piezometer tips. The presence of water in piezometer 4B is also judged to be partially the result of rainfall infiltration and seepage collection at the porous tip. Further, an inspection of the 4B plastic standpipe in early 1987 revealed a break approximately 2 ft below the refuse surface. The rather extreme fluctuations shown in Figure 6.12(b) for the water levels in 4B are most

Figure 6.13 Completed coarse refuse embankments for Pond No. 5

184

likely the result of embankment runoff feeding directly into the broken piezometer standpipe and alternately collecting within and draining from the porous tip.

The water levels shown in Figure 6.12(b) for deep piezometers 4A and 31A have remained relatively stable over the entire monitoring period and appear to be unaffected by fluctuations in the pond levels. The water level in deep piezometer 22A required several months to stabilize, followed by a slight decreasing trend similar to 31A. The data from all three piezometers support the preconstruction assumption of a low phreatic surface within the outslope portions of the embankment.

The water level readings for deep piezometer 13A suggest a significantly higher phreatic surface at this embankment location. No obvious explanation exists for this higher level of embankment saturation except that it may be reflective of a less well constructed clay core at this location or may be related to seepage within the foundation of the embankment construction. The natural ground near piezometer 13A has been observed to pond shallow water and remain saturated ever since the very early years of construction of the No. 5 Pond and is the location of a natural drainageway that existed prior to embankment construction. Monitoring activities for the deep piezometers will continue over the active life of the impoundment to detect any significant changes in the present water level trends.

Discussion

The completed coarse refuse embankments for Pond No. 5 have required a nine-year construction period to attain final design heights. The highest of these embankments which rise almost 90 ft above natural ground are shown in Figure 6.13. The pumpage of slurry will continue for approximately five more years before the impoundment is filled to design capacity with fine refuse. The completed closure plan for the impoundment will include the placement of a clay cover along the outer slopes and a clay cap over the impounded fine refuse, followed by mulching and seeding to establish a protective vegetative cover for final reclamation.

The design and construction procedures utilized for the Pond No. 5 embankments were influenced by both the functional adequacy of the early refuse disposal areas and the environmental concerns of uncontrolled acid water seepage from the impoundments. Early embankment construction did not adhere to rigid design and construction criteria established for earth dam structures, but no serious failures occurred and no interruptions in mine operations resulted. Seepage control within the present construction has been improved by incorporation of some design features and construction procedures adapted from earth dam technology; however, fundamental differences in design approach between coarse refuse embankments retaining fine refuse and earth embankments retaining free-water must still be recognized.

No embankment instability or saturated outslope areas are evident following nine years of active disposal operations at the No. 5 impoundment. Interpretations presented herein for embankment piezometer data collected over the last $2\frac{3}{4}$ years of the construction period generally support the original design assumption of a low phreatic surface in the embankment outslope areas. However, deep piezometer 13A identifies an embankment area exhibiting exceptionally high water pressure that is conceivably related to seepage from the impoundment. Additional piezometers at the crest location shown in Figure 6.9, installed in mid-1987, will provide supplemental piezometric data closer to the impoundment. These data will be utilized in continued studies to monitor embankment stability and to determine the potential need for drainage outlets through the proposed outer slope clay cover.

Soil/Fly Ash/Lime Containment Dikes

Background

The Central Illinois Public Service Company (CIPS) Power Station at Hutsonville produces fly ash as a by-product of the coal combustion process to produce electricity. The fly ash is recovered from flue gases and sluiced to an on-site disposal pond for long-term storage. When the existing fly ash disposal pond was nearly filled to capacity, the utility elected to construct a new disposal area that would serve the remaining life of the station. Hanson Engineers, Inc., was retained by CIPS to prepare a feasibility study and provide design and construction observation services for the new fly ash disposal facility. These services were initiated in the latter part of 1983 and completed in late 1986 when the new facility was put into operation.

Project Description

The new disposal pond required a storage capacity of 235 acre-feet which would ultimately accommodate 321,000 cubic yards of fly ash disposal. The land area occupied by the pond is approximately 14 acres, and the average height of surrounding dikes to contain the fly ash is approximately 22 ft. A preliminary geotechnical investigation was undertaken in September 1983 to determine the feasibility of the project and to identify construction difficulties that might be encountered. This study revealed shallow groundwater and bedrock levels in the proposed pond area which severely limited the amount of soil borrow that could be excavated from within the pond area and used for construction of the surrounding containment dikes. The levee section being considered at that time had a crest elevation of 466.0, and the natural ground within the impoundment was to be excavated down to Elevation 444 to provide natural soil materials for levee construction. However, it was deemed necessary to find a supplemental source of soil borrow to provide sufficient volume of materials for the construction of the dikes. The blending of fly ash and lime with the on-site soils was suggested as an alternate means of obtaining sufficient volumes of construction materials for the dikes, but the need for more detailed studies of this procedure was emphasized.

The Division of Water Resources of the Illinois Department of Transportation required a breach analysis to classify the impoundment as to the degree of threat to life and property in the event of a dike failure. The impoundment was initially categorized as a Class II structure (Significant Hazard Potential). However, the study resulted in a lower hazard classification of Class III (Low Hazard Potential) by demonstrating, through hydraulic calculations, that the adjacent property would not be impacted by an instantaneous failure of the dikes. The revised classification also resulted in a significant lowering in the magnitude of design floods required for sizing of the spillway structure.

In response to requirements of the Dam Safety Section of the Illinois Division of Water Resources, an analysis of dike stability and seepage was undertaken. This study was based upon the use of natural on-site soils for the dike construction and resulted in the adoption of 2.5H to 1.0V outside slope for the dike cross section. At this same time, a hydrogeologic study was conducted as part of the initial permit application to the Illinois Environmental Protection Agency (IEPA) for construction of the disposal pond. This initial application was based on an unlined pond (that is, no impermeable barrier between the stored fly ash and underlying aquifer system) and use of natural soil materials for construction of the containment dikes. Nine monitor wells were installed at the site of the disposal pond to establish: (1) pre-operational ground water quality and, (2) direction of ground water flow. The wells were also intended to monitor the effects of the disposal pond following construction.

Laboratory Study

Subsequent to the initial work just described, a laboratory study for soil/fly ash/lime containment dikes was initiated, and construction recommendations were developed. This study resulted in an economical approach to the construction of the containment dikes. The laboratory studies investigated the index and engineering properties such as permeability (hydraulic conductivity), compaction, and shear-strength characteristics of several test mixtures of the basic components stabilized with lime.

The constituent materials used in the soil/fly ash/lime mixture were the following:

1. *Soil.* The soil encountered in the proposed borrow areas was generally silty clayey fine to coarse sand. The moisture content of the soils varied from 16.1 to 21.3 percent. Test hole identification and grain size data are presented in Figure 6.14.
2. *Fly Ash.* The fly ash at the Hutsonville Power Station was randomly sampled. The grain size data for the randomly selected samples are presented in Figure 6.14. The grain size data show that the fly ash is a poorly graded material with primarily silt-size particles. The in situ moisture contents of the fly ash at the sampling locations are about 39 percent.
3. *Lime.* The lime used was Code L (a by-product material) produced by the Mississippi Lime Company in Ste. Genevieve, Missouri.

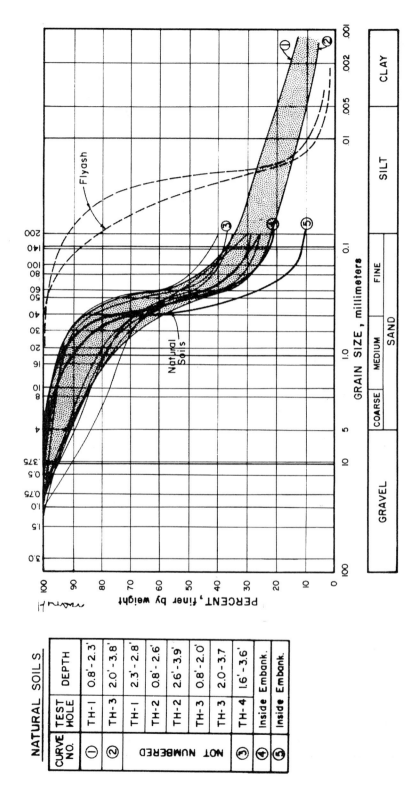

Figure 6.14 Sample depth chart and grain size distribution of on-site soils and fly ash

188

The mixtures for this study were proportioned (on a dry weight basis) as consisting of two parts soil to one part fly ash, and 5 percent lime as based on the combined dry weight of soil and fly ash. The soil materials used in the mixtures were from Test Hole TH-3 (2.0 ft to 3.8 ft) and Test Hole TH-4 (1.6 ft to 3.6 ft). In general, these samples represent the bounds of the gradation range for the natural soils incorporated into the dike construction, and the use of these soils provided representative test data for the actual field mixtures.

Standard Proctor compaction tests were carried out for two mixtures utilizing soil from TH-3 (2.0 ft to 3.8 ft) and TH-4 (1.6 ft to 3.6 ft). The data from these tests are plotted in Figure 6.15. These data show optimum moisture contents in the

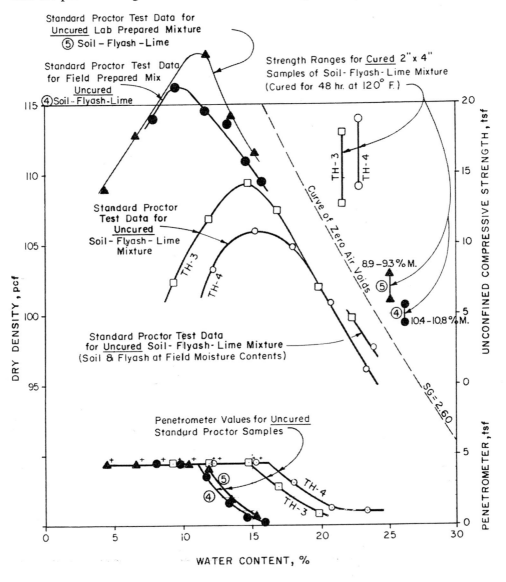

Figure 6.15 Strength and density data of soil/fly ash/lime mixture

range of 15 percent to 16 percent, and maximum dry densities in the range of 106 pcf to 109 pcf. In addition to this testing, one batch of each mixture was made up at the in situ moisture contents of the soil and fly ash and compacted according to Standard Proctor procedures. These data points are also shown in Figure 6.15. It is noted that the in situ moisture contents of the natural soil and fly ash result in mixtures that are several percentage points wet of the optimum moisture contents and several pounds lower than the maximum dry densities. The slight offset between the two corresponding compaction curves in Figure 6.15 is most likely the result of slight differences in sample preparation.

Strength estimates using a pocket penetrometer were determined for each Standard Proctor sample immediately following compaction. These estimates of unconfined compressive strength are plotted at the bottom of Figure 6.15. These data represent strength estimates prior to any significant pozzolanic reaction associated with the lime and fly ash. It is noted that the penetrometer values are low for those mixtures which have water contents corresponding to the in situ conditions of the natural soils and fly ash.

In order to evaluate potential strength gains of the mixtures as a result of pozzolanic action, two series of 2 in. by 4 in. compacted samples were made up at the in situ water contents of the natural soils and fly ash and of mixture densities close to those of Figure 6.15. Following compaction, these samples were sealed and allowed to cure in a moist environment for 48 hours at a temperature of 120°F, and then tested in unconfined compression. The 48-hour curing period at the elevated temperature is considered approximately equivalent to a 30-day cure period at 70°F.

The strength results are plotted in Figure 6.15 in relation to the water contents at which the mixtures were originally prepared. These data show significant strength gains resulting from pozzolanic action of the lime and fly ash. The TH-3 mixture exhibited an average cured strength of 16.0 tsf, and the TH-4 mixture exhibited an average cured strength of 16.9 tsf.

Laboratory constant head permeability (hydraulic conductivity) tests on saturated samples cured at room temperatures for approximately two months yielded coefficients of permeability in the range of 3.2 to 17×10^{-7} cm/sec.

Embankment Design

The soil/fly ash/lime design mixture selected for construction was proportioned on a dry weight basis as two parts soil to one part fly ash and 5 percent lime based on the combined dry weight of soil and fly ash. The two-to-one ratio of soil to fly ash was selected to make maximum use of the available fly ash at the site and to reduce the extent of excavations required for soil borrow.

Embankment Construction

The construction of the fly ash dikes was completed by Gust K. Newberg Construction Company and Mount Carmel Sand and Gravel Company. The project specifications were written as a performance type. Density requirements dictated that each lift (6 in. to 9 in., compacted) of dike material was to have a minimum compacted dry density of 100 pcf and a water content (dry weight basis) between 16 and 24 percent. The typical construction sequence was as follows:

1. The borrow area was stripped of all organic material and top soil.
2. Fly ash was placed in the borrow area, followed by the placement of lime (see Figure 6.16).
3. The combined soil/fly ash/lime was graded to an even thickness.
4. The soil/fly ash/lime material was blended into a uniform mixture by a Ray-Go rotor tiller.
5. The material was hauled and placed in the levee construction area (see Figure 6.17).
6. The blended mixture was graded and compacted by a sheepsfoot roller.

This sequence of construction was used throughout the project. Compaction requirements of the mixture were monitored for each lift, and problems were minimal. The amount of lime was monitored in the field by pH testing consisting of titration determinations of free lime which were correlated to laboratory test results.

Upon completion of the levee construction, limited studies of field permeability and in situ strength were conducted. The in situ field permeability testing was conducted using packer equipment. The permeability testing of the embankment at three locations yielded coefficients of permeability ranging from $(0.5 \text{ to } 55) \times 10^{-7}$ cm/sec. Samples retrieved from the three locations exhibited unconfined compressive strengths greater than 4.5 tsf.

Figure 6.16 Placement of lime and fly ash on soil borrow area. (Surface of soil borrow previously stripped of all organic matter)

Figure 6.17 Ash pond levee construction in background

Embankment Construction Using Scrubber Sludge

Background and Nature of Project

In 1982, Hanson Engineers, Inc. was engaged by Central Illinois Public Service Company (CIPS) to study stabilized scrubber sludge produced at the Newton Power Station by a Flue Gas Desulfurization (FGD) scrubber system and to recommend potential uses in construction. Figures 6.18 and 6.19 show the coal and waste materials from the mining operations to the power generating station.

A testing program (Mixes A through G) for stabilized sludge was formulated, and stabilized sludge was obtained from the pugmill associated with the FGD scrubber system. Sample preparation was conducted on site at the Newton Power Station. An attempt was made to prepare stabilized sludge samples in the HEI geotechnical laboratory to the same sludge proportions existing during the on-site sample preparation. The stabilized sludge ingredients were mixed by mechanical means and by hand, but difficulty was encountered in acquiring a sample consistency similar to the field-pugged samples. Therefore, laboratory stabilized sludge sample preparation was subsequently abandoned, and all sample preparation was conducted at the Newton Power Station utilizing actual field-pugged mixes.

Following initial studies, an embankment was constructed of stabilized sludge in conjunction with the development of a railroad track maintenance area at the Newton

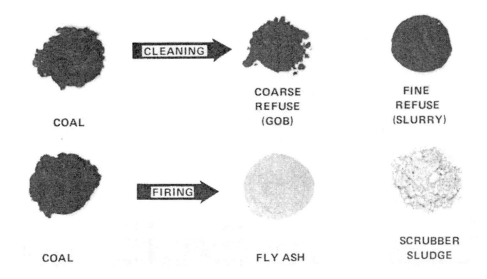

COAL

CLEANING

COARSE
REFUSE
(GOB)

FINE
REFUSE
(SLURRY)

COAL

FIRING

FLY ASH

SCRUBBER
SLUDGE

Figure 6.18   Coal and waste ingredients at the mine

Power Station. The stabilized sludge mixes included in the fill were monitored and tested. The results were correlated to the Mixes A through G prepared at the station.

Stabilized sludge had been used previously at the station as subbase for the maintenance road. Samples of the subbase were obtained and tested during this study, and those results are also included in this paper.

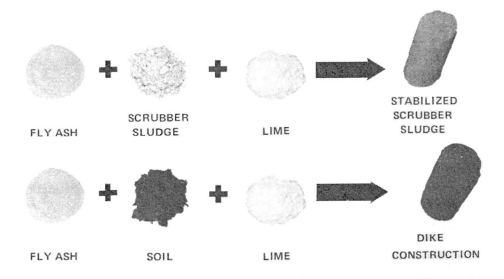

FLY ASH

SCRUBBER
SLUDGE

LIME

STABILIZED
SCRUBBER
SLUDGE

FLY ASH

SOIL

LIME

DIKE
CONSTRUCTION

Figure 6.19   Waste ingredients at the power plant

Constituent Materials in Stabilized Sludge

As indicated in Figure 6.19, stabilized sludge is a mixture of sludge (produced by the FGD system), fly ash, and lime. Initial information provided by CIPS indicates that approximately 95 percent of the stabilized sludge produced at the Newton Power Station has a fly ash-to-sludge ratio ranging from 0.5:1 to 0.8:1, and a lime content of approximately 2 to 4 percent (both computed on a dry weight basis).

The ranges of the *major* chemical constituents of the scrubber sludge are as follows:

Calcium sulfite	65–75%
Calcium sulfate	5–15%
Calcium carbonate	5%
Calcium oxide	1%

The solids content of the sludge after dewatering generally ranges from 50 percent to 65 percent.

CIPS has provided the following chemical composition of fly ash from a grab sample obtained at the Newton Power Station in 1978, which is representative of the fly ash presently being produced:

Silica	48.11%
Iron Oxide	14.36%
Aluminum Oxide	12.74%
Sulfates	8.99%
Calcium Oxide	6.35%
Potassium Oxide	2.20%
Magnesium Oxide	1.67%
Titanium Oxide	1.18%
Sodium Oxide	0.74%
Chlorides	0.44%

The Loss on Ignition (LOI) or percent combustibles of the fly ash obtained from the Newton Power Station ranges from 0.3 to 1.1 percent.

Lime used in the sludge stabilizing process is pebble quicklime supplied by Mississippi Lime Company. This material is guaranteed by the supplier to consist of a minimum of 92 percent calcium oxide.

The percent solids (dry weight basis) of the stabilized sludge produced at the power station is reported to vary from 60 percent to 75 percent.

Testing Program

The initial program involved two stabilized sludge mixtures consisting of fly ash-to-sludge ratios of 0.8:1 (Mix A) and 0.5:1 (Mix B). As previously discussed, stabilized sludge production operates 95 percent of the time within the aforementioned range. Operating procedures in 1982 prohibited fine-tuning the mechanical proportioning equipment at the Newton Power Station during the testing program, and the composition of Mix A exhibited a slightly lower fly ash-to-sludge ratio of 0.73:1. The weight-volume relationships for stabilized sludge Mixes A and B are given in Figure 6.20.

Ten Standard Proctor samples and 35 2 in. diameter by 4 in. high samples were made for each stabilized sludge mixture. The Standard Proctor samples, at the prevailing plant moisture content, were made according to ASTM D 698–71. The results are shown in Figure 6.21 designated as Mix A (pug mixed) and Mix B (pug mixed). The 2 in. by 4 in. samples of stabilized sludge were compacted to the same wet density as obtained for the Standard Proctor samples. All samples were cured in sealed metal containers at 100°F for strength and permeability (hydraulic conductivity) testing.

A parallel series of stabilized sludge samples (both Standard Proctor and 2 in. by 4 in.) was prepared in the *laboratory* utilizing the same mixture proportions as found in Mixes A and B. Laboratory samples were prepared to investigate the feasibility of conducting a testing program with variable fly ash-to-sludge ratios in the laboratory. However, difficulty in preparation of stabilized sludge to the same consistency of field Mixes A and B was encountered during the laboratory blending operations. Economic and time considerations prevented acquiring mechanical equipment to improve the mixing of the sludge constituents in the laboratory. Laboratory blended samples were prepared and cured in sealed metal containers at 100°F for strength and permeability testing. However, because of appearance and extremely low unconfined compressive strengths, the samples were later determined to be unrepresentative of pug-mixed stabilized sludge, and this procedure was eventually discarded.

A second series of stabilized sludge samples was prepared in the laboratory which involved variable water contents but maintaining the proportions of sludge, fly ash, and lime used for Mixes A and B. A Lancaster mixer and hand mixing were both utilized to blend the sludge ingredients. These samples were compacted to Standard Proctor densities, and the results are shown in Figure 6.21. Again, mixing difficulties were encountered.

A third series of samples was prepared in the laboratory utilizing the proportions of Mix A but substituting Ottawa sand for the sludge. These Standard Proctor samples were prepared to determine the pozzolanic reactivity that is obtainable between the fly ash and pebble quicklime in the absence of sludge. These samples were cured in sealed metal containers at 100°F for strength determinations.

To determine the effect of increasing the fly ash-to-sludge ratio and percent

	PUG MIXES FROM PLANT					
	MIX A	MIX B	MIX C	MIX D	MIX F	MIX G
% Solids (Scrubber Sludge)	55.2	61.7	59.8	55.5	53.9	51.6
Fly Ash To Sludge Ratio (Stabilized Sludge)	0.73	0.50	0.73	0.73	0.98	1.03
% Solids (Stabilized Sludge)	70.6	73.3	71.7	70.5	72.7	76.0
% Fly Ash (Stabilized Sludge)	41.2	32.8	41.0	40.4	48.1	48.9
% Lime (Stabilized Sludge)	2.49	2.18	2.99	4.04	2.81	3.63
Weight Proportions For 1.0 lb. Dry Wt. Of Stabilized Sludge 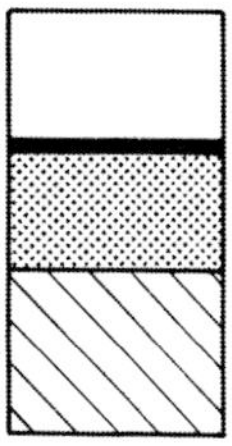						
Water[3] =	.416#	.364#	.395#	.418#	.376#	.316#
Lime =	.025#	.022#	.030#	.040#	.028#	.036#
Fly Ash =	.412#	.328#	.410#	.404#	.481#	.489#
Sludge =	.564#	.656#	.562#	.553#	.491#	.475#

NOTES:
1) All Data Shown On Dry Weight Basis
2) Mix Proportions Determined From Chemical Analyses Of Stabilized Sludge Samples Leaving Pug Mixer At Plant
3) Weight Of Water Based On % Solids Given For Stabilized Sludge
4) Mix E Had Fly Ash/Sludge Ratio = 1.15 Mix Too Dry And Was Eliminated From Testing Program

Figure 6.20 Weight-volume relationships for tests A through G

lime content, a testing program involving four stabilized sludge mixtures was conducted at the station. The mixtures (pug mixtures from the plant) consisted of fly ash-to-sludge ratios of 0.73:1 for Mixes C and D and approximately 1.0:1.0 for Mixes F and G. Mixes C and D contained approximately 3 and 4 percent pebble quicklime, while Mix G contained 3.6 percent pebble quicklime. Figure 6.20 includes the weight-

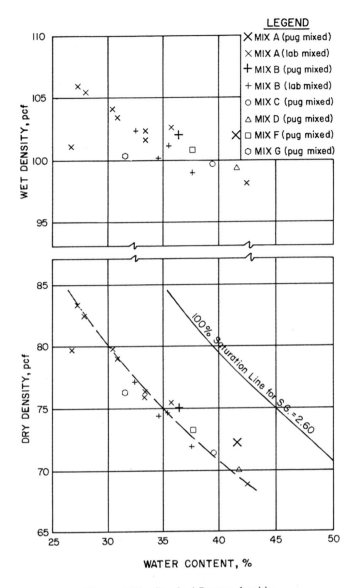

Figure 6.21 Standard Proctor densities

volume relationships for stabilized sludge Mixes C through G. The preparation of all samples was completed at the Newton Power Station.

Ten Standard Proctor samples and 18 2 in. diameter by 4 in. high samples were prepared for each stabilized sludge mixture (Mixes C through G). The 2 in. by 4 in. samples of stabilized sludge were compacted to the same wet density obtained in the Standard Proctor samples. The samples were cured in sealed metal containers at 72°F for strength testing. The samples were cured at 72°F in general conformance with the Illinois Department of Transportation Pozzolanic-Aggregate Mixture (PAM) Laboratory Evaluation/Design procedure.

Field Core Sampling

Several stabilized sludge samples were cored from two existing on-site locations. One site was a maintenance road consisting of approximately 1.5 ft of stabilized sludge overlain by 3 in. to 6 in. of crushed stone. The roadway was constructed in July 1981 by CIPS landfill operators. The other cores were obtained from the stabilized sludge land fill. Once the core samples were obtained, they were placed in sealed metal containers and cured at 72°F for future strength and permeability testing. These samples were placed in sealed metal containers and cured at 72°F for consistency in curing conditions.

Test Program Results and Interpretation

Figure 6.20 presents the weight-volume relationship of Mixes A through G. Note that Mix E is not shown in the figure since the mix was too dry (fly ash-to-sludge ratio 1.15:1) to compact and was considered impractical for sample preparation. Plant personnel indicated that the decreasing percent solids in the sludge from Mix C (59.8 percent) to Mix G (51.8 percent) can be attributed to the gradual plugging of the vacuum filter dewatering system that occurs during normal operations.

Figure 6.21 depicts Standard Proctor density-moisture content relations for all mixes studied. A well-defined relationship appears to exist between dry density and moisture content regardless of mix composition. Mixes A through G from the plant have water contents (percent of solids) on the wet side of the optimum water content associated with conditions of Standard Proctor compaction. While the optimum moisture content was not specifically determined by the testing program, it is believed that optimum moisture is approximately 25 percent or less. The vacuum filter de-watering system at the Newton Power Station is limited mechanically to dewatering of the sludge to 50 to 65 percent solids.

Unconfined compressive strengths plotted in Figure 6.22 for Standard Proctor samples of Mixes C through G indicate that Mix G increased in average strength from 185 psi at 14 days to 542 psi at 28 days. It should be emphasized that the results for Mixes A and B plotted in the figures were cured at 100°F, while Mixes C through G were cured at 72°F. Higher curing temperature accelerates the pozzolanic reaction, thus yielding high early strength values. The 28-day compressive strength values for Mixes B and G are almost equivalent. This can be attributed to a higher fly ash-to-sludge ratio and the increased lime content in Mix G. It is noted from the strength data of Mix D that a high lime content alone is not sufficient to achieve the high compressive strengths such as exhibited by Mix G. In general, samples tested after 180 days of curing showed increases in strengths between 50 percent and 100 percent of the 28-day values.

Stabilized sludge samples were also prepared in the laboratory for Mixes A

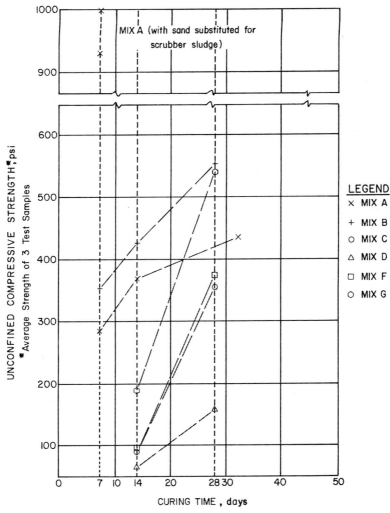

Figure 6.22 Strength data—Proctor samples

and B at the same water contents (percent solids) produced at the plant. Strength data (not plotted in Figure 6.22) exhibited considerably lower values than the plant-prepared mixes at seven-day curing time. The low laboratory strengths are believed to be influenced by laboratory procedures, since a pug mill type mixer simulating field conditions was not used. This datum has been discounted as an indicator of field behavior.

The laboratory samples prepared substituting Ottawa sand for sludge in Mix A revealed extremely high compressive strength values ranging from 930 to 1003 psi. These high compressive strengths indicate that the lime-fly ash constituents are creating cementing materials through the pozzolanic reactivity of the fly ash. The high compressive strength values also suggest that it may be possible to supplement the sludge with sand or coarse aggregate to achieve higher compressive strengths.

Cored samples of stabilized sludge obtained randomly from the existing on-site roadway and land fill gave unconfined compressive strengths of 346 psi and 428 psi, respectively. The ages of the samples had been estimated at 60 days for the land-fill and 52 days for the roadway. Proportions of stabilized sludge ingredients for these areas are unknown.

Permeability (hydraulic conductivity) tests were conducted on samples prepared from Mixes A through G produced at the power plant. It was found that results varied considerably, depending on curing conditions. For curing times between 30 and 40 days, the permeability values varied between 0.5×10^{-6} cm/sec and 1.5×10^{-6} cm/sec. Some of the higher permeabilities after 180 days of curing were undoubtedly the result of hairline cracks in the samples.

Maintenance Track Facility

Stabilized sludge was used as fill for a maintenance track facility at the Newton Power Station. Figure 6.23 shows a typical section through the embankment. The maintenance track fill was constructed by CIPS landfill operators, during May and June 1982.

The stabilized sludge used for fill construction was not proportioned to a predetermined mix design. Although the quality of the sludge was not controlled specifically for fill construction, it was monitored and recorded on a daily basis. Ranges of daily proportions of sludge components for the period of fill construction were recorded. Figures 6.24 and 6.25 show the wide variation of the fly ash-to-sludge ratio plotted against percentages of lime, water content, and solids.

The stabilized sludge was placed and compacted utilizing the same equipment used to dispose of the stabilized sludge at the on-site landfill. Stabilized sludge from the plant was stockpiled for as long as four days prior to placement at the site. During this time, the core of some of the stockpiles had begun to solidify. The majority of the stabilized sludge was hauled to the proposed embankment in 50-ton capacity International Harvester trucks with occasional loads by a scraper. A Caterpillar D-7 dozer was used to spread the stabilized sludge, and compaction was achieved by a steel drum vibratory compactor. It should be noted that additional compaction

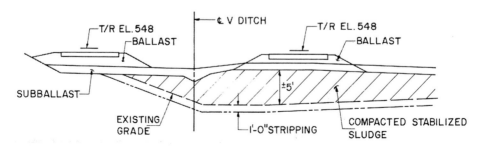

Figure 6.23 Typical section through tracks

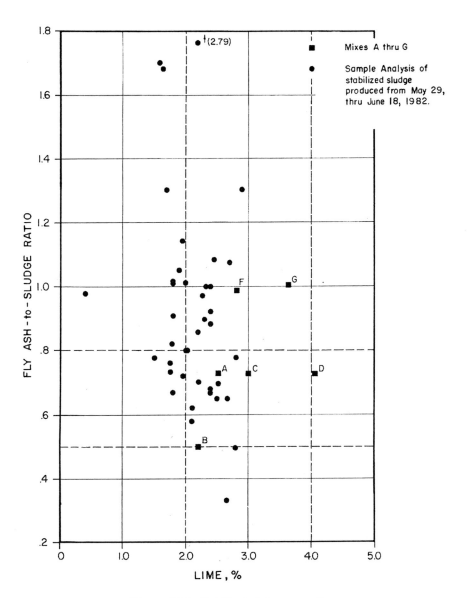

Figure 6.24 Stabilized sludge proportions

was also provided by the D-7 dozer during spreading operations and by the traversing of the site by the stabilized sludge hauling vehicles.

Due to the type of equipment used for the construction of the embankment, difficulty in controlling the lift thickness of the stabilized sludge was experienced. Loose-measured lift thickness ranged from approximately 12 to 30 in. after placement of the initial 24 to 30 in. working platform. Sixty-five field density tests were conducted on the stabilized sludge fill during construction. Field density test results indicated that adequate density was being achieved by two to three passes of the vibratory steel drum compactor. Forty-five of the 65 field densities conducted exhibited dry densities

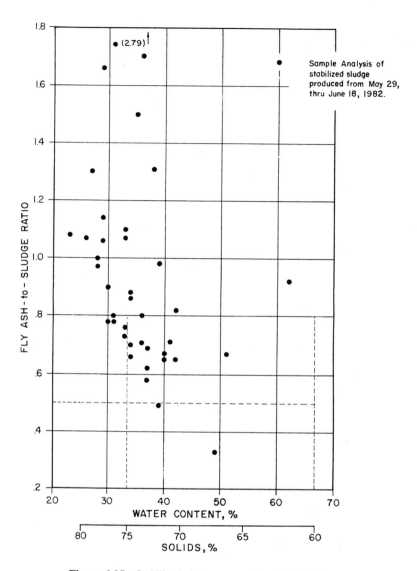

Figure 6.25 Stabilized sludge proportions in track fill area

higher than the Standard Proctor dry densities obtained for Mixes A through G (Figure 6.21).

Conclusions

Coal Mine Wastes

The first case history of this paper demonstrates that waste materials at coal mines can be managed to prevent failures of containment facilities and to use the waste materials themselves to achieve both adequate safety and favorable environmental economics. The parameters and constraints for design and construction, introduced by mine operations, make it impossible to design and build impoundment facilities with the same high degree of quality control which usually accompanies the construction of ordinary dams. In general, however, basic principles and procedures are identical to those used in the design and construction of ordinary dams and reservoirs. Nevertheless, such basic geotechnical knowledge must be tempered with good judgment, and usually with innovation to meet the client's needs.

Generating Plant Wastes

The second case history of this paper demonstrates the beneficial use of fly ash, mixed with soil and lime, to build containment dikes. The readily available on-site fly ash was a suitable substitute for off-site borrow and resulted in a cost saving equal to more than half the actual total project cost. Furthermore, the removal of fly ash from existing storage provided additional future storage space. Additional benefits occurring from the use of fly ash to replace soil in construction were steeper slopes and improved permeability of the dikes.

The third case history of this paper has demonstrated the feasibility of using stabilized scrubber sludge in embankment construction. Moreover, laboratory and field tests appear to indicate that, in addition to the railroad maintenance facility described in the case history, stabilized sludge is probably suitable for use in highway construction as elements of the pavement profile.

Future Research

It is important to note the need for further research, particularly in the uses of stabilized scrubber sludge. The research discussed in this paper has dealt primarily with the strength of stabilized mixes, and to a lesser degree with permeability (hydraulic conductivity). Since strength is only one of many properties required to define suitability for pavements and other uses, much future research remains to be accomplished. A large measure of this future research should be performed in the field and should include performance evaluations over periods of many years.

REFERENCES

1. L. H. Roth, J. A. Cesare and G. A. Allison, "Rapid Monitoring of Coal Refuse Embankments," *Proceedings of the Conference on Geotechnical Practice for Disposal of Solid Waste Materials* ASCE (June 1977), pp. 428–443.

2. National Ash Association, "Ash Production/Ash Utilization—1982," Washington, DC, August 1983.

3. "Design Guidelines for Coal Waste Structures," MESA Technical Support Centers, Denver, Colorado and Pittsburgh, Pennsylvania, May 1975.

4. Dames & Moore (for U.S. Department of Energy), "A Study of the Properties of Mine Waste in the Midwestern Coal Fields," November 1981.

The Old and New Clark Bridge

Walter E. Hanson and John E. Harms

Synopsis

This paper describes the existing Clark Bridge across the Mississippi River at Alton, Illinois, completed in 1928, and relates some history of the bridge dating back to the original promotion of the bridge. Also, the history and evolution of bridge engineering in general are noted by reference to certain periods of history and to significant projects other than the Clark Bridge. Finally, the new bridge at Alton that will replace the existing Clark Bridge is described, giving the reader a contrast of the proposed continuous cable-stayed spans with the original simple spans.

Introduction

The senior author, Mr. Hanson, first became acquainted with the existing Clark Bridge in 1951 when he was Engineer of Bridge and Traffic Structures in the Illinois Division of Highways. His interest in the bridge and in the "Three-River" region of the state of Illinois and Missouri has persisted since that time. For the past four years, Mr. Harms, the co-author, has been in overall charge of the planning, design, and preparation of the plans and specifications for the new bridge.

In a certain sense, this paper is the authors' attempt to bridge the gulf between pure technical analysis and design and all the other related aspects of what might be called "total bridge engineering practice" near the end of this, the 20th century. As in the case of most civil engineering projects in this day of increased concern for our environment, bridge engineering involves a wide spectrum of disciplines, of which many of those disciplines lie outside the realm of science and engineering. Bridges have always been more than a part of economic development; they have reflected, to some degree at least, the state of civilization.

The authors hope that this paper might serve to supplement senior and graduate-level courses in structural analysis to give students an indication of total professional bridge engineering practice. The reader will have to refer to other sources and persons

204

for some of the specific details of the structural analysis and design of the proposed Clark Bridge.

The authors wish to acknowledge and give due credit to the many firms and persons who have helped in the planning and design of the new bridge. These include: the Illinois Department of Transportation (District 8 and the Bureau of Bridges and Structures); the consulting engineering firms of Figg & Muller Engineers, Inc.; Sheppard, Morgan and Schwaab; Globetrotters Engineering Corporation; Fox Drilling, Inc.; and Wells Engineers, Inc.

Evolution of Bridge Engineering

Although the evolution of bridges began with creations of nature (before primitive man made any contributions), the Roman military engineers are commonly considered the first consequential practitioners of bridge engineering. The Roman Empire has been called the first nation of bridge builders as well as rulers of the world. One of the restored Roman bridges, located near Mortarelli, Spain, is shown in Figure 1. It is believed by some historians to be the oldest of the remaining Roman bridges, probably built prior to the Punic Wars between Rome and Carthage, circa 219-202 B.C.

Figure 1. Restored Roman Bridge near Montorelli, Spain.

It has been written (1) that after the fall of Rome, historical bridge construction made little progress until the 11th and 12th centuries. During those centuries, much of the bridge engineering was practiced by religious orders. An example of a beautiful 12th century bridge is the St. Benezet structure in Southern France, shown in Figure 2. According to legend, St. Benezet was the leader of the French Brotherhood of Bridge Builders (2). It is interesting to note that about this same period in history, the foundations consisting of long piling were begun for London Bridge (1).

During the Renaissance period—the 14th, 15th, and 16th centuries—many scientists and artists contributed considerably to the

Figure 2. St. Benezet Bridge at Avignon, France.

evolution of bridges. However, it was not until the 17th and 18th centuries that science advanced, and fundamental laws were discovered that provided the basis for rational theory, analyses, and design of bridges. During this period, such scientists as Galileo, Hooke, and Bernoulli, paved the way for Coulomb, Hodgkinson, and Euler. It was also in the 16th century that the truss structure was invented by the Italian architect, Palladio, which contributed immeasurably to the evolution of bridges as well as to buildings. Indeed, the invention of trusses made possible the building of countless long span bridges, of which the existing Clark Bridge is one.

Dr. J.A.L. Waddell and Collegial Bridge Engineers, Circa 1900

It is difficult, if not impossible, to select the most outstanding bridge engineer in all of history, but in this paper, at least, there is a valid reason for awarding such an exalted title to Dr. J.A.L. Waddell. He, in addition to being a world renowned bridge engineer and promoter of major bridge projects, was a skilled and comprehensive writer. An example of his writing is the monumental treatise, *Bridge Engineering* (2), published in 1925, consisting of two volumes and more than 2,000 pages. Dr. Waddell was a strong advocate of the selection of engineers for engineering assignments judged on their capabilities and experience. He was known to have been somewhat arrogant and egotistical in his personal relations. Such a personality is probably reflected by the title sheet of his *Bridge Engineering*, shown in Figure 3, which cites more than 25 degrees,

BRIDGE
ENGINEERING

BY

J. A. L. WADDELL

C.E. (Rens. Poly. Inst.); B. A.Sc., Ma. E., D.Sc. (McGill Univ.); D.E.
(Univ. of Neb.); LL.D. (Univ. of Mo.); Kogakuhakushi
(Doctor of Eng., Imp. Univ. of Japan)

Correspondant de l'Institut de France dans l'Académie des Sciences; Correspondiente de la Real Academia de Ciencias
y Artes de Barcelona; Correspomsal de la Sociedad de Ingenieros del Perú; Knight Commander of the Japanese
Order of the Rising Sun; Ordre de Bienfaisance de la Grande Duchesse Olga of Russie, Première Classe; Second
Class Order of the Sacred Treasure of Japan; Second Class Order of the Sacred Grain of China; Cavaliere
dei Ordine della Corona d'Italia; Consulting Engineer New York City; Member of the American Society
of Civil Engineers; of the American Institute of Consulting Engineers; of the Franklin Institute; of La
Société des Ingénieurs Civils, Paris; of the Engineering Institute of Canada; of the Western Society
of Engineers; of the Society for the Promotion of Engineering Education; of the American Association for the Advancement of Science; of the American Society for Testing Materials; of
the International Society for Testing Materials; of the American Railway Engineering
Association; of the China Society of America; of La Société de Géographie de France;
of the National Conservation Association; of the National Economic League; of the
Liberal League of the Authors Club London; and Honorary Member of the Chinese Institute of Engineers; of the Association of Chinese and American Engineers; of the Chinese Railway Association; of the Association Nacional de
Ingenieros Industriales de España; of the Kogoku Kyokai (Engineering
Society of Japan; of the Engineers Club of Kansas City; of the Société
Internationale d'Études de Correspondance et d'Échanges Coo-
cordia, Paris; of the Phi Beta Kappa Society; of the Sigma
Xi Society; and of the Tau Beta Pi Society

IN TWO VOLUMES

VOLUME I

FIRST EDITION
FOURTH THOUSAND

Yours faithfully,
J. A. L. Waddell.

NEW YORK
JOHN WILEY & SONS, Inc.
London: CHAPMAN & HALL, Limited
1925

Figure 3. Title Page of <u>Bridge Engineering</u>

awards, and honors, including the Doctor of Engineering bestowed upon him by the Imperial University of Japan.

Another important reason for giving special recognition here to Dr. Waddell is that he founded at least three bridge engineering firms. However, of equal significance are the many other prominent firms founded by his former partners and associates, most notable of which was Harrington, Howard & Ash, the engineering firm of record on the existing Clark Bridge in the 1920s. Some years later, the firm's name became Ash, Howard, Needles & Tammen, and then Howard, Needles, Tammen & Bergendoff, the latter of which exists today. Several other well-known, present-day firms can trace some of their roots to Dr. Waddell or to one or more of his colleagues.

History of Existing Clark Bridge

Prior to the construction of the Lewis and Clark bridges, the Alton area of Illinois was acutely isolated from Missouri to the south. Since the turn of the 20th century, and even earlier, there had been dreams about bridges across both the Mississippi and Missouri Rivers, but it was not until 1923 that interest grew to active promotion and organized civic involvement.

In March 1926, the *Alton Evening Telegraph* reported that U.S. Congressman Clarence Cannon of Missouri had introduced a bill in Congress authorizing the total Lewis and Clark project. By June of that year, thirty-three Alton businessmen had subscribed the funds needed to make a financial feasibility report for the toll project. The report, completed in October, concluded that the project was financially sound and that "good profits can be realized from the tolls collected."

The test borings for the bridge in the natural geological materials below the Mississippi River were completed in November 1926. It is interesting to note that even in 1926 a form of penetration test was used to determine the depth of rock and to evaluate the density of the sands, gravels, and other types of soil. On Sheet No. 2 of the plans for the bridge, the following note appeared:

> "Probings: Probings are shown on profile with depth below surface in feet given. These were made March 18, 1927 by driving down iron rods with a 15-pound maul until solid material was struck except the following: No. 4, down 37 feet, no rock; No. 7, down 27.5 feet and broke rod; and No. 8, down 17 feet and broke rod."

The U.S. War Department approved the bridge plans in December 1926, provided the truss spans of the Missouri River Bridge would be increased from five to six, Early in 1927, the Alton, St. Louis Bridge Company, which sold bonds and stock to finance the bridge and which collected tolls to amortize the liabilities, was officially and legally organized.

On March 16, 1927, the Alton newspaper published a special 10-page supplement devoted to the new bridges. The various articles and congratulatory advertisements emphasized the increase in trade which the new bridges should surely bring to the Alton community. One article noted that the Missouri farmers were really a part of Alton and that the new bridges would mean new paved roads into the city. Another article gave due credit to the engineering firm of Harrington, Howard & Ash, "one of the leading bridge engineer organizations in the United States."

Construction contracts totaling approximately $2,400,000 for both bridges were awarded in May 1927, and the Kansas City Bridge Company and the Wisconsin Bridge Company were the principal builders.

The formal opening of the bridge was set for August 1, 1928. However, it is interesting to note that on June 30, 1928, according to the *Alton Evening Telegraph*, the first vehicle to cross the new bridge was an ambulance on emergency call to West Alton.

Many interesting events and periods of anxiety have occurred during the life of the existing Clark Bridge. After the indebtedness of the Bridge Company had been retired, circa 1950, tolls were discontinued for a brief period. However, the City of Alton soon resumed the collection of tolls to provide for maintenance and operational expenses. The states of Missouri and Illinois eventually signed a joint maintenance agreement, but not without much discussion and even disagreements on the condition of the bridge and respective responsibilities. The senior author of this paper was privileged to have participated in some of those negotiations from 1951 through 1953.

Type and Condition of Existing Bridge

U.S. Route 67 accommodates traffic movements between rural northern St. Louis County and the City of Alton, Illinois. The Lewis Bridge in Missouri carries U.S. 67 over the Missouri River, while the Clark Bridge carries the same highway over the Mississippi River at Alton. The original Lewis Bridge in Missouri was replaced by the Missouri Department of Transportation in the late 1970s.

As shown in Figure 4, the existing Clark Bridge is located downstream, parallel to the Burlington Northern Railroad Bridge. Both bridges extend over existing Lock and Dam No. 26. The construction of the new Lock and Dam No. 26 approximately two miles downstream is well advanced. The Corps of Engineers raised the pool at the site of the new Clark Bridge in January 1990. The Burlington Northern Railroad Bridge is being removed as part of the existing Lock and Dam No. 26 demolition contract. The existing Clark Bridge will be removed after the new replacement bridge is completed.

Figure 4. Clark Bridge Site Showing Existing Bridge, Lock and Dam, and Existing Burlington Northern R.R. Bridge

209

The existing 3,640 ft. long Clark Bridge is a two-lane bridge with a roadway only 20 ft. wide. The Missouri approach spans consist of three concrete girder spans with a concrete deck. These spans, all of which are simple spans, are supported by concrete columns and concrete footings on timber piles.

The existing main river spans consist of seven steel, through truss spans with a concrete deck, all of which are simple spans. The piers for these spans consist of two cylindrical, concrete columns connected by a full height concrete wall. The piers are supported by concrete footings on timber piles.

The existing Illinois approach spans consist of nine steel, deck truss spans and four steel, through girder spans with a concrete deck. The deck truss spans are supported by steel towers with four steel columns at each pier location. The foundations for these towers consist of concrete pedestals on timber piles. The through girder spans are supported by two steel columns at each pier location, and the columns are supported by concrete pedestals founded on rock. Like the Missouri approach spans and the main river spans, all of the Illinois approach structures are simple spans.

At present, the deterioration of the existing bridge is serious, the substructure elements in the river require continual protection by riprap against local scour, and the bridge is too narrow to carry the present amount of traffic. These main deficiencies justify complete replacement of the existing bridge.

History of Studies for New Bridge

The need for additional capacity on the Clark Bridge Crossing has been recognized for at least two decades. In 1958, H.W. Lochner & Company prepared a report: *Recommended Solution of the Lewis and Clark Bridge Problem, Alton, Illinois*. In 1961, Harland Bartholomew and Associates compiled a report: *The Comprehensive Plan; Alton, Illinois*. The firm of Howard, Needles, Tammen & Bergendoff in 1967 prepared a report: *City of Alton, Illinois; Mississippi River Bridge Location Studies*; and in 1969, another report: *Corridor Location Report: U.S. Route 67 Extension Through Alton* was produced by the same firm.

None of the recommendations of these prior investigations was implemented, mainly because the studies also included some form of north-south cross town highway through Alton. Although the need for improved north-south highway capacity has never been refuted, none of the proposed plans received acceptance by the community due to associated neighborhood severance and displacement problems.

In 1981, DeLeuw, Cather & Company undertook another study, in which an evaluation of possible locations for a new bridge in and near the Alton area resulted in a finding that the most suitable location, both environmentally and economically, was in the vicinity of the existing bridge. The study concentrated on two alternative locations, one immediately adjacent to the existing bridge and another beginning near the abutment of the existing bridge in Missouri and terminating approximately 2,000 ft downstream of the existing bridge in Illinois. These two alternatives are shown in Figure 5.

The second alternative alignment was recommended and approved by the Illinois Department of Transportation in the February 15, 1985 "Design Report" by DeLeuw, Cather & Company.

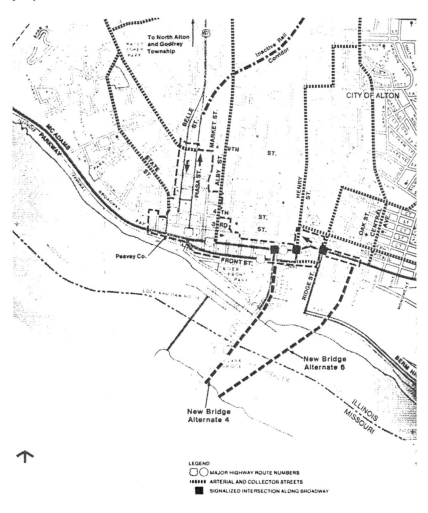

Figure 5. Alternative Horizontal Alignments of Proposed Bridge.

Final Studies and Design

In 1985, Hanson Engineers Incorporated, with Figg & Muller Engineers, Inc. of Tallahassee, Florida as a subconsultant, began a "Bridge Type Study Report" for the approved alignment. Initially, a 600 ft. right angle navigation channel, with the Illinois main span pier located behind the extension of the existing lock guide wall, was proposed and submitted to the U.S. Coast Guard's Second District for approval. A coordination meeting was subsequently held with U.S. Coast Guard officials in St. Louis to discuss navigation requirements. Concern was expressed about the location of the Illinois pier north of the navigation channel, because prevailing river currents caused natural drifts of barges toward the Illinois shoreline.

After the initial meeting with the Coast Guard officials, the St. Louis District, Corps of Engineers performed a bridge pier model study at the Waterways Experiment Station in Vicksburg, Mississippi. The size and location of the new bridge piers were studied under existing and future river pool conditions to identify the impact of the piers on commercial navigation. Based on the results of the Corps' study, the Coast Guard presented the options of either building a rock dike extending downriver from the existing lock or moving the Illinois pier 150 ft. toward the Illinois shore. The Illinois Department of Transportation decided for economic reasons to increase the main span length by 150 ft. and accordingly, an 850 ft. main span, which provided 750 ft. of horizontal clearance, was submitted and tentatively approved by the Coast Guard.

However, subsequent to the submittal of the final "Bridge Type Study Report", the Corps of Engineers decided to provide additional navigational safety by building the rock dike extension downstream from the existing Lock and Dam No. 26. The Illinois main span pier was then placed in line with the rock dike, which allowed the main span length to be reduced from 850 ft. to 756 ft.

Steel and Concrete Alternative Designs

The Federal Highway Administration policy mandates that alternative bridge plans in steel and concrete be prepared for major river crossings. The "Bridge Type Study Report" considered a tied arch, a continuous truss, and cable-stayed main spans for the steel alternative. Cable-stayed and box girder bridges were considered for the main spans of the concrete alternative. Based on economic studies, cable-stayed spans were recommended and approved for both main span alternatives. Steel parallel flange, plate girders with a cast-in-place concrete deck were selected for the steel alternative approach spans, and twin precast box sections, which are to be post-tensioned longitudinally, were selected for the approach spans of the concrete alternative.

The replacement bridge is 4,620 ft. long, with the cable-stayed spans being 1,360 ft. long. The new bridge will be a four-lane bridge with accommodations for a bicycle path in the outside shoulders. The structure is skewed 20 degrees with the river flow. A five track railroad corridor on the Illinois side of the river will be relocated to provide an adequate connection between the bridge and Illinois Route 143 in Alton.

Both cable-stayed alternatives are very similar in nature. The two lines of cables are arranged in a fan type arrangement as shown in Figures 6 and 7. One end of the stay is anchored to the deck system and extends up over the top of the pylon in a "saddle" 176 ft. above deck level and descends to the deck level on the other side. The stays consist of 0.6 in. diameter, epoxy coated strand impregnated with a grit. The strands are surrounded by a metal pipe or polyethylene pipe with grout placed in the pipe after all the stays are adjusted. All jacking of the stays will take place below deck level.

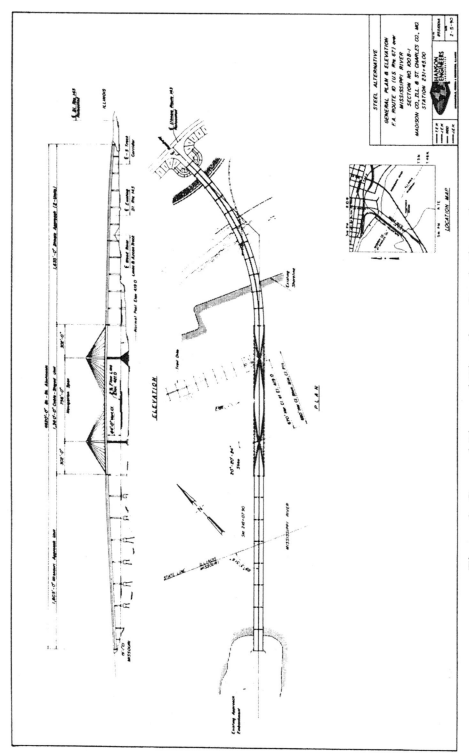

Figure 6. General Plan and Elevation: Steel Alternative.

213

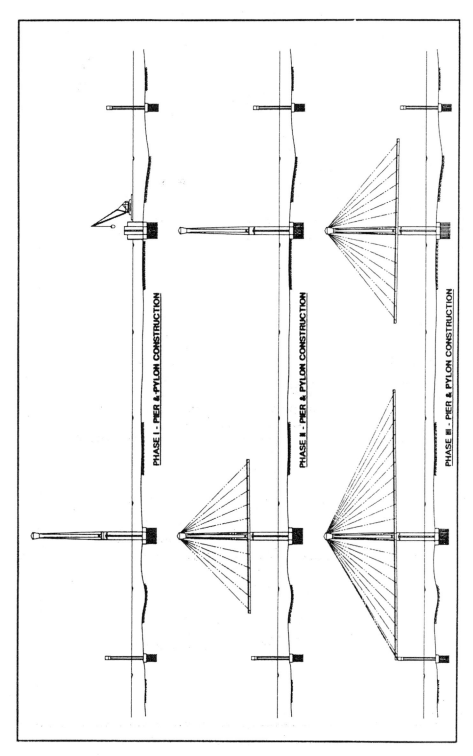

Figure 7. Balanced Cantilever Erection Scheme for Main Spans.

As indicated in Figure 7, the structure will be built by the balanced cantilever method by alternating from one side to the other side of the pylon. The metal pipe section in the saddle will be locked into the saddle at the top of the pylon. The strands in the pipe will rely on friction to resist any unbalanced loads. A special testing program to verify the coefficient of friction was conducted by the firm of Wiss, Janney, Elstner Associates, Inc.

The deck system for the cable-stayed spans of the steel alternative consists of longitudinal, solid precast concrete deck panels supported by transverse, steel plate girder floor beams, as indicated in Figure 8. The floor beams are, in turn, supported by two longitudinal, steel edge girders, to which the cable-stays are attached, as indicated in Figure 9.

The deck system for the cable-stayed spans of the concrete alternative is precast box sections, which span transversely. The box sections are post-tensioned together longitudinally, and the stays are attached to the ends of the box sections, as indicated in Figure 10.

Specifications and Special Studies for Foundations, Scour, and Earthquake

In the "Type, Size, and Location" phase of the project, a geotechnical investigation, hydraulic and scour study, and a seismicity study were performed. Also, the "Criteria for: The Design of Bridge Piers with Respect to Vessel Collision in Louisiana Waterways," produced by Modjeski and Masters in 1974 for the Highway Research Board, was used as a guide to develop a barge collision force for analysis and design.

The geotechnical investigation included a soil boring program and a geotechnical report. The geotechnical report recommended steel "H" piles driven to bedrock for the Illinois approach spans, the main spans, and the Illinois abutment. The piers for the Missouri Approach spans will have both "H" piles driven to bedrock and "H" piles in friction. The Missouri abutment will have "H" piles in friction. This report also recommended a mid-height berm be placed in the Illinois roadway embankment to provide stability and safety against liquefaction from earthquakes.

The basic Design Specifications for the bridge include:
    1988   AASHTO Standard Specifications for Highway Bridges
    1983   AASHTO Guide Specifications for Seismic Design
    1980   AASHTO Guide Specifications for Horizontally Curved Bridges
    1986   P.T.I. Recommendations for Stay Testing

The hydraulic analysis included the various discharge-water surface elevation relationships and bridge backwater values. The scour study provided estimates of scour at bridge piers and abutments.

The seismic design of the approach spans will be developed in accordance with the AASHTO Guide Specifications for seismic design. However, the seismicity study, which was prepared by Dr. Douglas A. Foutch, University of Illinois, provided some modifications of the equations and concepts given in the AASHTO Guide Specifications. The following main recommendations for the cable-stayed spans by Dr. Foutch include:

(1) The bridge should be considered as "Essential"
(2) The design should follow "Seismic Performance Category C"
(3) The acceleration coefficient should be 0.15
(4) A "Multimode Spectral Analysis Method" should be used for design

Construction of the main span foundations will start in the late spring of 1990, with completion anticipated in late 1991. The remaining portions of the main spans are projected to start in the winter of 1990, with anticipated completion in 1993. The Missouri and Illinois approach spans are scheduled to start in the late spring of 1991, with completion anticipated in the latter part of 1993.

Conclusions

In a general sense, this paper has described bridge engineering at the beginning and at the end of the 20th century. The differences in the nature and scope of engineering work required for a major bridge project, such as the Clark Bridges, have been the result of many aspects of change besides the advancement of the states-of-art of structural analyses, building materials, and construction techniques. These changes include: demographics of commerce and population, environmental and economic factors, and other societal concerns—even the preservation of history.

From the standpoint of structural engineering, the most notable difference between the old and new Clark Bridge is the degree of indeterminacy of the main spans. Dr. Waddell and his peers in 1927 believed that all bridges should be as nearly statically determinate as possible. Today, the redundancy of cable-stayed structures is usually considered to represent added safety. Of course, the electronic computers have made possible the analyses of such structures. It is a reasonable conjecture that Dr. Waddell would approve the new Clark Bridge—with some suggested changes, no doubt.

Endnotes

[I]   Founder and Special Consultant, Hanson Engineers, Incorporated, Springfield, Illinois.

[II]   Partner and Head of Bridge Section, Hanson Engineers, Incorporated, Springfield, Illinois.

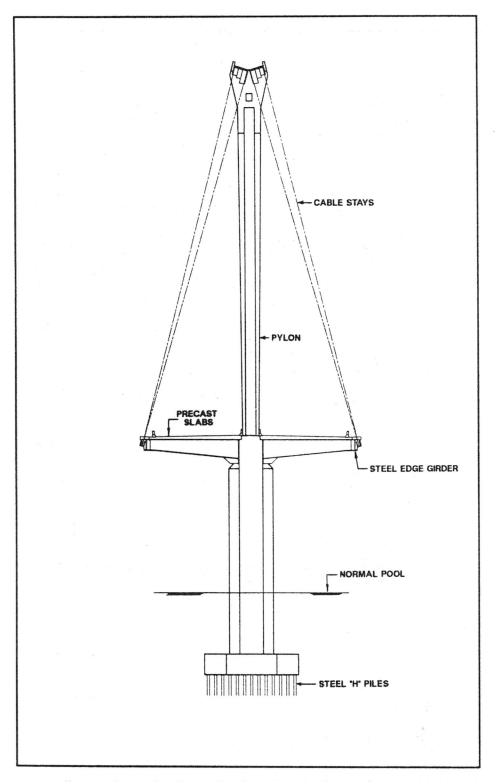

Figure 8. Cross Section: Steel Alternative.

217

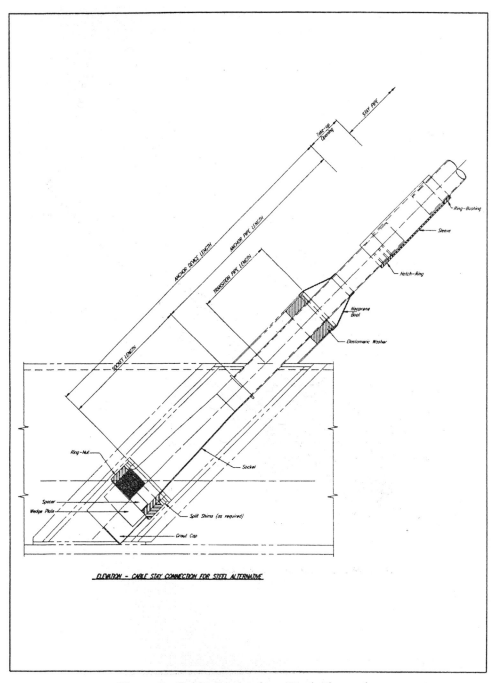

Figure 9. Cable Connection: Steel Alternative

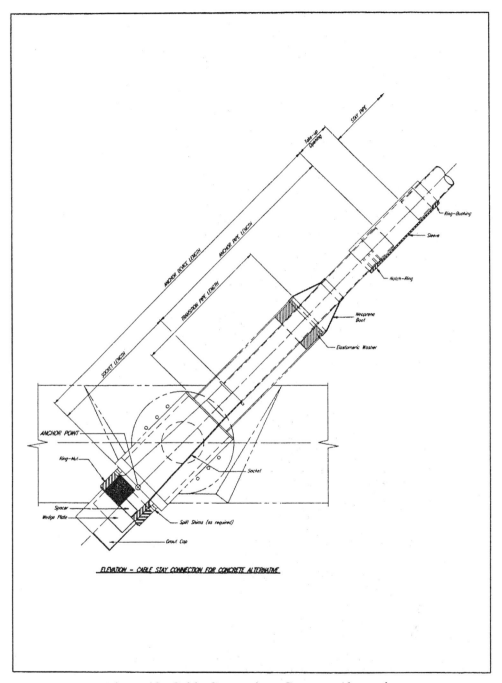

Figure 10. Cable Connection: Concrete Alternative

SELECTED PRESENTATIONS

———••●••———

Author's Note: The camera slides named in some of the following presentations have been lost. We trust that these omissions will not detract appreciably from the text material.

———••●••———

"County Highway Bridges— Engineering Requirements and Types of Construction"

Tenth Annual Highway Conference
For County Engineers and Officials
American Road Builders Association, Springfield, Illinois
September 30-October 3, 1962

Introduction

In Illinois, county and township bridges represent a very important part of the overall highway program of planning, design and construction. Surely the same can be said for most of the other states represented at this convention. Unfortunately, the serious magnitude of the problem of repair and replacement of county and township bridges is not always appreciated; and where the problem is appreciated, the construction funds just do not seem to be available.

The Illinois Division of Highways reports that there exist on the roads of this state nearly 24,000 bridges which range in length from 20 to 160 feet. It is important to note that nearly 20,000 of these bridges are located on county and township roads. But of greater importance is that fact that nearly 3,000 of these 20,000 bridges are reported to be in poor structural condition. The structural condition of another 6,000 is only fair. Many thousand more are deficient because of other reasons, such as deficient roadway width and poor alignment.

220

These are alarming statistics which indicate that more than one-half of the existing county and township bridges in the state of Illinois should be either repaired or completely replaced. These are bridges that are not eligible for 90 percent federal participation in the construction costs. Indeed, in many instances the cost of construction must be derived entirely by county or township taxation. Needless to say, the demands of traffic, waterway requirements and other engineering requirements must be satisfied as cheaply as possible. At the same time, however, the solutions in the form of new structures must be such as to eliminate unreasonably large maintenance requirements.

During the next few minutes, I want to talk about a few of the engineering requirements of county bridges. Most of my remarks will be limited to waterway and foundation requirements and their influence upon the choice of type of structure, with particular emphasis on the substructure. I shall conclude my discussion with a number of slides that will demonstrate my comments and, at the same time, will give an overview of the different types of county bridges used in Illinois.

Preliminary Engineering

General Discussion

First, I want to stress the importance of preliminary engineering when we are considering the construction of a new bridge or replacement of an old one. By preliminary engineering, I mean the evaluation of site conditions such as waterway requirements, foundation conditions, and all the other work that must be accomplished before one has a proper basis for comparative estimates of cost and for final judgment in the selection of span combinations and type of bridge.

Present and future traffic must be estimated, because the traffic establishes the importance of the bridge. It is obvious that the magnitude and type of traffic over the top of the bridge should establish the roadway width across the bridge as well as the horizontal and vertical alignments of the approaches. It is sometimes not so obvious that this same traffic should also affect decisions concerning design floods, types of substructure and span arrangements.

The degree of difficulty and amount of effort which must go into the preliminary phase of bridge design is not a function of the size and cost of the bridge. Sometimes more time is required in the preliminary engineering for a small $10,000 bridge than for structures costing 10 or 20 times this amount. It is at this early point of the development of bridge design that important decisions have to be made. If they are properly made, the best economical structure is conceived. If not, thousands of public tax dollars may be wasted.

Hydrology and Hydraulics

Certainly, during the past few years, important results of experimental and analytical research have improved the methods that are available to predict flood flows at bridge sites. Notable among these, at least in Illinois, are the so-called Mitchell method and the

Chow method. But let me indicate to you some points in connection with the hydraulics of bridge structures that require engineering judgment even though a design discharge is computed as accurately as present knowledge permits.

First, I want to comment on the importance of determining as accurately as possible a high water elevation which is consistent with the design flood. Too often, the waterway opening computed for a 10- or 15-year frequency storm is furnished below a high water elevation which more nearly corresponds to a 50-year flood. It is important to realize that a given waterway requirement furnished below a water elevation that is too high will result in a bridge that may have difficulty in passing even the design flood. It is even more deficient for floods of greater magnitude. So it is important to realize that it is not always conservative to use the highest high water of record for purposes of design of county bridges. The design values of flood discharges and high water elevations must be as consistent as possible.

Secondly, it is important to realize that the hydraulic design of small bridges sometimes extends much farther upstream and down than the limits of the right-of-way lines along the road. In some instances, a considerable amount of channel work may be necessary. Trees, brush and other channel constrictions, together with the discharges from ditches and secondary tributaries near the site, may cause floods to converge and establish turbulence at the bridge opening. It must be remembered that the general direction and characteristics of stream flow during floods may be quite different from normal flow confined to the natural banks of the stream.

Lastly, in connection with hydrology and hydraulics of new bridges, I would emphasize the importance of evaluating the performance of the old bridge. Let us say that an old bridge has been in place for 50 or 75 years, and during this period it has handled all floods satisfactorily. If nothing is proposed in the way of future construction which would increase or otherwise alter the characteristics of the flood discharges to be handled by the new bridge, there would appear to be very little, if any, justification for a larger waterway opening. Indeed, there are instances when the waterway opening furnished by the new bridge need not be as large as that supplied by the old bridge.

Foundation Conditions

Another important part of preliminary engineering is the analysis and evaluation of foundation conditions. For small county bridges, it is not always possible to obtain, or even to justify, foundation borings in accordance with State standards for structures on primary and interstate highways. Nevertheless, it is important to have some quantitative basis for the evaluation of the consistency and compressibility of the subsoil, even if exploration consists only of hand auger borings or driving a reinforcing bar into the subsoil.

It is important to realize that it is not whether the subsoil is brown or blue that is important; it is the degree of softness or hardness that must be known to determine the appropriate and most economical type of substructure. For example, pile bents for bridge piers cannot be used if subsurface conditions do not permit adequate penetration. Sometimes, if piles are required for the support of closed concrete abutments, a three span bridge with spill-thru slopes is more economical.

Frequently, abutments and piers are caught in deep-seated failures of creek banks due to the added weight of approach embankments. A thorough program of test borings and appropriate testing is justified if, for any reason, such unfavorable subsoil conditions are suspected to be present. Sometimes a relocation of a road to a more favorable site from the standpoint of foundation conditions may result in a cheaper bridge and less overall cost of the project.

Types of Substructure

Let us consider the bridge substructure which, for purposes of discussion, includes slopewalls, abutments and piers.

Concrete Slopewalls

Complaints are frequently heard about the maintenance requirements of concrete slopewalls at bridges. Even if they do not wash out, they sometimes experience large settlements and lateral displacements. Because of difficulties of slopewalls of some sort or another, some counties have tended to look with disfavor on the so-called spill-thru abutment. There is no question about the sizeable initial cost of slopewalls, and sometimes they do present rather serious construction and maintenance problems, but a few unfortunate experiences with concrete slopewalls should not be considered sufficient reason for the elimination of all spill-thru abutments.

On the other hand, more consideration should be given, at least in some instances, to the substitution of flatter slopes and wider berms for the use of concrete slope protection. The cost of concrete slopewalls for a small bridge can sometimes be made 10 or 15 feet longer, providing an increase in waterway opening of say 20 or 30 percent. This possibility should always be considered in the preliminary engineering phase of bridge design.

Abutments

There are two common types of abutments for small bridges: 1) the spill-thru type, which requires a rather inexpensive support at the end of the bridge, and 2) the closed abutment, which may in some instances be quite costly, because it not only supports the end of the bridge but serves also to retain the overturning forces of earth pressure. The use of the spill-thru type results in a longer bridge and sometimes increases the number of spans. However, the added cost of superstructure is frequently less than the cost of construction of a high closed abutment.

It is possible that more frequent use should be made of abutments that are more or less a combination of the spill-thru and closed types. Such an abutment is one which derives its stability partly from an earth berm and slope at a lower elevation on the stream side and partly from anchorages and the structural strength of the abutment itself. Dumped stone or broken concrete riprap may be used as added protection on the slope in front of the abutment. The use of an abutment of this type results in a bridge length about midway between the requirements of a complete spill-thru and a fully closed type.

Examples of the use of precast and prestressed concrete planks in various types of abutments will be shown later in some of the slides.

Bridge Piers

Probably the most common type of intermediate support for the spans of a small bridge is the pile bent. Various types of piles may be used, depending upon subsoil conditions and other factors.

Where piles cannot be driven to sufficient penetration, columns may be supported on spread footings which rest on satisfactory soil or rock below any anticipated effects of scour and frost. Round columns which utilize standard soni-tube cylinders for construction forms are very economical. Such a pier is much less expensive than the solid shaft type. They are quite appropriate for small bridges when piles either cannot or need not be driven.

On the other hand, larger bridges sometimes require solid piers, either supported by piles or by spread foundations resting on satisfactory soil or rock. The trend over the past several years has been toward the use of the so-called hammerhead pier where solid shafts are deemed desirable.

Summary and Conclusions

As county engineers and other officials who have lived for a number of years with your old bridges—and who expect to live for many years to come with at least a few new ones—you should realize that you are best qualified to answer many of the questions which provide the necessary judgments involved in the design of your bridges. You should become familiar with and have respect for new scientific developments and new methods of construction. At the same time, such respect should not lead to the erroneous and dangerous impression that all bridge problems are susceptible of direct scientific solution. Unfortunately, the whims of nature and the demands of economy combine to eliminate this possibility.

Even though a bridge may be small, sometimes it can present big problems. The importance of thorough preliminary engineering cannot be emphasized too strongly. Many man hours are required to design and prepare a set of plans and specifications for a bridge, even if standards are used; but the most important investigations, judgments and final decisions must be made beforehand. And if they are wise decisions, well substantiated, the public is the beneficiary.

Theory, Practice and Assumptions

Joint Meeting of the
Peoria Branch, Central Illinois Section, ASCE
and the Student Engineers Club, Bradley University
December 12, 1963

Introduction

Dean Finch, in a recent article entitled "Rankine: Theory and Practice"[1] discusses the impact of Rankine's writings upon the engineering profession about 100 years ago. Rankine's teaching, publications, and his philosophies of engineering practice contributed much to the development of the scientific approach to engineering design. At the same time, as Dean Finch points out, Rankine condemned the idea that theory and practice should be "contrasted and placed in opposition, as denoting two conflicting and mutually inconsistent ideas." Rankine criticized the "lack of communication between men of science and men of practice," and he endeavored to further a liaison between science and engineering.

There is much spoken and written these days about the relationship and interdependence between science and engineering. As Dean Finch says in his article, "A proper balance between the teachings of science and due attention to the needs, requirements, and conditions of practice still remains a major educational problem." We all know that the solution of an engineering problem by scientific methods usually uncovers several other problems to which the answers are unknown. The engineer still meets many problems where he must, as Rankine said, "rely in many cases on less exact available data and sound judgment."

So we are confronted with the ageless problem of bridging the gap between theory on one hand and practice on the other; between analysis and design; from research to application; and from the office, classroom, and laboratory to the construction project in the field. There must be proper balance in the abutments of knowledge of such a bridge; otherwise, the bridge cannot be stable or even exist at all. As these abutments of knowledge and experience grow in properly balanced proportions, the gap becomes smaller and the bridge more stable. No engineer has been able, nor can any one of us expect, to close completely the gap between theory and practice. The late Doctor Karl Terzaghi came as close as anyone in this century thus far.

What Are the Assumptions?

This evening, I should like to visit with you for a few minutes on the subject of engineering assumptions. This is because I believe that in our teaching and in our practice of engineering, too often, we either lose sight of the assumptions altogether, or else fail to recognize the effects of conceivable variations in the assumed parameters of the problem. After all, the science, theories, and methods of analysis with which we deal are literally overflowing with assumptions. The same can be said of our empirical procedures that are based upon laboratory research and field observations.

Recently, I heard a young engineer lament, "The problems in practice never seem to possess any similarity to those dealt with in my undergraduate and graduate courses at the University. My analysis, too often, has to be repeated because the project engineer points out the unreasonableness of my assumptions. I'm beginning to question whether science and theory have any place at all in the design office." This young man is beginning to bridge the gap. But there is also danger at this stage. He must not devote all of his future efforts to the building of the abutment of knowledge on the practice side of engineering. Remember: knowledge of theory and practical applications must grow together, side by side, in the successful practice of engineering.

Let us consider some of the assumptions, or should we say judgmental decisions, involved in the preliminary planning, structural analysis, and engineering design of a typical continuous highway bridge.

Waterway Requirements. The hydrology and hydraulics of bridges are far from exact sciences. We must make certain assumptions as to design flood frequency, runoff characteristics, velocities, and the like, after which we assume that certain theories and empirical methods which in themselves contain many other assumptions, can be applied to the analysis.

Foundation Conditions. The scattering of results of test borings and laboratory tests must be evaluated. A type of foundation must be selected based upon many assumptions as to foundation loads, probable average characteristics (and variations from such averages) of the subsoil, and apparently feasible construction methods. Moreover, the engineer must keep in mind the effect of one assumption upon another.

Substructure Analysis and Design. Once the foundation type is selected, the substructure elements themselves must be analyzed and designed. Needless to say, many assumptions must be made relative to the loadings on a bridge pier. Even though many of these uncertainties are covered by codes and specifications, the recommendations contained in the codes cannot be considered more than reasonably good guides for judgment. The engineer must be constantly on guard, or else he will apply a code recommendation to a structure that, for some reason or other, cannot possibly respond as assumed.

Superstructure Analysis and Design. How many H-20-S-16 trucks travel on the highways? Such a vehicle simply does not exist; yet it represents the live load for which thousands of highway bridges have been, and continue to be, analyzed and designed. Furthermore, the basic assumption underlying the theory of analysis and the computation of moments and shears is that the piers do not settle under load. Professor Hardy Cross, in a paper entitled *The Relation of Analysis to Structural Design*,[2] discusses three kinds of stresses in addition to normal structural action. His paper does a good job of relating analysis to design within a truly engineering prospective of theory and practice. The concept of the whole project must be kept in mind at all times.

Only a few of many assumptions common to civil engineering practice have been discussed. I shall not discuss more, because I do not want to give the impression that science, theory and analysis are not necessary and essential to successful engineering practice. They are important, but any reasonably intelligent technician on electronic computer can apply scientific and empirical methods to the solution of engineering problems. But the problems themselves, the choice of theory, and the associated assumptions must be initially tested and organized by human brains, as do the final answers.

So, in conclusion, let me leave you with two thoughts, neither of which is original.

Karl Terzaghi: *"The same pattern of development can be detected in the life of almost every engineer who has acquired a justified reputation for 'sound judgment.' As a student in the classroom, he worked with his head, advancing as far as logical reasoning could take him. After he embarked on his professional career, the useful portion of what he learned became part of his subconscious, and then, but not earlier, he could attempt, without serious risk, the solution of problems in the field of engineering which cannot be solved by rational procedures. Students who observe such an engineer in action may arrive at the conclusion that the time they have spent on absorbing theory is wasted, but this conclusion would be erroneous indeed. The object of their scrutiny would never have risen to his high level of perfection without having first learned and thoroughly digested every bit of information with a direct bearing on his professional activities. The details of the theory may escape his memory, but the essence becomes more and more active as the years go by. Therefore, the secret of efficient professional education resides in persistent emphasis on what is worth being absorbed and subsequently digested, and on the inevitable uncertainties associated with the application of mathematical theories to engineering problems."*[3]

To Dr. Terzaghi's grand statement can be added the warning expressed by the English scholar, **T. R. Glover**, who pointed out that a little sound knowledge is often a dangerous thing. No matter how sound it may be, it does not always show a man his ignorance. There may not be anything wrong with the knowledge, but it does not necessarily give him the range and perspective he needs. Our abutments of knowledge that support the bridge across the gap between theory and practice must never be considered so good that we are satisfied and have no ambition to keep learning. In other words, we must recognize our ignorance or else we become a public danger. This is not an assumption; it is a fact.

—•—

Education for Professional Practice: A Perspective of Analysis and Design

World Congress for Engineering Education
Illinois Institute of Technology
June 23, 1965

Introduction

At the present time, I am not an engineering educator; but I was one between 1942 to 1951. I was in engineering practice a few years prior to the decade of teaching and fourteen years of practice have now passed since I left the teaching profession. I shall try to view my subject objectively from a context of experience both inside and outside the proverbial ivory towers.

Let me say at the outset that I do not expect either engineering educators or practicing engineers to agree with all of my ideas. During this presentation, I may strike some sensitive nerves on both sides. If stimulation of thought rather than indignation is promoted, I will have accomplished my purpose.

In the February, 1965 *Journal of Engineering Education*, Dean Elmer C. Easton, president of ASEE, took to task speakers from industry who claim that industry should have more to say about curricula and that engineers need more work in the humanities. He suggested that such topics have been talked to death and should be buried. Dean Easton further advised that speakers be assigned specific topics which are fresh and stimulating such as classroom teaching, research, and administration.

A brief comment in rebuttal to Dean Easton's statement cannot be suppressed. I doubt very much that engineering educators will very soon have the pleasure of serving as pallbearers at the funeral of the notorious trouble maker – the curriculum man. He cannot be buried alive; it seems to me that he possesses more life today than ever before.

I have, however, taken my cue from Dean Easton's suggestions, and I shall not dwell on the subject of curricula, per se. Rather, I should like to express some views on the <u>presentation</u> of curricula. Presentation means the methods and efforts expended by the teacher which are so paramount to the name and content of the course. It is the

228

presentation that trains the young engineer to think for himself, to innovate, and to realize, as science is learned, the limitations of the scientific methods. It is the presentation, more than the name of the course and its content, that plants the seeds which may grow slowly into the conceptual skills necessary to fit engineering systems to changing economic and socio-political patterns.

Therefore, the only purpose of this paper is to present a plea for balance in engineering education—balance between science and due attention to practice, between research and application, between theoretical analysis on one hand, design on the other.

Analysis and Design in Perspective

In some respects, it is unfortunate that the young engineer has to learn analysis before design. As a result, he sometimes never develops beyond the scientific ingredients of engineering education. He knows how to analyze the problem, but he doesn't know how the problem came about in the first place. Neither does he realize the inevitable uncertainties associated with the application of mathematical theories to engineering problems.

It is not suggested that engineering design precede instruction in science and theoretical analysis. Neither is it recommended that scientific courses be replaced by courses in design. But, in the presentation of most engineering curricula these days, the emphasis appears to be somewhat unbalanced on the side of science and theoretical analysis.

I know from experience that analysis is easier to teach than design. Lectures require less work in preparation and examinations less time to grade. Moreover, instruction in the use of scientific methods is mainly an impartation of knowledge. The teaching of design, on the other hand, requires stimulation of the student's latent abilities to think for himself; and as you know, this is no small task in some students.

Example: Let us attempt to place analysis and design into an integrated perspective by considering for a few minutes the judgmental decisions involved in the preliminary planning, structural analysis, and engineering design of a typical highway bridge.

The hydrology and hydraulics of bridges are far from exact sciences. Certain basic assumptions must be made concerning flood frequency, runoff characteristics, velocities, and the like. Then certain theories and empirical methods, which in themselves contain many other assumptions, are applied in the analysis.

The scattering of results of soil borings and laboratory test data must be evaluated. A type of foundation must be selected based upon many assumptions as to foundation loads, probable average characteristics of the subsoil and variations from such averages, and apparently feasible construction methods. Moreover, the engineer must keep in mind the effect of one assumption upon another.

Once the foundation type is selected, the substructure elements themselves are analyzed and designed. Actually, they must be designed before the analysis can be made. Needless to say, many assumptions must be made relative to the loadings on a bridge pier. Even though many of these uncertainties are covered by codes and specifications, the recommendations contained in the codes cannot be considered more than reasonably good guides for judgment. The engineer must be constantly on guard, or else he will apply a code recommendation to a structure that, for some reason or other, cannot possibly respond as assumed.

The analysis of the superstructure is based upon the application of standard truck loadings given in the specifications published by the American Association of State Highway Officials. Such a vehicle simply does not exist on the highways; yet it represents the live load for which thousands of highway bridges have been and continue to be analyzed.

The bridge is now designed and the analyses of its various parts have established its overall structural adequacy. But, why was the bridge needed in the first place; and what will be its effect on the economics and social welfare of the community and the public which it will serve? Engineers in practice have to answer these questions too.

Conclusions

Science, theory and analysis are necessary and essential in the practice of professional engineering. Engineering curricula must be strong in this respect. But, it must be realized that intelligent technicians and electronic computers can apply scientific and empirical methods to the solution of engineering problems. The problems themselves, the choice of theories, and all the related assumptions must be tested and organized by the human brains of engineers, as do the final designs.

It is imperative that engineering education for professional practice be supplied within an integrated perspective of analysis and design, and, in this connection, it is the presentation in the classroom that counts.

We in private practice offer to you in engineering education our cooperation and assistance. We have probably shirked our duty too long. If the balance in engineering education of which I have spoken is our responsibility, let us hear from you.

What are the Assumptions

Student Chapter, ASCE, University of Illinois
November 7, 1967

Introduction

We in engineering practice, just as you as students, are confronted with the integration of theory on one hand and practice on the other—between analysis and design—from research to application—from the office, classroom, and laboratory to the construction project in the field. In order to have a successful integration there must be compatibility between the two parts. In other words, does the theory suit the project? And what are the limits of its suitability? Of course, this all assumes that you have conceived a project in the first place that satisfies the basic need and environment.

I would like to discuss with you for a few minutes this evening the subject of engineering assumptions. I believe that too often we lose sight of the assumptions, and as a result we fail to recognize the effects of conceivable variations in the parameters used for purposes of analysis and design. Sometimes when this happens, a high claim of extra expense becomes due to the contractor. Or, more important, public safety and life may be involved.

In this connection, our professional liability insurance is sometimes called "insurance against poor assumptions."

The other day I checked the dictionary definitions of the word "assumption." The first one was "a supposed bodily ascent into heaven." I believe we should leave this first definition to the space program and theologians. Other definitions were "anything taken for granted; supposition; presumption." I was reminded of several soils reports that I have seen recently which stated: "It is recommended that a <u>presumptive</u> allowable soil pressure of so many tons per square foot be used for purposes of design." After so many claims on a firm's professional liability insurance, such words creep into reports and, after still more claims, the words are underlined.

EXAMPLE:

Let us attempt to place analysis and design into an integrated perspective by considering for a few minutes the assumptions (or should we say judgmental decisions) involved in the preliminary planning, conceiving, design and analysis of a typical highway bridge.

The hydrology and hydraulics of bridges are far from exact sciences. Certain basic assumptions must be made concerning flood frequency, runoff characteristics, velocities, and the like. Then certain theories and empirical methods, which in themselves contain many other assumptions, are applied in the analysis.

The scattering of results of soil borings and laboratory test data must be evaluated. A type of foundation must be selected based upon many assumptions as to foundation loads, probable average characteristics of the subsoil and variations from such averages, and apparently feasible construction methods. Moreover, the engineer must keep in mind the effect of one assumption upon another.

Once the foundation type is selected, the substructure elements themselves are analyzed and designed. Actually, they must be designed before the analysis can be made. Needless to say, many assumptions must be made relative to the loadings on a bridge pier. Even though many of these uncertainties are covered by codes and specifications, the recommendations contained in the codes cannot be considered more than reasonably good guides for judgment. The engineer must be constantly on guard, or else he will apply a code recommendation to a structure that, for some reason or other, cannot possibly respond as assumed.

The analysis of the superstructure is based upon the application of standard truck loadings given in the specifications published by the American Association of State Highway Officials. Such a vehicle simply does not exist on the highways, yet it represents the live load for which thousands of highway bridges have been and continue to be analyzed.

If your theories suited the project, and if your assumptions were reasonable, the bridge is now designed and the analyses of its various parts have established its overall structural adequacy. But why was the bridge needed in the first place, and what will be its effect on the economics and social welfare of the community and the public which it will serve? Engineers in practice have to answer these questions too. Indeed, they had to be answered before the bridge began to come into being in the first place.

Conclusion

I have mentioned and shown only a few of many assumptions common to civil engineering projects. It is very important that I not leave you with the impression that science, theory and analysis are not necessary and essential to successful engineering practice. They are important. Yet any reasonably intelligent technician or electronic computer can apply scientific methods to the solution of engineering problems.

Of equal importance, however, is a realization that the problems themselves, the choice of theory, and all the assumptions must be initially organized and tested by human brains, as do the final answers. At least, that's the way things stand at the present time.

Best wishes to all of you.

Civil Significance

Chi Epsilon Initiation Banquet
University of Illinois
December 4, 1972

Introduction

Thanks for inviting me back after nearly 24 years to participate in your initiation festivities. I don't believe that, strictly speaking, I am an honorary member of Chi Epsilon. As I recall, a young man named Bill Sands was one of the officers of Chi Epsilon in 1949. He is now Director of Public Works in Decatur. One day, Bill came to my office in Engineering Hall and said, "Professor Hanson, we'd like to have you become a member of Chi Epsilon, but we really don't have an appropriate category. You are not a student, and we can't find any real good justification to classify you as an honorary member." Well, I was pleased, to say the least, to be initiated.

Time passed. About six or eight months ago, I was in Narbey Khachaturian's office. He informed me that he had located an old ledger book in the Chi Epsilon archives and was surprised to find that I was listed as an honorary member. This is how I squeaked in as an honorary member of your fraternity, and why I'm here tonight.

General

It seems to me that Chi Epsilon stands for much more than personal excellence in one or more of the various disciplines within our civil engineering profession. Chi Epsilon brings us together as civil engineers and gives emphasis to the civil significance of our profession.

In this day of future shock and the rather severe and sometimes unjustified criticism directed toward engineers and scientists, we must be careful not to turn inward against ourselves. It is easy to become distressed; to ask "What's the use?"

In an effort to counteract such a tendency, I frequently think about the projects with which I have been associated, at least in some small way. Sometimes I also reflect upon the accomplishments of my former students, my partners, and others with whom I have been associated. Usually, it is not difficult for me to find civil significance in the projects, as contrasted with the technical and personal points of view. Of course, in my reflective analysis, I am biased. Moreover, my idea of civil significance may not agree with yours, and yours may not agree with your counterpart in social science on the

233

"south campus." Since we are now getting into a philosophical discussion of special interests and value judgments, and I am not qualified as an expert, I think we should relax and look at a few slides of civil engineering projects.

These slides have been selected in an attempt to optimize three criteria: 1) interest as determined by the technical and special engineering requirements, 2) interest as I evaluate the civil significance of the projects, and 3) quality of the photography (which, with only a few exceptions, is not mine).

DAMS IN ILLINOIS: 1. Loud Thunder, near Rock Island; 2. Henry County, near Kewanee; 3. Nauvoo State Park; 4. McLean County, between Farmer City and Bloomington; 5. Douglas County, east of Arcola; 6. Washington County, south of Nashville; 7. Crisenberry Dam, west of Murphysboro; 8. Lake Yaeger, near Litchfield; 9. Lake Springfield, showing undeveloped campus for SSU and LLCC.

SSU AND LLCC: 10. Aerial view in 1971; 11. Close-up aerial view of SSU in 1971.

OLD CAPITOL COMPLEX: 12. Demolition of Old Capitol; 13. Project under construction; 14. Project under construction; 15. Project under construction; 16. Completed project - exterior view; 17. House of Representatives; 18. Underground Garage; 19. State Historical Library.

SANTO DOMINGO: 20. New Santo Domingo Airport; 21. Old restored Columbus' Son's Palace; 22. First University in the Americas; 23. Sabaneta site.

Summary

"Civil" is defined as "of, or made up of, citizens." It also means "pertaining to the whole body of citizens, or the state or their interrelations." Today, we should extend this definition to the "family of man."

Clearly, therefore, civil engineering is more than the hydrology and the hydraulic analysis and design of the dams shown in the slides; more than the complicated analysis and design of the H-P slabs on the Old Capitol project; more than the foundation design of a new library for SSU; more than the design of irrigation canals in the Dominican Republic.

On the other hand, we should not fail to emphasize the significance of proficiency in the application of the scientific method to the design, as well as the significance of personal satisfaction (the human ego and the salary and bonus checks are important too).

So let us recognize (1) that technical competency is important, (2) that a personal sense of accomplishment, as well as due recognition, is important, but, unless these technical and personal ingredients are mixed in a matrix of "civil significance," we are not really practicing civil engineering. And, what a hollow life that would be!

Never were the challenges greater, nor the opportunities more extensive, nor the future brighter. Perhaps not to be exploited in the spirit of the old American frontier, but the challenges and opportunities are there, nevertheless. I hope to partake of them for several more years, and I envy you younger people and the future that lies ahead of you. Good luck and best wishes to everyone.

————••◆••————

Settlement of Construction Disputes

Illinois Associated General Contractors
February 11, 1982

Introduction

The actual construction of projects of all kinds and the engineering practice associated with construction methods are at best risky businesses, because uncertainties are inherent in the evaluations of ground water conditions, the interpretation of boring logs and laboratory tests, and in the choice of forces to be resisted and the methods of resistance. (These risks were evident this morning in the presentations by Don Bartlett.) But those inherent risks are frequently aggravated by poor personnel policies, unsatisfactory personal relationships and administrative rigidities. Frequently, it is the aggravation of inherent risks that cause disputes to arise.

No engineering design can be guaranteed and no construction job can possibly be made free of all risk. However, what we can strive toward as owners, engineers and contractors are: (1) a reduction of risk by doing a competent job of our respective responsibilities as team members and (2) if a disagreement should arise, settle it as expeditiously and as fairly as possible. It is toward this second aim (a fair settlement) that our attention will be directed today.

Litigation

Courts have been the traditional means of ultimately allocating responsibility and liability for problems that have developed in the construction industry. However, it has been estimated that the legal process itself consumes approximately 83 percent of the loss dollars. Thus, even the winner of a lawsuit may be a loser.

The court as the mechanism for resolving disputes and allocating liability in itself creates problems and frustrations. One disadvantage in litigation is that the dispute is usually not settled until long after the project is completed—sometimes even completed by a bonding company. Disputes should be settled the same day, or at least as soon as possible, not 10 years later after volumes and volumes of depositions, claims, counter-claims, motions, continuances and other delays.

Another distinct disadvantage of litigation is that judges, juries and attorneys are not usually knowledgeable in the technical areas involved. Consequently, disputes can-not always be resolved equitably in the courts. But the root of the sometime unfairness of court decisions goes much deeper than lack of technical knowledge. Juries and judges have been swayed by the showmanship of witnesses and lawyers, resulting sometimes in unfair judgments.

Arbitration

An alternative to litigation, which can be final and binding in most states if agreed to, is arbitration. Construction Industry Arbitration Rules {there are 53 rules) have been developed by the Joint Construction Industry Arbitration Committee of the American Arbitration Association. Contractor organizations represented on this committee are: Associated General Contractors; American Subcontractors Association; Associated Spe-cialty Contractors, Inc.; and the National Utility Contractors Association, Inc. Six other organizations are represented on the Joint Committee, covering various engineering and architectural interests.

The American Arbitration Association is a non-profit organization, founded in 1926. It promotes the voluntary resolution of disputes through arbitration, mediation and other peaceful means. It has 24 regional offices, including one in Chicago at 180 N. LaSalle Street. The Association claims to have 60,000 persons registered on their impartial panels as prospective arbitrators who have agreed to serve. (I should say that arbitrators agree to be asked to serve, while reserving the right to accept or reject assign-ment to any given dispute.)

I have been on the AAA list of construction industry arbitrators for about twenty years. During that period of time, I have served on quite a few 3-person panels and as a single arbitrator in several cases. I prefer a 3-person panel of which one panelist is a lawyer. Lawyers are usually involved on both sides of an arbitration case and they invari-ably try to make the arbitration proceedings conform to the style of the courtroom. It is therefore beneficial to have a lawyer on the panel as a consultant, because no arbitration proceeding is totally free of legal ramifications.

I think that you can appreciate that conventional arbitration is not a cure-all for the settlement of construction disputes. Sometimes arbitration takes as long as litiga-tion, and legal fees may be just as large as for the route through the courts. The biggest advantage in arbitration lies in the fact that arbitrators are supposedly selected from panels of knowledgeable persons from various sectors of the construction industry.

There is another advantage to arbitration that I always try to induce when serving as an arbitrator. Since the proceedings are less formal than those in a courtroom, it is sometimes possible by carefully worded questions and comments to promote an early negotiated settlement between the parties. Many cases have been settled either before or soon after a pre-hearing conference. Others have been resolved by negotiation between the parties after several days of hearings. On the other hand, a large percentage of arbitration cases, like litigation, run the full gauntlet and culminate in a determination and award issued by the arbitrator(s).

Mediation

The previous discussion gives you the impression that neither litigation nor arbitration may be an altogether satisfactory method of settling disputes. Litigation and arbitration are both time consuming and costly, and both are adversary transactions. So, surely there is a better method for settling disputes.

About two years ago the National Construction Industry Arbitration Committee formulated and published its Mediation Rules. Even prior to that time, provisions for mediation had been incorporated into certain contracts, mainly those between owners, architects and engineers, but endorsement by AAA has added much stature to the procedure.

In the words of the AAA: "Mediation consists of the effort of an individual, or several individuals, to assist the parties in reaching the settlement of a controversy or claim by direct negotiations between or among themselves. The mediator participates impartially in the negotiations, advising and consulting the various parties involved. The result of the mediation should be an agreement that the parties find acceptable. The mediator cannot impose a settlement, but can only seek to guide the parties to the achievement of their own settlement."

The AAA further suggests that the following clause be used in contracts: "If a dispute arises out of or relating to this contract, or the breach thereof, and if said dispute cannot be settled through direct discussions, the parties may agree to first endeavor to settle the dispute in an amicable manner by mediation under the Voluntary Construction Mediation Rules of the American Arbitration Association, before having recourse to arbitration or a judicial forum."

It is possible to name a mediator in a contract. Sometimes a panel is designated and actually serves as a board of consultants to both sides of a dispute. The advantages of having a predetermined mediator or panel already named are obvious. These persons can be brought into the conflict immediately after it develops to help resolve such matters as changed conditions and to make recommendations to mitigate the losses.

Mediators do not write reports unless the parties agree otherwise. It is important to recognize that nothing that transpires during the mediation proceeding is intended in any way to affect the rights or prejudice the position of any of the parties to the dispute in any later arbitration, litigation, or proceeding.

I am not qualified to speak about the legality of contractual agreements, but I am of the impression that two parties to an agreement can decide just how much authority shall be given to a mediator or to a mediating panel. In other words, responsibility and authority might vary from merely advisory to what for all intents and purposes might be called true arbitration under the AAA rules.

Mediation Program in Atlanta, Georgia

In August 1981, the Metropolitan Atlanta Rapid Transit Authority (MARTA) of Atlanta, Georgia adopted a mediation process administered by the American Arbitration Association. (This morning Don Bartlett showed you some slides of our construction engineering work on this project.) As far as I know, MARTA is the first public authority to establish a mediation program for construction disputes.

It is important to note that MARTA and two of its main contractors, and a large subcontractor, agreed to underwrite a modest budget for the AAA to train a panel of mediators and to establish mediation procedures. It is interesting to note the backgrounds of the persons chosen to be trained as mediators in Atlanta: (1) a public utility contractor who also holds a law degree; (2) an engineer who is also a sub- and specialty contractor; (3) a registered architect; (4) an engineer who is also a certified city planner and practicing attorney; (5) a consulting structural engineer; (6) a general contractor who is also a graduate engineer; and (7) another registered architect. My only comment would be: they overlooked the most important type of mediator—the engineer who knows soils and soil-structure interaction. Perhaps the structural consultant chosen as mediator has this dual expertise.

Mediation/Arbitration

The American Society of Foundation Engineers, over the past 15 or so years, has devoted a lot of time and spent a lot of money on research and development aimed toward reducing conflicts by improved contracting procedures and improved performance. My friend, John Gnaedinger, Chairman of Soil Testing Services in Northbrook, has been very active in this cause. They have also looked into methods of resolving disputes independent of the performance of the soil and foundation engineer on the project. They have given considerable thought and study to what they I call the mediation/arbitration procedure, sometimes referred to as just MED/ARB.

The mediation/arbitration method for settlement of disputes might be characterized as strengthened mediation or as less formal arbitration. It is therefore a compromise for those of us on one hand who believe that both litigation and arbitration are almost always too costly and slow, and those on the other hand who feel that mediation is too unstructured and without authority. I think it is just possible that the MED/ARB procedure will emerge as the fastest and fairest method of settling many disputes. Of course, there will always be conflicts that can only be resolved in the courts. But wouldn't it be great to reduce the workload of lawyers and judges and get resolutions in a day or a week rather than sometime within the next ten years?

Conclusion and Recommendations

An overview of various methods of resolving construction disputes has been presented. But, let us not overlook the fact that engineers, contractors, architects and all the other members of the "building team" have, first of all, the responsibility of eliminating insofar as feasible the basic cause of disputes. That is, remove risks from the job. To the engineer, this means a competent design and accurate contract documents. To the contractor, this means doing a competent job of building the project. Competence plus competence equals few risks and not many disputes to settle. Incompetence plus incompetence means disaster and more conflict than any method of settlement can get settled.

In conclusion, I would consider this discussion incomplete without making a few specific recommendations, or perhaps I should say suggestions. I am speaking now mainly to the contractors or to their organizations.

Why don't you form a task force to check into the MARTA operation in Atlanta? Find out firsthand how mediation is working for settling disputes. At the same time the task force should check into MED/ARB. There are lots of papers and reports that cover the subject in much greater depth than I have done this afternoon. If I can help in the future, please let me hear from you.

I am going to devote the remainder of the period to your questions and discussion. But, remember we are here to talk about methods of resolving disputes, not about what a lousy, unreasonable, SOB resident engineer you had on a job you finished three years ago, because that resident probably had the same opinion of you. The question is: How can we bring the two of you together quickly and fairly to resolve the dispute and to build the project for the benefit of the owner?

Questions?

Other points for discussion are:

- Importance of qualifications of mediators and arbitrators

- Importance of paying well for this expertise

- Importance of first meeting between mediators and arbitrators with parties of the dispute.

Cross-cultural Aspects of Engineering Practice
(With Emphasis on Work in the Dominican Republic)

CE 295
University of Illinois
September 29, 1982

Introduction

The management of any engineering endeavor, whether in the U.S. or some foreign country, involves human relations, and sometimes these aspects dominate over the technical engineering; but those in the U.S. do not usually involve the blending of cultural differences. That is, we may have communication problems, but they are not complicated by bilingual inadequacies. We may have conflicts of personal egos, but they are not fueled by national pride and prejudice. We may have environmental compromises to make, but not within a context of a developing nation and an altogether different economy. Unless the U.S. engineer in foreign practice recognizes from the beginning that the "way to do it" in the good old USA may not necessarily be appropriate in the host country, he's likely to be headed toward a most unsatisfactory experience. On the other hand, foreign practice can be more challenging and rewarding, at least in personal satisfaction, than practice in the U.S.

This afternoon, I intend to be just technical enough to establish an adequate case history about the interrelationship between the human and cultural ingredients and the technical matrix of engineering practice. To do this, I'd like to use the Sabaneta Dam in the Dominican Republic as the project example. As we view some slides of the country and of the construction of the dam, I hope that what you see will generate questions in your minds. I will finish the slides at about 4:40, leaving some time for your participation.

It is my privilege to salute the many Dominican engineers who were responsible for the design and construction of the Sabaneta Dam, especially Ingenieros Augusto Rodriguez, José Betances, José Ordiex, Nelson Morales, and Manuel Gomez Achecar.

(Read three paragraphs from speech given by Antonio Ortiz Mena, president of the Inter-American Development Bank, at the Los Angeles World Affairs Council in Los Angeles on September 17, 1973):

The countries of the region realize that they need foreign capital and know-how, in pragmatic businesslike terms. Every nation has the sovereign right to determine independently whether or not it is willing to import foreign private capital and technology,

240

and if so under what terms and conditions; conversely, foreign investors must know with reasonable certainty the policies and procedures under which their capital and technology will be acceptable. More often than not, they will find in Latin America high rates of return and conditions propitious to a successful investment. This is so particularly if the foreign investor associates with local entrepreneurs, in lasting associations that are rewarding for all parties involved.

Frankly speaking, I am convinced that there is an urgent need to apply greater imagination and creativity to this issue. Great benefits are being repaid in our region by entrepreneurs who have learned how best to adjust to local development policies. This generally means contributing to the generation of local employment, of export revenues, of a technological and managerial infrastructure and of industrial development in the host countries.

Herein lies the essence of the concept of partnership, between business men as well as between nations. The more bridges we manage to throw across the gaps which separate us, the better will our interests converge, and the more meaningful shall our interdependence be. The favorable climate for foreign enterprise requires a quid pro quo, in the form of new patterns of corporate behavior. Foreign corporations must also be good citizens. When only a few fail in this duty, the damage can be disproportionate. In other words, for a foreign investor to be successful, he must display the qualities of adaptability to local conditions, of empathy and forbearance.

Prime Minister of Chile, October 10, 1973, to United Nations: "It is one thing, gentlemen, to evaluate a foreign experience from afar, seated in comfortable armchairs or in discussion around a well-served table. It is quite another to live it."

Chronology of H-R, S.A.

1954   José Capacette from Puerto Rico at U. of I.

1956   Capacette teaches at Santo Domingo. Engineer C. A. Rodriguez in class. Uses Peck, Hanson & Thornburn. Engineer C. A. Rodriguez teaches at University of Santo Domingo.

1961   Dictator (since 1930) Rafael Trujillo assassinated.

1962-1965   Political strife. Civil war. Engineer C. A. Rodriguez comes to U. of I. Partner José Ordiex to Puerto Rico.

1965-1968   Engineer C. A. Rodriguez obtains M.S. Additional graduate work at Minnesota. Adopts 3 children (U.S. citizens). Returns to Dominican Republic.

1968-1971	Engineer Rodriguez works in Dominican government. Resumes partnership with Ordiex. Teaches at University of Santo Domingo.
Jan. 1971	Phone call from Dr. Deere of U. of I. Initial trip to Santo Domingo for meeting with Engineer Rodriguez.
Spring-	Organization of H-R, S.A. Contacts with Caterpillar. IDB. Alternate Summer business arrangements. Meetings with lawyers.
Aug. 1971	Obtained first job (Sabaneta). Competition. Selection Committee.
March 1972	Second contract. Meeting with president. Statement of H-R policy.

Present Status of Jobs: Division of work.

Prospects of Future: President's annual address in February 1973. Political stability.

Discussion Topics

1. Mr. Antonio Ortiz Mena's statement on September 17, 1973, regarding business partnerships.

2. His statements on September 18, 1973, regarding effects of devaluation of US$ and continuous changes in the international rages of exchange.

3. Necessary ingredients in foreign aid programs. Register editorial.

Discussion Questions

1. What skills are essential in cross-cultural situations?

   The how may be as important, if not more so, as the what.

   Communicate respect, encouragement and sincere interest. (Actions speak louder than words.)

   Display empathy and understand the other point of view. (Face-saving and self-respect are important in any culture.)

Learn when to tolerate ambiguity rather than press for exactness.

When speaking English, speak clearly and enunciate.

2. What brings on cultural shock and irrational behavior?

   Many things. Usually a combination of circumstances. Living conditions, loneliness, family situations, and especially inability to speak the native language.

   Whole communities are sometimes built for construction workers and families. Even schools and health facilities are included for large jobs of long duration.

   Some companies employ a professional anthropologist and/or psychologist.

   Persecution complex.

3. How many engineering firms are involved in foreign work?

   28 percent of the medium-sized firms (60-100)

   40 percent of the large firms (greater than 100)

   Some of these firms do very little; others derive almost 100 percent of their fees from foreign work. We have never been higher than 15 percent.

4. How do you obtain foreign work?

   U.N. Forum (newspaper of the United Nations) includes notices of IDB and World Bank projects.

   Commerce Business Daily for US AID projects.

   Other sources, such as Engineering News-Record.

   Local agents and partners

   Selection and negotiation processes.

5. How do you find a compatible and qualified local partner or associate?

   Discuss how Hanson-Rodriguez, S.A. came into being.

Discuss how Tony Burnett in Dominica was found.

We are looking in Jamaica and other countries. Drop us a line if any of you are interested when you return to your native country.

———•+•——

Assumptions and Judgments 100:
A Prerequisite for Computer Science 101

Panel on High Technology and Higher Education
Adlai E. Stevenson Lecture Series
October 25, 1984

Introduction

Don't you long for the "good old days" when hardware meant hammers, screw-drivers and wrenches? And a byte was associated with eating? And CAD meant an ill-mannered boy, not computer aided design?

I confess that I often have such longings, but I'm also aware of all the good things that computers do for me. There is the nice voice that talks to me at the Eisner check-out counter, and all the mail that I receive regularly from President Reagan, Senator Percy and "Aspiring Senator" Simon. Jesse Helms, Ralph Nader and Reverend Falwell also write me frequently. Yes, it is great to live in this compassionate, computer age!

In a more serious vein, it seems to me that the subject of high technology and higher education has two main aspects. This is because not everyone—probably no more than a small percent of the university students—will be involved later in the design of computers and the development of programs that cause them to sort, analyze, display, print, etc. Nevertheless, almost everyone will use computers in the future, or at least be indirectly affected by what the amazing machines can accomplish.

So we probably should consider two broad categories of higher education: (1) the curricula for those who will conceive and design the hardware of the future, as well as the necessary operational software, and (2) the education of those persons who will be living in this high tech age, and who, because they are in the majority, will make most of our societal decisions as they pursue other lines of endeavor.

There is, of course, also the training necessary to learn to operate the equipment,

244

but this is technical/vocational in nature. Although some of this "hands on" training is essential, whether we speak of computer science or some other curriculum, it is not really a core part of higher education. Surely primary and secondary education and vocational/technical institutions will handle this aspect of future education.

Analysis and Design

I have chosen as a title for my remarks: "Assumptions and Judgments 100: A Prerequisite for Computer Science 101." In order to make my point, I should remind you of the difference between analysis and design. Analysis is defined as the solving of problems by means of equations or as the examination of the relations of variables. Design, on the other hand, means a plan or a project. Usually, designs are obtained through analysis whether we use a man-made computer or our God-given brains.

Analyses and designs require that assumptions and judgments be made. This is why computers don't always give good answers, despite what the advertisements and salesmen tell us. They don't always give good answers for numerous reasons—the most common reasons being (1) unreliable data bases from which the basic assumptions are taken, (2) unreasonable assumptions relative to parameters of behavior, and (3) computational models that fail to take into account the interactions within the problem.

But don't blame the computer. If properly used, it can judiciously test your assumptions and determine the effects of variable parameters. This is analysis. Without fail, judgments must be applied to the output in the determination of the most reasonable and, hopefully, the best answer. This is the design—the plan or the project.

It is important to remember that your assumptions and judgments may differ from your neighbors. Individualized value judgments are difficult for a computer to handle. This is why computers will not replace referenda in a democratic, free society. At least, I hope not.

Design of the Prerequisite Course

"Assumptions and Judgments 100" is actually a philosophy that should permeate all courses regardless of curricula. It may be even more important in science and engineering and in other professional education than in liberal arts. If "Assumptions and Judgments 100" were a formal course, I believe it should be, in essence, a history course. Just think of all the case histories that could be found to demonstrate good and bad assumptions and good and bad decisions, some of which have had profound effects on mankind.

I believe that such a course, or its philosophy injected into other courses, should also emphasize that decisions have to be made sometimes without much analysis, simply because there isn't time or because the data and programs are insufficient. Furthermore, such a course, or its philosophy, should demonstrate that analysis can't be substituted for judgment, and that the beneficial objective of analysis is a plan or a project, not analysis for its own sake.

In addition to case histories, I would be inclined to include a bit of the late C. P. Snow's philosophy in such a course. Remember his little book entitled "Two Cultures and the Scientific Revolution?" Snow was a scientist, writer and educator who emphasized that scientists should think beyond mathematics, physics and chemistry. On the other hand, he was equally critical of writers, artists and others who were not at all versed in the scientific areas of knowledge. C. P. Snow wrote his book in the 1960s. I believe that his theme of bridging the gap of cultures and special interests is even more timely today.

Conclusion

I hope that I haven't left the impression that computers are unreliable, monster machines to be avoided. To counter even such a remote possibility, I would like for you to visit our office in Springfield where our PRIME 550 and all its associated terminals, modems, and printers are a vital part of our operations. It does engineering analyses, job cost control, billings, payroll, backlog reports, word processing and mailings. It ties together our offices in Springfield, Peoria and Rockford. All this hasn't happened overnight. It started about 20 years ago, and we have learned "Assumptions and Judgments 100" by doing quite a few things wrong. But we learned from our mistakes and things are going well at the present time. However, more credit is due to people than to the computer.

Engineers: Changing Ideas Into Reality

Southern Illinois University
February 21, 1985

Introduction

Thanks for the invitation to speak to you tonight. It's been a number of years since I was last in your neck of the woods of Illinois, and I'm glad to be back.

My first trip to southern Illinois occurred while I was a professor at the U. of I. That was long ago. I was helping the Illinois Department of Conservation study the feasibility of their small dam north of Murphysboro. A few years later, as Illinois bridge engineer, I was down this way frequently for meetings at the District 9 office. I remember well the design and construction of the bridges across the Big Muddy. That was also quite a while ago. Some years after the bridges, our firm designed the Kincaid Lake project. Incidentally, those were the days before we had so much good private engineering competition in southern Illinois.

Before talking more about engineering, I would be remiss if I didn't tell you how very much we appreciate the S.I.U. Medical School in Springfield. Dean Moy has developed a very fine school of medicine. It is vitally important to Springfield and to all of central and southern Illinois. I hope that you will convey "Springfield" thanks and appreciation to your colleagues in the medical school here in Carbondale.

Once a year, engineers get together at events like this all across the country to honor our first president and our profession. In our enthusiasm, we may sound a bit egotistical to our friends in other lines of endeavor. However, during Engineer's Week we have a license to agree with Dizzy Dean's statement when someone accused him of bragging. Dizzy said, "If it's true, it ain't bragging." And there is also Frank Lloyd Wright's self evaluation that suits us during Engineer's Week. He has been quoted as saying, "I must agree that I am a great architect. To not do so would be hypocrisy." I'm not sure that the great architect had the same feeling toward any engineer. In fact, when you read the book "Fallingwaters" by Donald Hoffman, you get the distinct impression that Frank Lloyd Wright may have had considerable distain for engineers.

Success (and Failure) of Engineering Works

Turning ideas into realities usually connotes the creation of public benefits and being of service to humankind. In this public connotation, we engineers like to believe that we are primarily responsible for turning ideas into real projects, products, and services, and that we have improved life in America, and even around the world. However, there is a somewhat more sobering aspect of all realities. Seldom is a reality created where we can be 100 percent sure that it is "100 percent right." By "100 percent right" is meant all benefits, no detriments. To obtain zero risk usually involves so much cost as to make the reality economically infeasible.

In a recent article in the magazine of the American Society of Engineering Education, Professor Koen, a mechanical engineer at the University of Texas, asked the question, "Can you name a profession that is affecting your life more incisively than is the engineer's?" He continued to say, "The effect of the atomic bomb, telephone, computer, airplanes—all undeniably the products of engineering work—on our health, stress levels, and happiness, makes this a difficult question."

Professor Koen used the adjective "incisive," rather than "beneficial," in speaking about engineering realities. It seems to me that most ideas turned into realities—at least, the major ones—have been incisive; but we have to admit that benefits do not always materialize as expected. In some instances, adverse effects more than offset the benefits. Indeed, as we all know, even complete failures occur. Of course, these unsuccessful realities are infrequent and unintentional events. They usually happen because correct answers to right questions were not determined by engineers, or else answers were obtained to the wrong questions, to say nothing of the non-engineering decisions in the political, social and economic areas.

Every college of engineering should offer a required course called "Technology in the Real World." I would think that it should be offered in the last semester of the engineering curriculum. In such a course, the required readings should include an address by Dr. Benjamin C. Dysart III, delivered to the Association of College Honor Societies last year. Dr. Dysart is president and chairman of the National Wildlife Federation and a member of the faculty at Clemson University. His talk was titled "Some Thoughts on Academic Excellence, Character, and Making a Difference in the World." It was both scholarly and pragmatic (scholarship and pragmatism are not mutually exclusive; in fact there should be more PhD's earned with such a dual emphasis). Dr. Dysart placed in good perspective the interrelated aspects of turning ideas into realities. He discussed certain unchanging things, getting at the right questions, the black and white and the gray areas, value judgments, responsible people, and he presented a really tough case history as an example of our complex world. I thought his talk really hit many nails squarely on their heads. It was published in the 1984 Spring *Journal* of Chi Epsilon, the Civil Engineering Honor Society.

Actual Projects

Most of my previous remarks have actually dealt very briefly more with pre- and post-environmental impact assessments of ideas and realities than with real projects in fact. Now I'd like to show some slides of real projects. All are related to water resources.

Most, in my opinion, have been successful and beneficial, although not everyone would agree with me. In order to keep things in proper perspective, I have also included the Teton Dam, which almost became a reality prior to its disastrous failure.

Let us commence our inspection trip in the Dominican Republic for two reasons. First, that's where our firm has been most involved with large dams, and that allows me to "tell the truth, which ain't bragging." Secondly, it is a beautiful Caribbean country. Perhaps you will want to visit it some day. I can certainly recommend that you do so.

Now, for a few slides of the Teton Dam failure. This project was to have provided flood control, hydropower, a recreational lake and, most importantly, water to irrigate 100,000 acres of arid land in Nevada. When it failed during its initial filling in 1976, eleven persons and 20,000 head of livestock were killed, 25,000 people were left homeless, and property damage was about half a billion dollars.

Conclusion

In conclusion, I'd like to leave you with sort of a visionary, yet disturbing, thought. Nearly forty years ago, following World War II, Dr. Karl Terzaghi, the founder of the International Society of Soil Mechanics and Foundation Engineers, was asked: "What future engineering achievement would hold the greatest benefit for mankind?" He quickly responded: "Peace on Earth!" I have often wondered how engineers can be more effective in making Dr. Terzaghi's idea become a reality—one beyond doubt and without risk—that is 100 percent right. That might be the greatest engineering challenge, even today, just as it was forty years ago.

Thank you all so much for your kind attention and for the hospitalities shown me today and tonight. I hope that we can get together again soon. Good night!

Civil Engineers, Lawyers, and Other People

ASCE Student Chapter and Alumni Dinner
University of Illinois
October 4, 1985

Introduction

Time was when civil engineers would design a bridge across the Mississippi River without a corridor study; without the slightest environmental impact assessment; without a design report; without a bridge type study report; without a hydraulic model study; without an aerodynamic analysis of the bridge; without checking substrata for seismic liquefaction potential; without even one public hearing to acquaint people with the features of the proposed project. In those days, as is still true today, the project design was done by structural engineers who had become experienced in bridges. But the geotechnical work consisted of field borings and logs which were interpreted by the bridge designers, not geotechnical engineers. Hydraulic work consisted mainly of Talbot's formula, applied with judgment by the bridge engineers, not hydraulic engineers. The bridge engineers even designed the highway approaches. That's the way it was when I worked on my first bridge across the Mississippi at Dubuque, Iowa.

In the 1960s, about the time you students were born, this civil engineering profession of ours became much more multidisciplinary, and not just in engineering aspects. Have you heard in our courses about the interaction of civil engineers with other professions such as biologists, sociologists, economists, lawyers, and with the general public and political agencies? Sometimes this interaction even extends beyond design and construction into operation of civil engineering projects, and if something doesn't work out, that's when lawyers may come into the life of the civil engineer and stay for a long time. Needless to say, when this happens, the civil engineer must engage his or her own legal counsel.

Richard Meehan is president of the consulting firm called Earth Sciences Associates, and he has written a book entitled "Getting Sued and Other Tales of Engineering Life." He tells about an engineer who is being sued and who wants to defend himself rather than pay for the services of his attorney. His attorney, however, handily convinced him otherwise by telling the story about an accused purse snatcher who thought he could defend himself. On cross examination, his first question to his accuser was, "Did you actually see my face when I took your purse?"

Dick Meehan is also a consulting professor at Stanford University, and I can recommend his book as interesting and enjoyable reading (much more so than your *Foun-*

dation Engineering text). It contains memoirs and case histories (Dick calls them anecdotes), and the book is full of good, subtle humor, sprinkled with irony about life in general. Only the last chapter deals with his experiences in a lawsuit.

Dick and I, along with several lawyers and other engineers, are working on a lawsuit at the present time. I'd like to tell you more about that controversy, but since the case is still in preparation, not much should be said about it at this time. Instead, during the next few minutes, I'd like to recount two anecdotes of my other experiences as an expert witness and as an arbitrator.

The Case History of the Martin Oil Company

I recall that this was my first experience as an expert witness and first exposure to the rigors of testimony and cross examination in a courtroom before a judge and jury. It is significant to me because it was my first, not because of its size or complexities. The case involved a new filling station in Rantoul, Illinois. You would think that such a small project could be built without litigation, but the site was cleared of an old house prior to construction, and the demolition was what led to the controversy.

The owner of the house on the lot adjacent to the filling station filed suit for damages alleged to have been caused by the wrecking operations. The claim was simple: vibrations had caused cracking of the plaster walls. The case was to be tried in Urbana, and a Champaign attorney, Mr. Franklin, asked me to be a witness on his side. He was representing the Martin Oil Company.

As a matter of course, I visited the site, reviewed the soil and foundation report, and examined the drawings for the new filling station. There was no mention of instrumentation or protection of the adjacent house during construction. No "before and after" photographs had been taken. That is, observational data was non-existent, except for the visible cracks in the adjacent house, which I had concluded had not been caused by clearing the construction site next door. Mr. Franklin said the trial would probably be a battle of judgments of experts on both sides, and he sure was going to have to depend heavily on me. My ego was inflated, but I was suffering the nervousness of inexperience. The trial turned out to be more than a confrontation of experts, because the judge took the entire jury on an inspection trip of the house in question. There was to be no conversation during the inspection, but I overheard one juror whisper to another, "Lord, I sleep under worse cracks than these every night." Suddenly, my nervousness seemed to diminish.

The opposing expert witness was an architect and, since he represented the plaintiff's side, was called before me. I was allowed to listen to his testimony, which is unusual in such cases. Usually, you wait outside the courtroom for hours, and even days, sitting on a hard chair in a dim passageway. Mr. Franklin's cross examination was not a friendly exchange, to say the least, and I actually felt sorry for the architect, even though I had suggested many of the questions being asked. During this cross examination, the jury heard that the architect was not a structural engineer; that he had never done a soil and foundation investigation; that he had never seen a seismograph; that he didn't know the definition of damping and peak particle velocity. It was determined, however, that the architect was an expert on plaster walls. At the same time, the jury learned that such walls cracked frequently due to changes in weather and temperature.

By the time I was called to the witness stand, I honestly believe my testimony accomplished little. The case had already been won by Mr. Franklin's cross examination of the plaintiff's expert witness. Mr. Franklin must have had a similar feeling, because he instructed me not to get carried away with theory in my testimony. The opposing attorney showed me a photograph and asked, "Mr. Hanson, I show you what is identified as Plaintiff's Exhibit No. 13. Do you recognize this round object?" "Yes, sir," I replied. "Will you tell the court what it is?" asked the lawyer. "It is a wrecking ball, sometimes called a headache ball," I answered. "Mr. Hanson, how much would you say this wrecking ball weighs?" was the next question. "I don't know," I answered. "You don't know!" snorted the lawyer, "You have just testified that you have had years of experience in construction. Is that not correct?" "Yes, but wrecking balls come in various sizes. If I knew the volume of the ball in cubic feet, the weight in pounds would be approximately 450 times the volume." The lawyer changed the subject, and I was dismissed from the witness stand later without having had to guess the weight of the headache ball.

Mr. Franklin called me the following day to report that the jury had decided in our favor. I was happy, because I believed it was a fair and just verdict.

The Case of la Plaza de Ponce

The Ponce Plaza is a large shopping mall in the city of Ponce, Puerto Rico. It took a year to construct the drilled pier foundation for the building, instead of the 60 days originally estimated by the contractor. Such delays, for whatever reason, invariably lead to claims for extra compensation, and sometimes to litigation or arbitration. The Ponce Plaza was no exception—claims by the dozen, and eventually a request for arbitration.

I was asked by the opposing lawyers in this case to serve as the arbitrator. Although the case was to be heard under the rules of the American Arbitration Association, special terms of reference were handled by formal agreement between the lawyers and myself. I sent them an agreement, which was quickly signed and returned, and within a couple of weeks I was deeply involved in my first (and probably my last) foreign arbitration case.

Time does not permit my telling you about all the interesting aspects of this arbitration case. It presented a combination of political problems, debatable civil engineering design decisions, bidding procedures and contracts, construction supervision and, of course, much in the realm of people relationships. The hearing was also an exciting and interesting exercise in bilingual communication between lawyers, witnesses and myself, because Spanish was the first language of most of those involved, while the contractor and his personnel and I were from the U.S. The hearing room in San Juan was full of bilingual court reporters and all kinds of recording equipment. The transcripts, however, were excellent and were furnished in both English and Spanish.

The case required approximately two weeks of hearings, and after reading the lawyers' summary briefs, I wrote my findings in accordance with the rules of the American Arbitration Association. No single party involved in a controversy such as this is really satisfied with the outcome, because of the complex interrelationship of responsibilities and liabilities. This case was no exception in this regard, and I'm not sure that I made a single friend in Puerto Rico. In fact, I believe that I may have lost one or two.

I was going to tell you about the case of Krannert Center and the case of Memorial Stadium, but my wife, Sue, read my talk and said, "Remember, I've never heard a bad 10-minute after-dinner speech."

Conclusion

May I quote again from Dick Meehan's book. He says:

"I used to be a designer, and <u>once</u> I knew the secret and satisfaction of transforming a concept into reality; but that's dangerous business these days, and there is not much of a market for it, either."

He goes on to say:

"But if you watch the lawyers, in time you learn the trick of trafficking with words. My firm has tripled in size since [we were sued the first time]. We write environmental impact reports now, some of them so big it takes more than one strong man to lift them, and we earn a good profit performing studies and analyses required (but I suspect not read) by bureaucrats."

"Forensic Engineering. It's the new way, and business is booming," says Dick Meehan.

Personally, I'd like to say that Dick Meehan has made a good point, but we must remember that we are civil engineers. I'm sure that you agree that civil engineering is the greatest of all professions. We must acknowledge and appreciate the big picture, and the interrelations of our specialties and professions with lawyers and other people.

Whatever Became of the Foundation Engineer?

ASCE - West Branch, Central Illinois Section
December 17, 1985

Let me introduce my subject today by reading from the November issue of *ASCE News*, in which, on page 13, the following advertisement appeared under the section "Faculty Positions Available:"

> *Geotechnical Engineering—Stanford University. A tenure track position in the Department of Civil Engineering is available for a geotechnical engineer with expertise in one or more of the following areas: computational mechanics, constitutive modeling, soil dynamics, and earthquake engineering. Interests in innovative areas such as computer-aided engineering and expert systems are desirable. The appointee will be expected to develop active research programs and to teach at both the undergraduate and graduate levels.*

Most of you have upon occasion designed foundations—some of you have designed many kinds. In doing so, you have used the basic principles of statics and even dynamics. Are your calculations now known as computational mechanics—a special expertise?

Some of you have also designed retaining walls and braced excavations. In doing so, you have taken into account the stiffness and strength of your structures and the stress-deformation and strength properties of your soil materials. Is this now known as constitutive modeling—a special expertise?

I wonder whatever became of foundation engineering. Has specialization extended beyond its optimum worth to civil engineers in practice? Having asked this question, let me say that I don't want to minimize the need for specialization, for research, for the development and verification of old and new hypotheses. Moreover, I recognize my personal bias toward transfer of technology from theory to practice, and that I can't be totally objective in evaluating research and specialization. But can an engineering educator/researcher be any more objective in evaluating the practical value of his research, particularly if he has had no experience in design and construction?

We need what could be called a closed circuit with all the advantages and benefits of feedback from theory to practice and from practice back to theory. Such a circuit should be regulated by two-way modulation. Sometimes I think our situation is analogous to a circuit containing two condensers—one located between research and practice and the other between practice and research. There is a little current flowing in the system, but it is not well regulated, to say the least.

Civil engineering has evolved (perhaps it has been more than evolution) into a profession of many special disciplines over the past thirty or forty years. In this connection, I looked over my shelves of ASCE proceedings and transactions which now span more than four decades. Prior to 1950, the proceedings of ASCE contained papers of all specialties. For example, the index of the December 1949 proceedings contains a listing of papers and discussions on many subjects—buckling loads and finite differences, tunnel construction, anaerobic digestion of sludge, pile driving in soft clay, multi-purpose reservoirs, and several other subjects. Every ASCE member received these proceedings.

I note on my shelves also that in January of 1950 I began to receive what was called separates from newly created divisions of ASCE. At that time, I subscribed to the publications of the structural division and of the soil mechanics and foundation division. Just now, I am wondering if in 1950 I changed, to some small degree at least, from being a civil engineer to a structural engineer with a significant interest in soils and foundations.

But the change in 1950 was not the end of specialization. In my opinion, as years passed, the bonds between structural engineering and soil mechanics seemed to become strained sometimes to the yield point. Specialization and research in both areas of expertise continued until the engineers in both areas—whether in research or in practice—only talking to each other in their respective divisions.

Then, in 1973, there was a complete divorce when soil and foundation engineers voted to change the name of the ASCE division of soil mechanics and foundations to the geotechnical division. (With reluctance, I decided to vote with the conservative minority against the change, perhaps because of my great interest in structures.)

Nowadays foundation engineers don't develop from courses in colleges. Perhaps you will say that they never developed, except with experience. And I would be inclined to agree, except to say that I have always favored more emphasis in the geotechnical classroom on the structural engineering aspects of foundation engineering. On the other hand, will the new tenure track professor at Stanford be expected to teach foundation engineering? I don't think so. Moreover, is there likely to be a tenure track professor of structural engineering at Stanford who would have the special knowledge of soils and be qualified to teach foundation engineering? It is possible, but not probable, in my opinion.

Whatever happened to foundation engineering? Well, it's still around, and somehow we manage to design foundations. And I'll have to admit that I believe that our designs are better than they were forty years ago. I'd like to show you a few slides of projects designed by civil engineers who have learned to bridge the gap between structures and soil mechanics, and who deserve the special title of foundation engineer—all in spite of, or perhaps because of, their specialized education.

From Research To Practice, Or Vice Versa?

Illinois State Water Survey
March 23, 1988

Thanks for inviting me to visit with you today. I am most appreciative. I am always glad to return to Champaign-Urbana. This was my home for about ten years, interrupted by a three-year military leave in the Navy. I boast about being the only practicing engineer in Illinois who first obtained tenure in the U. of I.'s Civil Engineering Department. When I was around this neck of the woods, Arthur Buswell was your chief. I numbered Herb Hudson, John Stahl, Jack Roberts and other Water Survey engineers as good friends. Those were the days! Later, much later, it was Bill Ackerman who asked me to serve on the Board of Natural Resources and Conservation. But I assume that I was not invited here to reminisce.

The title of my talk surely indicates to you that I shall not give a paper that would survive a peer review for publication in a scientific journal. Its best hope might be the *Professional Issues Journal* of the American Society of Civil Engineers. This publishing uncertainty emphasizes, more or less, the gulf between research and practice.

I wonder sometimes whether the gulf between research and practice is wider now than in years past. I believe I could take either side in this ageless debate. More than a century ago, the great scientist and engineer, Sir William Rankine, condemned the idea that theory and practice should be "contrasted and placed in opposition, as denoting two conflicting and mutually inconsistent ideas." The important thing, in my opinion, is to appreciate that a gulf, wider or smaller, does still exist which needs the best possible facilities for two-way communication. I believe that the Illinois Department of Energy and Natural Resources and the three scientific surveys offer the very best means to facilitate such interaction. Some of you have already heard my sermons on this subject at meetings of the Illinois Board of Natural Resources and Conservation. Even though I no longer serve on that board, I shall continue to promote the same ideas as a member of the board of the society for the scientific surveys.

The mandate of the legislation that governs the surveys is problem solving, accomplished through research. Therefore, we should work constantly to maintain the feedback model between research and practice. New and better ways of doing things have to be monitored to test and prove the applications of research. When field observations get back to the laboratory, the circuit is complete, and a new cycle, if necessary, can be commenced.

I recognize that the building of, and more importantly, the maintenance of the two-way bridge between research and practice are easier said than done. It is almost trite these days to say that we live in a complicated, interrelated environment. Sometimes we dare not specialize; at other times, we dare not, not to specialize. The Hugh matrix (or is it better described as a mosaic?) must include social, economic and psychological ingredients. Remember the *New Yorker* cartoon that showed a wife escorting a physician into her sick husband's bedroom, saying, "This is the man who ate the steak that came from the steer, that grazed on the grass that grew in the field, where roamed the cat that caught the bird, that ate the fish that fed on the bugs, that floated in the oil slick?" Sooner or later, of course, the lawyer enters the fray and takes charge. A year or so ago, I gave a talk to the U. of I. ASCE students titled "Civil Engineers, Lawyers and Other People." It was a recitation of some case histories from my personal experiences in forensic engineering. The message was that we must acknowledge and appreciate the big picture—the interrelations of specialties and of whole professions. And let's not forget the general public and those whom we elect to represent us in government. These days, just who are our peers? Or are we in a peerless society? — So much this morning for the philosophy, psychology, and politics of research and engineering practice.

I was torn in preparing for this talk between going into depth and details on a single case history or "broad brushing" several project experiences. I decided on the latter, but I will return, if invited, to fill in more details.

However, for the benefit of some of my friends in the audience, I will admit to the temptation to present my case on the reliability of the diversion of the Sangamon River for a supplemental water supply for Springfield. I only want to assure you that this subject will continue to be a prime example, at least in my book, of the imprecision of the applied science of hydrology, particularly without continuous stream flow data. The quandary will not go away in Springfield, and you will no doubt hear more about it here in the Water Survey.

Conclusion

Every constructed project represents research in the field. In the projects shown in the slides, there were lessons learned, and what was learned would benefit future designs and construction.

Clearly, research and practice are not mutually exclusive. Whether the voltage in our circuit analogy be the research scientist in the laboratory or the engineering practitioner in the field, feedback, tuning and tempering are essential. So just now, if you please, may I please change the title of my talk to "From Research to Practice, and Vice Versa ?" Thank you kindly.

The Gray Area of Ethics and Money

Cracker Barrel Club, Springfield
April 20, 1989

The son of a successful businessman had just finished his MBA program at Harvard, and his father was giving him some advice about the real world. He said, "Son, always remember that in business, as in life, honesty is the best policy. And I'd urge you to keep up on your corporation law, because you'll be amazed at what you can do and still be honest."

Can't you sort of picture the father in this story as being Mr. Wright, Mr. Meese, Mr. Wilken, or you can take your pick of many individuals in public positions, and in private businesses too, who have no doubt kept up on their corporation law, but who may have had some recent difficulties in separating the ethical and the legal aspects of their opportunities to make money. "Don't tell me what's ethical; just tell me what's legal." That seems to be a standard by which decisions in business and politics are being made.

Up until last week I was going to talk tonight on the subject of "The Environment and Debt." I thought that I should acquaint you with some of the global environmental problems, such as the "greenhouse effect," the "holes in the ozone layer" and "acid rain." Then I would give you some thoughts on how environmental cleanups and the protection and wise management of what we have left of natural resources are bound to be related to the solution of the international economic and debt crises.

But I changed my mind about the general thrust of my talk. It seemed to me that back of most of the environmental and world debt problems are the ethical/money aspects. That is to say, somebody, or some government, or some company did something for money that created the problem. More often than not, it was a matter of short-term profits versus longer-term detriments; hence, it was money versus ethics.

Another reason why I changed the thrust of my talk came after hearing the Ruth and Lester Friedman lecture on public affairs at SSU a week ago tonight. Mr. Richard Franke, CEO of John Nuveen & Co., spoke on the subject of "A Businessman's View of Responsible Participation in Democracy." I guess I was hoping that Mr. Franke would discuss some case histories of his or his firm's dealings with lawyers, members of toll highway commissions, city councils, and various other individuals and entities involved in the business of tax exempt bonds. Surely Mr. Franke could have told us about some gray area requests for political contributions, consulting fees, and commissions which might have most appropriately fallen into the category of money exchanged for influence, or even outright bribes or kickbacks. On the other hand, I can appreciate the many other aspects of responsible participation in democracy; so I am not critical of Mr. Franke's speech. I enjoyed it. However, I can be more straightforward in my remarks tonight, because you are all sworn to confidentiality—it's written right in the Cracker Barrel Constitution.

I would like to mention a few viewpoints about the black and white and gray of my subject before discussing some of my own experiences. I guess it's true that all, or nearly all, decent, educated persons can readily tell right from wrong in clear-cut, black and white situations. In the gray area, however, where we seem to be more often than not these days, the old saying, "just do what is right" may not get you to first base. Indeed, can you think of any important public policy question in the real world that is not played out in the gray zone?

Let me give you a hypothetical tough example of the gray area of ethics and money which I have taken from a speech by the president and chairman of the board of the National Wildlife Federation. It deals with one type of problem that scientists, engineers, and industrial managers have to cope with.

"As a manager—as the project manager—how much should you treat the twenty drums a day of concentrated deadly toxic witch's brew which is one waste from your factory? How much money should be spent, how sophisticated should the technology be, what should be the time frame—the next few months, the next few years, or forever? If you under-treat the waste, or cut too many corners, or look the other way, when you should be exercising due diligence, unaware of your public trust responsibilities, you may have some problems or, at best, a mixed bag. In the short run, profits and employment may be up. That's all good. You're making money for the stockholders, you're producing or maintaining jobs for society, and paying taxes.

But what about the long term? What can happen to profits if you find that you are losing a bunch of very bad toxic wastes to the environment—leaking out of that big unlined pond—out of sight on the back 40? On the other hand, if you really do a super job of treating, perhaps way over-treating (whatever that may be), you will adversely impact profits and future growth of your corporation. If you guess right, if your hunch is right, if you're going with technology that pans out, things are good, jobs are created, everybody's happy. But if not, you and the corporation could go down the tube, or maybe worse you could be sent to prison. You, as a decision maker, are going to be considered reckless if you waste the corporation's dollars and resources today. You're also going to be reckless and irresponsible if you foul up things for tomorrow—or forever.

This hypothetical example is the real thing of everyday practice for the good people in the Environment and Waste Management Section of Hanson Engineers, Inc. Incidentally, the cost of professional liability insurance for this line of work is very expensive, if it can be obtained at all. Who should pay for such insurance? That is a subject for a future talk at Cracker Barrel.

Now for the personal brushes with ethics and money quandaries—some white, some black, and most in the gray area. I left the faculty at the University of Illinois at an early age to come to Springfield to be bridge engineer for the State Division of High-

259

ways. I was certainly naive in the arena of politics and state business, but I survived in pretty good shape. It wasn't until I went into private engineering business that I was really confronted with the gray area of ethics influenced by money. It's usually the money aspect of situations involving ethics that make the decisions in the gray area so difficult.

Within weeks of my going into business I was visited by a lobbyist for cement interests who offered to obtain jobs for me for a commission of five percent of the fee that would be received from the client (the State Department of Public Works). Of course, he did not reveal who else might be scheduled to receive a portion of the five percent commission. We, that is myself and the company, have not used this form of business development, but the question remains whether this is greatly different from paying the salary of a regular employee to solicit work. There must be a difference, at least in the minds of certain officials—state and federal, because some years ago it became necessary to sign an affidavit to the effect that no one except a regularly salaried employee had been paid to solicit the state work being contracted for. Commissions treated as deductible business expenses have gotten some individuals and firms in hot water when the recipients failed to report money received as taxable income.

In the 1950's and 1960's, my firm did most of its engineering work under subcontractual arrangements with other companies. That is, the other firm would hold the prime contract with, say, the Illinois Division of Highways for the design of a 10-mile section of interstate highway, and we would sub-contract to design the bridges. Such a procedure provided us with insulation from any political contributions associated with the project, whether it be finder fees, kickbacks, or even the purchase of tickets to fundraisers. But there came a time, about 1970 in our business, when our special services were not so much in demand. (We had trained our competition in the art of bridge design.) So, in order to grow, indeed to survive, we began to undertake more and more contracts as the prime engineering firm. Perhaps a few personal experiences with business ethics and money during the '60s and '70s would be of interest to you.

1. The unsuccessful attempt to legislate ethics in 1967, and the demise of HB 684 introduced by the Illinois Society of Professional Engineers.

2. The ISPE Ethics Case of the 1960s in Gary, Indiana.

3. In the 1970s, the evolution of procedures for the selection of engineers for public works projects: prequalification, advertisement of work, selection committee, negotiation of scope of work and compensation.

4. Surviving an investigation by the FBI in 1975-76.

5. Experience with "concrete block" ethics in the Dominican Republic and advice from the U.S. Ambassador.

6. Saudi Arabian ethics.

I have talked mainly about the gray area of ethics and money in dealings with individuals on public works projects. This is, of course, only a small fraction of the big picture of ethics and money. What about the ethics and money aspects of takeovers, golden parachutes, and junk bonds in private business? Don't you think that many of these transactions make the Jim Wright case look rather light gray? But, that's a subject for another Cracker Barrel talk!

(Endnotes)

[1] *Consulting Engineer*, Nov., 1963
[2] ASCE *Transactions*, Vol. 101, 1936.
[3] "Presidential Address," Fourth International Conference of Soil Mechanics and Foundation Engineering.

Walt Hanson attends the wedding of his secretary Claudie to Nelson Morales in Santo Domingo on September 15, 1973, serving as father of the bride.

Hanson-Rodriquez:
From Springfield to the Dominican Republic

By
Claudie Morales

As Walt Hanson's secretary from 1961 to 1973, I had the opportunity to experience firsthand some the early formative years of the Hanson company. I came to work for Walt in June of 1961 when the firm, known then as Walter E. Hanson & Company, was still young and struggling. There were only 12 employees at that time. From the very beginning, I found it to be a wonderful place to work. When I came to work in the morning, I never knew what interesting and exciting project I might be working on before the day was done or where in the world it might be located. I remember that my first job assignment was to transcribe a report Walt had dictated on one of the current projects, a wharf being constructed at a port in Guayaquil, Ecuador. I also remember that I had to look up Guayaquil in Webster's to see how it was spelled!

From our first meeting, I was impressed by Walt's deliberate approach to things, his rather dry sense of humor, and especially by his optimism and enthusiasm about the future of his company. As a boss, he was patient, fair, and genuinely concerned about the welfare of his employees and their families. He also had that very special ability of making you feel that you were working "with" him, not "for" him. While we all respected his wisdom and his position of authority, we mostly just thought of him as the nice guy who shared the morning and afternoon breaks with the rest of us in the downstairs coffee room and took an active part in the humorous give and take that normally went on there.

My position at Hanson's could definitely be described as "multi-tasking." I answered the phones, greeted visitors, typed, took shorthand, ordered office supplies, kept all the office machines running, did the payroll, handled accounts receivable and payable, and made travel arrangements for the engineers. I also assisted with job cost accounting by reviewing the employee time sheets and converting the hours worked, travel expenses, phone calls, etc. into invoices for the jobs. When the need for additional clerical help arose after a few years, I handled the recruiting and testing process and helped to train and supervise the new employees once they were hired.

As the years passed, the Hanson company grew very rapidly and its dedication to excellence earned it an impressive client list. The firm also began entering into joint

At the beginning of the surveys for the Sabaneta Dam, Gery Millar, geologist (shown above), and Nelson Morales, hydraulist, lived in small tents for several weeks during the geological studies prior to construction.

ventures with other companies for special projects. Of all these joint ventures, the one which was probably closest to Walt's heart was the association created in 1972 with an engineering firm in the Dominican Republic. Walt received a telephone call one afternoon from Don Deere, a professor at the University of Illinois, inquiring whether he would be interested in working with a former student from the Dominican Republic who was looking for an American company to work with him on some hydroelectric projects in that country. That engineer was Augusto Rodriguez, who had met Walt Hanson while he was studying for a master's degree in engineering at the University of Illinois from 1966 to 1969. Rodriguez had then returned to the Dominican Republic to form his own engineering firm. Walt thought it over and decided that he was, indeed, interested, so he flew to Santo Domingo to meet with Rodriguez and discuss the work. He still recalls that when he picked him up at the airport, Rodriguez assured him, "You can trust me."

Rodriguez told Walt that he was interested in submitting a proposal to the Dominican government's National Institute for Hydraulic Resources (INDRHI) for the design of a large hydroelectric dam. The funds for this project were to be loaned to the Dominican government by the International Development Bank, and one of the bank's requirements was that the firm who was awarded the contract must have an American engineering company as a partner. Rodriguez wanted Walt to form a joint venture with him to submit a proposal for the project.

After checking Rodriguez' references, Walt decided to accept his offer, and a partnership corporation was formed on April 24, 1972. Walt says that when they were trying to come up with a name for the firm, he suggested Rodriguez-Hanson, but Rodriguez didn't think that was a good idea because there were too many Rodriguez in the phone book, so they decided on Hanson-Rodriguez because there would probably not be more than one Hanson. The project proposal was completed and submitted, and they were successful in getting the contract.

The Hanson-Rodriguez joint venture proved to be both interesting and challenging. At that time, the Dominican Republic was just beginning to emerge as a viable democracy after 31 years of dictatorship by Rafael Leonidas Trujillo, and it was undergoing drastic social and economic changes. Trujillo had assumed control of the country in 1930 after a series of *faux pas* on the part of both that country and the United States. In the early 1900s, there had been heavy American investment in the sugar industry of the Dominican Republic. By 1916, the country was on the verge of bankruptcy and heavily in debt to the United States. Things had become so politically and economically unstable that the United States sent military forces to occupy the country in order to protect its investment from a European takeover. The population was disarmed by the American military, and the Dominican army was disbanded and replaced by a new, better trained army whose purpose was supposed to be to maintain law and order. The commander of this newly created army was Rafael Trujillo. Trujillo immediately began using his new position of power to enhance his personal wealth by embezzling funds from the government through the purchase of military supplies.

The U.S. military occupation of the Dominican Republic was withdrawn in 1924, leaving Trujillo still in command of the Dominican armed forces. The country held its first free elections that year, and a new president was elected, but Trujillo repeatedly used his military power to block the new president's attempted reforms. In 1930, he was able to gain complete control of the country, and his dictatorship began. His tight-fisted reign of power lasted for 31 years, and during this time he systematically looted the country's treasury and forced peasants from their lands so that he could take them over. By the time of his assassination on May 30, 1961, he had become one of the wealthiest men in the world, with a personal fortune estimated at $500 million deposited in foreign banks.

The president of the Dominican Republic at the time of Trujillo's assassination was a Dominican lawyer named Joaquin Balaguer, whom Trujillo had appointed as a figurehead president in 1960. Following Trujillo's assassination, Balaguer was deposed as president, a new Dominican constitution was formulated, and a new president, Juan Bosch, was elected. Bosch's socialistic reforms were considered too extreme by the United States, who feared that the country was leaning too far in the direction of communism and might eventually suffer the same fate as Cuba. Also, the armed forces that had kept Bosch in power began blocking all of his legislative programs, making it impossible for him to accomplish anything, so after only nine months as president, Juan Bosch was overthrown and replaced by a three-man triumvirate chosen by the Dominican military. Two years of political and economic chaos ensued before the working classes, aided by a dissident military faction, mounted a revolution against this triumvirate. In April of 1965, U.S. Marines were again sent to occupy the country, using the pretext that communists were leading the revolution. A cease-fire was eventually negotiated by the Organization of American States, and the revolution ended. When new elections were held in 1966, both Joaquin Balaguer and Juan Bosch were candidates for the presidency. Balaguer won the election and thus became president of the Dominican Republic for the second time.

By the time the Hanson-Rodriguez joint venture took place in 1972, President Balaguer had finally been able to bring some stability to the country, and it was beginning to make some forward progress, but there were still serious political and economic problems. Poverty was the rule rather than the exception, and living conditions for the majority of the country's population were extremely bad. There were very few paved highways, and those that existed were in bad condition and extremely overcrowded. One of the most serious problems was a crippling shortage of electric power and water resources. In the capital city of Santo Domingo, a city of about 1.5 million people, the power was off almost as much as it was on, and water was generally available in the taps for only a few hours each day. The tap water that was available was not safe to drink. The power and water shortage was even worse in other parts of the country.

The project for which the Hanson-Rodriguez joint venture was initially formed was a direct response to the Dominican Republic's severe power and water shortages. The Sabaneta Dam, to be constructed on the San Juan River in the province of San Juan de la Maguana, would provide much-needed hydroelectric power as well as irrigation for thousands of acres of farm land in the southern part of the country.

Walt and Augusto Rodriguez assembled a distinguished panel of consultants to work with them on the Sabaneta project, including Walt's co-authors of *Foundation Engineering*, Dr. Ralph B. Peck and Dr. Thomas H. Thornburn, as well as two other highly-respected professors of engineering from the University of Illinois, Dr. Don Deere and Dr. Ven T. Chow. William Wagner, Director of the U.S. Bureau of Reclamation's Hydraulics Research Laboratory in Denver, Colorado, would serve as a consultant for the hydraulic model of the dam's spillway.

Work on the Sabaneta Dam project began in the summer of 1972. During the first few months, Walt flew to Santo Domingo several times a month, sometimes accompanied by his wife, Sue. During these visits, the Hansons spent quite a lot of time getting to know the Rodriguez family. Augusto's wife, Helena, was a very successful architect, and the couple had three children, two daughters and one son. The Rodriguez' also took Walt and Sue to visit other parts of the country. They traveled to Puerto Plata on the north coast, Santiago in the central part, and to the Rodriguez' second home in La Romana on the east coast. Wherever he went, Walt was impressed by the friendliness, the ingenuity, and the work ethic of the Dominican people.

About a year after it was formed, the Hanson-Rodriguez joint venture resulted in a merger of a different sort. On September 1, 1973, I resigned my job at Hanson's to move to Santo Domingo and marry Nelson Morales, a Dominican engineer who was one of the key figures on several of the Hanson-Rodriguez projects. I had met Nelson in October of 1972 when Augusto Rodriguez had sent him and another engineer, José Betances, to Springfield to work on the Sabaneta Dam design. Both of these young engineers were bilingual and very well educated. José Betances had received a master's degree in engineering from the University of Illinois. Nelson Morales was a graduate of the University of Santo Domingo and had completed postgraduate studies in hydraulic structures at Delft University in Holland under a scholarship from the United Nations and the Dutch government.

I remember that when Walt introduced José and Nelson to me, I thought that Nelson had the most infectious sparkling white smile I had ever seen. A week or so later, he came by my office, on the pretense of asking me a question, and invited me to have lunch with him. That was the first of many lunches, and we quickly became good friends. Nelson was very surprised to learn that I spoke some Spanish, and he encouraged me to continue studying it. José and Nelson remained in Springfield until mid-December of 1972. During that time, Nelson told me a lot about the history of his country and how beautiful it was, and before he left, he invited me to come and visit him in Santo Domingo.

During 1973, I made several trips to the Dominican Republic. During my first visit, I arrived in the country in the middle of an attempted coup de etat by some Dominican guerillas who had come from Cuba and entered the country along one of its coasts. When I arrived at the airport, I was surprised to see soldiers with machine guns everywhere. When I asked Nelson what was wrong, he said the government had issued a 9:00 p.m. curfew, which he had had to violate in order to come to the airport to pick me up. On the way from the airport to the hotel, we were stopped by soldiers carrying machine guns and the car was searched. When Nelson explained that I was his American fiancé who was visiting the country for the first time, the soldiers apologized profusely, but told Nelson he was in violation of the curfew and needed to get off the streets as soon as possible. Nelson took me to my hotel, dropped me off, and left immediately. Needless to say, I didn't sleep much that night.

The next morning, I walked out on the balcony of the hotel and saw tanks and armed soldiers surrounding the hotel. It goes without saying that at that point I wondered what I had got myself into. There was no curfew during the day, so Nelson was able to take me to see some of the sights of Santo Domingo. We were stopped by soldiers occasionally, but they were always very polite and apologetic when they found that I was an American. I stayed in the country one week on that visit. Before the end of the week, all the guerillas were captured or killed, and things returned to normal. Nelson told me later that when he put me on the plane to come home, he thought he would never see me again.

I did, however, make more trips to the Dominican Republic and Nelson returned to Springfield several times, and our friendship gradually turned to love. During the summer of 1973, we decided to get married. Since Nelson was very involved in the design of the Sabaneta Dam at that time, that meant we would have to live in Santo Domingo. I knew from what I had already seen that it would not be an easy adjustment for me, but I agreed to at least try it.

Although the Dominican Republic was a very beautiful country, it was also very primitive and had a lot of unrest and political problems. There were few paved highways, and those that existed were in very bad condition. The streets and highways were filled with vehicles in extremely poor condition, especially the public taxis, called "publicos," which operated like buses on set routes and which often had bad brakes, no tail lights, and sometimes had parts that were literally wired together. There was a severe shortage of power and water, and few people in the country spoke English. The capital city of Santo Domingo was surprisingly cosmopolitan in many respects, with opera and ballet and American movies, etc., but in other cities it was not uncommon to see pigs, chickens and goats in the streets. As you drove through the countryside, you saw children playing naked in their yards.

I know that Walt was very concerned about whether I was making the right decision, but before I left he graciously organized a lovely reception for Nelson and me at the Holiday Inn East in Springfield. The next morning, Nelson and I left for Santo Domingo. During the flight, from Miami to Santo Domingo, when the reality of what I was doing finally hit me, I reflected on my years with the Hanson organization. Over the past 12 years, the staff had grown from 12 to 40. The company was now involved in much larger projects, many of them international, and had become a highly respected member of the engineering community in the United States Walt's vision for his company was definitely well on its way to realization.

Nelson and I arrived in Santo Domingo late in the evening of September 8 with less than a week to complete plans for the wedding, which was scheduled for September 15. The Hanson-Rodriguez joint venture was to be well represented. Two of the young lady engineers who worked with Nelson were to sing my favorite Spanish song, "Eres Tú," and an architect who worked with Nelson would serve as photographer. Augusto Rodriguez would serve as best man, and Walt was to walk me down the aisle and give me away. Walt took his role very seriously. He was a little concerned, because the ceremony would be conducted in Spanish, and he was worried that he wouldn't know when he was supposed to stand up and say "I do" when they asked who gave the bride's hand in marriage.

Because a church wedding alone is not legal in the Dominican Republic, Nelson and I had to be married twice. On the afternoon of the wedding day, we went to the dingy little office of a justice of the peace for the civil ceremony. It was very hot, and there was no air conditioning, so the door was left open, and while we were taking our vows a chicken walked in the door, clucking and pecking at the cracks in the tile floor, apparently looking for ants and other insects. She continued to peck and cluck contentedly throughout the entire ceremony, while the judge ignored her as if it were just an everyday occurrence.

Ironically, the country's severe power shortage was the cause of a major wedding day crisis. While I was having my hair done for the wedding, the power went off and didn't come back on again for about seven hours. Nelson picked me up at the salon, with my hair still wet and in rollers, and took me back to our apartment. Augusto and Walt were to pick me up at there at 6:00 and take me to the church. The power was also off at the apartment, so I spent about an hour desperately fanning my hair dry with a newspaper. By then it was getting dark outside, so I had to get dressed and put on my make-up by the light of a single candle.

When we arrived at the church at 7:00 p.m., the power was still off. However, since this was such a common occurrence, the church was well prepared, and the service was performed by candlelight, which for me made it even more romantic. Augusto stood beside Nelson, beaming proudly as best man, and Walt said his "I do" at precisely the right moment. Despite my rather stressful day, I was holding up very well until the moment when Nelson handed me a handful of small silver coins as a symbol of his intentions to provide for me for the rest of my life, but at that moment I completely lost it and cried throughout the rest of the ceremony. Following the ceremony, we went back to our apartment where the reception was being held. Luckily, the power was back on by that time, and the reception went very well.

The next morning Nelson and I flew in a small two-engine plane to Puerto Plata for a short honeymoon. The plane landed at the Puerto Plata "airport," which consisted of a bumpy grass landing strip and a small wooden hut with a Hertz Rent a Car sign swinging in the breeze. We spent our honeymoon at the Montemar, Puerto Plata's only hotel. The hotel's dining room was called the Candlelight Room, which we thought was very appropriate because the power went off during dinner every night and you had to find your way back to your room by candlelight! We went to a different beach each day. There were no facilities of any kind at the beaches, so we took wine, bread, fruit and cheese to eat, but sometimes a local woman would come by, build a little fire, and cook us deep fried fish and sweet potatoes slices, which tasted absolutely marvelous under those circumstances. Since there were very few tourists in the country at that time, we were always the only people on the beach.

———◆———

By early 1974, work on the Sabaneta design was nearly completed. The dam would provide 12,000 KW of hydroelectric power and irrigation for 75,000 acres of cultivated land. The zoned earth fill embankment was 230 feet high and 2800 feet long, and the reservoir encompassed 770 acres. The primary spillway was an 80-foot diameter morning glory spillway with a 26-foot horseshoe type outlet tunnel. Hanson-Rodriguez was responsible for the entire Sabaneta project, including the feasibility study, design, preparation of plans and specifications and construction supervision. A hydraulic model of the proposed spillway was constructed on some vacant land on the outskirts of Santo Domingo, and Nelson worked closely with the U.S. Bureau of Reclamation consultant, William Wagner, to observe its operation closely over a period of several months.

Before the design of the Sabaneta Dam was completed, Hanson-Rodriguez had already been successful in obtaining another contract in conjunction with two other international engineering companies, Acres International of Canada and ILACO of The Netherlands. The contract was for a large irrigation project on the Yaque del Norte River near the country's second largest city, Santiago. The Yaque del Norte project involved the design and supervision of construction of a diversion dam and a network of irrigation canals to bring water from the Yaque del Norte River to thousands of acres of the country's best farmland in the Cibao Valley. A large volume of tobacco and much of the country's supply of food crops such as sugar cane, bananas, plantains and rice were grown in this valley.

The Yaque del Norte project was scheduled to begin early in 1974, and Augusto asked Nelson to move to Santiago and serve as the Dominican project engineer on the job. Nelson was very nervous about breaking this news to me, because I was already having a difficult time adjusting to the living conditions in the Dominican Republic. He told Augusto that the move to Santiago might be the end of our marriage. Luckily, I had been taking daily Spanish classes to improve my communication skills, and was getting pretty fluent in Spanish, so Augusto asked me to work as a bilingual secretary for the project. I agreed to try it, and going back to work turned out to be just what I needed. Fortunately, I also fell in love with Santiago at first sight and was much happier there than I had been in Santo Domingo.

Santiago was a very picturesque city of about 250,000 people located at the foot of the country's central mountain range in the heart of the beautiful Cibao Valley. From the highest point in the city, where the towering monument to the heroes of the restoration stood, you could look down on the city and see the ancient church spires, the brightly-colored wooden houses, and the Yaque del Norte river which ran along one side of the city.

Santiago was much less modern than Santo Domingo. Part of its transportation system still consisted of colorfully painted red, yellow, and blue horse-drawn carriages which clip-clopped through the narrow, congested streets, weaving perilously in and out among the speeding cars and trucks and public taxis whose drivers drove more with their horns than anything else.

When the project first started up in Santiago, the office was located on the top floor of the Hotel Matum in what was called the Trujillo Suite. This suite had been Trujillo's home when he visited Santiago during his dictatorship. It consisted of two bedrooms, kitchen, dining room, living room, sitting room and balcony, all of which were furnished with beautiful antiques. It was situated on the back side of the hotel, and a special outside stairway had been constructed so that Trujillo could enter and leave without being seen or could make a fast escape in case of a threat on his life. Because the new house that we had rented was not yet completed when we arrived in Santiago, Nelson and I spent several weeks living in the Trujillo Suite. It gave me an eerie feeling to know that I was sleeping in the same bed where one of the cruelest dictators in the history of the world had slept.

After a month or so, the project moved into its permanent offices on the second floor of a bank building overlooking one the of the city's small parks. Once we moved into these quarters, we all agreed that we would work "tropical hours," which meant that we started work at 7:30 in the morning and worked straight through until 2:30 in the afternoon, and then we were finished for the day. The office maid would serve a light soup or some crackers and fruit and drinks at noon. Sometimes we drank coconut milk directly from the coconut with a straw.

The staff of the Yaque del Norte project was a very eclectic group. The project director, Henry Sauve of Acres International, was from Canada and spoke both English and French. Other Acres and ILACO engineers and draftsmen were from England, Scotland, and The Netherlands, and I was American. There were about 50 Dominican employees, including chauffeurs, secretaries, engineers, draftsmen, and "macheteros" (men carrying machetes who cut a trail through the brush for the engineers and surveyors).

Language was definitely a problem on this project. All the foreign professionals were supposed to be bilingual, but in reality most of them spoke only a few words of Spanish, so both Nelson and I spent a lot of time serving as interpreters and mediators between the foreigners and the Dominican personnel, especially at the beginning when the foreign personnel were getting acclimated to the culture and the slower pace of work in the Dominican Republic. This problem improved gradually as the two groups developed a mutual understanding and respect and began to form a more cohesive unit. But we did have some fun with the language problem, too. The men were always leaving the office bathroom door open, so one day the office manager put up a sign saying, "Please close the door" in Spanish and then below that in English. Before the end of the week, the sign had been amended, in several colors of Magic Marker, to read, "Please close the door" in Spanish, English, Welsh, French, and Dutch, and below that was another line of garbled letters that nobody could ever understand.

Nelson was in charge of the Dominican personnel on the project. On more than one occasion, he received a call at home early on a Monday morning to come and bail one of his macheteros out of jail so he could work that day. It was usually just the result of a minor altercation or from having too much rum on a Saturday night. Sometimes there were also some labor disputes that had to be resolved, and there were frequent problems with equipment breakdowns, scheduling, etc.

Country-wide strikes are a very common occurrence in the Dominican Republic, and several of them occurred during the Yaque del Norte project. These general strikes, or "huelgas" as they are called, are staged to protest anything from the price of beans, sugar, or rice to the price of gasoline or even a taxi ride. The prices of all these things are set by the government, so during a strike it is not uncommon to see cars bearing government plates being stoned, overturned, or burned in the streets. All the foreign personnel of the Yaque del Norte project, including Nelson and me, were driven to and from work every day in cars bearing official government plates, but during these strikes Nelson and I always used our personal car, just to be on the safe side.

There wasn't that much for the foreign project personnel to do in Santiago. Despite its population of 250,000, the city had only one fairly modern movie theater and an older, bare cement floored one where you could see a movie for only 60 cents. At either one, the power always went off in the middle of the movie and the audience would sit there entertaining themselves by making funny comments in the dark for sometimes 15 or 20 minutes until the generator was fired up and the picture started again, always to a burst of applause from the audience.

Santiago was also the home of one of the country's four professional baseball teams, the Aguilas (Eagles), where many of the American major league players came to play in their off season. Two other professional teams were based in Santo Domingo (one of them was coached by Tommy La Sorda) and another in San Pedro de Macoris. In the entire city of Santiago, there was only one good restaurant, one outdoor pizza place, an ice cream shop, and two supermarkets. There was also a country club, but we couldn't afford to join it. Luckily, there was another less luxurious private club, the Centro Español, which we could afford, so Nelson and I and several of the other project personnel became members. This club had an open-air bar/restaurant and dance floor, a swimming pool, tennis courts, a soccer field, miniature golf, a baseball diamond and an outdoor bowling alley, and there were peacocks strutting proudly about the grounds. Nelson and I usually spent our Sundays there (the maid's day off) and often went to the outdoor dance parties they had every Saturday night. If we didn't go to the Centro Español on Sunday, we often loaded up the car and drove to the north coast to the beach.

Because there was not much to do in Santiago, the project personnel also spent quite a bit of time together on weekends, taking turns hosting parties and dinners. It was interesting to meet all these international engineers who had worked in so many remote and interesting places around the world. It was also nice to meet their wives and hear about how they had learned to cope with life in all the remote places their husbands had been stationed. A couple of them gave me some good advice about learning to relax and roll with the punches that life dealt me. They sometimes had some very humorous things to say. One night we were hosting a cocktail party at our house when a mosquito landed in the drink of the wife of one of the ILACO engineers. She was a doctor of tropical medicine and had spent a great deal of her life living in Africa and other tropical places. When the mosquito landed in her drink, I offered to fix her another one. She said, "Oh, that's okay. I'm in the fourth stage of tropical life now." When I asked her what she meant, she explained that when she first went to live in the tropics, if a mosquito or a bug landed in her drink, she was horrified and had to have a completely new drink in a different glass. As time passed, she progressed to the point where she just threw out the drink and made another one in the same glass. Eventually she progressed to the point where she just fished it out and then finished the drink, but now she was in the fourth stage of tropical life where she just left it there and drank around it!

Even though Santiago was much smaller and less modern than Santo Domingo, I found life there more enjoyable. It did have its bad moments, however. As in Santo Domingo, the power was off almost as much as it was on. Because of the power shortage, we were not allowed to use the air conditioner we had bought, so the windows were always open, and there were no screens. One night, as I was hooking up the mosquito netting over the bed by the moonlight shining through the window, I noticed a big black spot on the white bedspread. When I lit a candle to see what it was, I saw that the black spot was actually a 5-inch diameter hairy-legged tarantula which had crawled in through the open window and dropped onto the bed. On another occasion, I reached for my bath towel and found a scorpion perched on it, and late one night, as I walked down the hallway to the bathroom in the semi-darkness, I got "splatted" in the face by a big green frog. It took a long time, but I also eventually got used to the small lizards that scurried about the house and slept beneath the pictures on the walls.

In September of 1974, Nelson and I learned that we were expecting our first child. Our son, Nelson Edward Morales, was born in Santiago on May 2, 1975. There is a custom in the Dominican Republic that when a pretty woman walks down the street, men often make suggestive remarks to her. I had always detested that custom until one morning, when I was about 8½ months pregnant, as I approached the door to the office, an old man standing by the door smiled at me and said in Spanish, "What an enchanting woman." Somehow, at that particular point in time, I didn't find that custom so despicable!

—·+◆+·—

In addition to the two projects previously discussed, the Hanson-Rodriguez joint venture completed the design of three other hydroelectric projects in the Dominican Republic. Rincon Dam, on the Jima River in the province of La Vega, is a 165 foot high concrete gravity dam designed to provide irrigation to 25,000 acres of farm land, generate 10,000 KW of hydroelectric power, and provide potable water for 300,000 people. Hatillo Dam, on the Yuna River in the province of Sánchez-Ramírez, is a 170 foot high rockfill embankment designed for flood control purposes as well as to provide irrigation for 30,000 acres of farm land and generate 8,000 KW of hydroelectric power. Monción Dam, on the Mao River in the province of Valverde, is a 400 foot high rockfill embankment designed to provide irrigation to 50,000 acres of farmland, generate 56,500 KW of hydroelectric power, and provide flood control and potable water for several towns downstream from the dam. In 2002, the Monción Dam was awarded the international prize of the prestigious San Benito de Alcantara Foundation of Spain for its social importance and because it was the highest rockfill dam in the Antilles.

Hanson-Rodriguez was responsible for 100 percent of these three hydroelectric projects. This included a complete geological investigation for site selection and type of dam, an integrated program for a hydraulic-agricultural-energy development of the re-

Walt Hanson confers with Professor Don Deere and Hanson-Rodriguez engineers at the Monción Dam site, circa 1980.

gion, preliminary and final design of all components of the project, final plans and specifications for construction, and the international bidding documents. It also included supervision of the construction of the Hatillo and Rincon Dams. The Monción dam was not constructed until several years later.

All of these Dominican projects were plagued by serious problems, including bad roads, power shortages, lack of well-trained personnel, language problems, government red tape, and delays in payments for services. At times, the wheels seemed to turn at a agonizingly slow pace, but somehow a way was always found to resolve each problem and get on to the next one until the job was completed.

There were also sometimes dangers involved with working on these projects located in very remote areas. Gery Millar, an American geologist, loves to tell the story about the time he and Augusto Rodriguez were kidnapped by armed bandits while working on the Sabaneta Dam project. Millar and Rodriguez were on their way to set up a field exploration camp at the dam site, which was located in a very remote and undeveloped part of the country. When they stopped at what appeared to be a military checkpoint along the road in a remote mountain pass, they were taken captive by eleven armed bandits dressed as Dominican army personnel. The bandits were apparently planning to hold up a police jeep which regularly transported a shipment of money from the small banks in the southern part of the country to Santo Domingo.

The police jeep normally came through this mountain pass at about 6:00 every Tuesday morning, but for some reason it had been delayed that day. When Millar and Rodriguez stopped at the supposed military checkpoint at about 7:00 a.m., four of these heavily-armed bandits got into the car with them, and the rest of them got into another car they had, and they drove at great speed down the mountain toward the town of Azua, apparently thinking they could intercept the jeep carrying the bank shipment there.

Once they arrived at the town, the bandits (with Millar and Rodriguez as their captives) ran through a checkpoint at a police fortress, hitting the fortress' speed bump at about 60 miles an hour, and then continued driving the wrong way down a one-way street. At that point, Rodriguez grabbed the steering wheel, causing the car to veer out of control, hit another vehicle, and tip over, dumping the bandits, their captives, and all their weapons into the street. Rodriguez and Millar fled the scene in opposite directions. Rodriguez ran back to the police fortress, identified himself, and reported the incident. Millar was captured a few minutes later by a police patrol, who thought he was one of the bandits and proceeded to rough him up a bit. He was then taken back to the fortress, where Rodriguez identified him as being his employee and not one of the bandits.

Both Millar and Rodriguez remained under suspicion of some kind of involvement in the incident, and were held by the police for 11 hours until Mrs. Rodriguez, in Santo Domingo, learned of the incident and contacted one of her friends who was a high-ranking army official. That official sent an army patrol to Azua to free Rodriguez and Millar from police custody.

Augusto Rodriguez was very concerned that Walt Hanson not learn about this incident, because he thought that Walt might possibly re-think his involvement in the Sabaneta project. Millar, on the other hand, was more concerned about the fact that he would have to travel through that same area frequently during the next several months to get to the dam site, especially since only two of the eleven bandits had been captured. As an American, he would be very easy to spot, because there were few Americans in the country at that time. His solution was to grow a thick beard as a disguise.

My role in the Dominican Republic "adventure" ended early in 1977 with the completion of the design stage of the Yaque del Norte Irrigation Project. By that time, Nelson and I had decided that opportunities were far greater for us and for our son in the United States than in the Dominican Republic. By this time, I had grown to love the

Dominican Republic and its people very much, and I knew that I had been afforded the opportunity of a lifetime to have the personal experiences that I had had and to be a part of the important and exciting work that Hanson-Rodriguez was doing there. However, I wanted our son to grow up in the United States and receive an American education. Also, Nelson had learned of a special training program for foreign engineers which was being offered by the U.S. Bureau of Reclamation in Denver, Colorado, and he was very interested in participating in that program.

In March of 1977, we left the Dominican Republic and moved to Denver, Colorado. When Nelson completed his training with the Bureau of Reclamation a year later, he was hired by the Hanson firm in Springfield as a hydraulics engineer. He is now in his 28th year with the company. Our son, Edward, who received master's degrees in both architecture and engineering from the University of Illinois, joined the Hanson "family" in 2000 as a design architect in the Hanson offices in Orlando, Florida. He is now married and expecting his first child, a son, in March of 2006.

———————•••◆•••———————

There is no question that the Hanson-Rodriguez joint venture was a significant risk for Walt Hanson to take. As Nelson Morales says, "There is no doubt that it took a lot of courage for Mr. Hanson to make such a substantial investment in a small, underdeveloped country. He put the future of his own firm at risk, and fortunately the results were very positive for everyone involved."

Besides the obvious benefits of helping to alleviate the serious power and water problems in the Dominican Republic, the Hanson-Rodriguez joint venture had a positive effect on the that country in other ways. Augusto Rodriguez says, "In its 33 years of existence Hanson-Rodriguez has carried out the design and supervision of construction of dams, highways, bridges, irrigation canals, etc. and is recognized as one of the most respected and experienced firms in the field of water resources in the Dominican Republic. The role that Hanson-Rodriguez has played in the history of engineering in the Dominican Republic can be summed up in a few words: it has demonstrated that the Dominican engineer is capable of studying, calculating and designing important projects of great magnitude and with great risks from an engineering point of view."

Gery Millar believes that Walt Hanson also made a significant personal contribution to the future of engineering in the Dominican Republic. He says, "Walt's greatest legacy in the Dominican Republic was the instillation of confidence in the ability of Dominican engineers who were involved in the massive infrastructure development that characterized the 1970s. This experience prepared an entire generation of Dominican engineers, many of whom continue today as high-level consultants and government officials working in public and private infrastructure capacities. Walt's patience with these young engineers was his most endearing quality, followed closely by his genuine interest in their professional development."

José Betances also believes that Walt Hanson made an important contribution to the Dominican Republic. José says, "I have always deemed an honor the opportunity I had to meet and work with Mr. Hanson. He revealed at all times a fine professional and human conduct. These qualities and his practical experience were fundamental in the successful completion of several major dam projects in the Dominican Republic. He made a significant contribution to the overall future of Dominican engineering."

The Hanson-Rodriguez joint venture was also an exercise in international relations which demonstrated definitively that many people from diverse cultures could successfully work together toward a common goal. Walt's eyes still light up when he talks it, and he is justifiably proud of the important contribution it made to the overall development of the Dominican Republic.

Past and present CEO's of the Hanson engineering companies, left to right:
Walter E. Hanson, Sergio A. Pecori (present CEO), Eugene R. Wilkinson, Leo J. Dondanville.

Recollections of Associates and Friends

Lee Dondanville

Perhaps the most difficult, yet most important, thing for a founding partner to do is stand aside as a new executive team pursues its vision of the future. To Walt's everlasting credit, he did this after the firm weathered the early 1980's, a slow economic period for many professional engineering organizations. By 1985 the new group had been kept together, gained experience and maturity, and was ready for increased authority and responsibility. They were prepared for an exciting period of remarkable expansion.

After his retirement from executive responsibility and ownership interest in 1985 Walt was available but did not intrude. Those of us who were fortunate enough to lead the firm the next decade and into the new millennium experienced the thrill and satisfaction of the growth of the firm from about 60 professionals in 1985, to over 100 in 1995, and to over 300 at the turn of the century.

I will be forever grateful for the pivotal role during that first 10 years of Gene Wilkinson, a fine executive who took over as CEO after I retired in 1995. Also, long-time key associates Jack Healy, John Hine, Dutch Miller and Don Oglesby had worked with Gene and me since the early 1960's and they gave support to the mature staff. The confident charge into the new century is under the leadership of Satch Pecori, John Coombe and Bob Cusick. We all approached our practice with the assumption that our clients deserved a professional service of excellence, but would continue as clients only if they enjoyed the experience.

A landmark project in the late 1980's and early 1990's was the Clark cable stayed bridge across the Mississippi River at Alton, Illinois. This "signature bridge" was developed under the leadership of John Harms. It was conceived, designed and built with no distracting lawsuits involving either the owner, engineer or contractor—quite an accomplishment.

One of the things I most value about my career with Walt was the freedom and license granted to follow special interests such as the marketing of professional services, development and retention of clients and staff—the "people" side of a professional business firm. Our progress in these areas was not a common thing in the 1960's and 1970's and it helped set the character of our organization.

Eugene Wilkinson

My first awareness of the person Walter E. Hanson came as a student in the Civil Engineering Department at the University of Illinois. I worked as a student employee for Dr. Thornburn, who was co-author with Dr. Peck and Walt Hanson of *Foundation Engineering*, the text book used in soils and foundation design classes.

I recall a conversation with Dr. Thornburn at the time I began seriously considering employment opportunities after graduation. This was late in 1960. We talked a bit about the consulting firm started a few years earlier by Walt Hanson. As I recall, Dr. Thornburn mentioned that the Hanson company was going through reorganization and that it might not be the best time to inquire about employment opportunities. Pursuing other opportunities led to a structural design position with a large design-build company in Pittsburgh, Pennsylvania.

Pittsburgh and I were not compatible, and after about ten months I communicated once again with Dr. Thornburn expressing my interest in returning to Illinois. The Hanson organization at that time was growing and looking for structural engineers. The next thing I knew I was in telephone communication with Walt, receiving an offer to join the Hanson group, which I accepted without ever having personally met him, or him having met me. While not a customary method of filling a position, or of accepting a job offer, there was a reasonable amount of comfort due to both of us relying on Dr. Thornburn's judgment and recommendations.

Well, that was the beginning of my relationship with Walt and the consulting engineering business. It was a fortunate career move for me, and created an opportunity to be mentored by Walt himself as well as by the extremely talented group of managing engineers assembled under his leadership. Participating in the growth and development of the company from a staff of around 15 when I joined to over 350 has been an extremely exciting and rewarding journey. My gratitude to Walt for the opportunities afforded me is immeasurable.

John "Jack" Healy

In the fall of 1961 I was finishing work on my masters degree in civil engineering at the University of Illinois (majoring in geotechnical engineering) and started looking for employment with a consulting engineering firm. As I found out later, Walt Hanson and Lee Dondanville were also looking to add to their staff in Springfield. At that time, Walter E. Hanson & Co. was a small ten- or eleven-person firm located in Springfield, Illinois. They had just been awarded a contract by AT&T to provide foundation engineering investigation services on their nationwide program to construct microwave communication towers and blast harden coaxial cable structures. Those services previously had been provided by Dr. Peck and Ireland at the University of Illinois. With Walt's close relationship with Dr. Peck and the need for them to pass these services to a private firm outside the university, the Hanson firm was recommended and was awarded the contract. This coincided with the time I was receiving my degree, and I had the training necessary for the position they wanted to fill. Lee still comments that I am the only employee that he interviewed and hired in Pub on Green Street in Champaign. I had a job offer with a firm in Philadelphia, Pennsylvania at the time, but being from Illinois and liking the type of work the Hanson firm provided, it was a natural for me.

Looking back now after some forty-four years, I consider myself very fortunate for the opportunities my employment has provided. I love to travel for short periods, which the AT&T and other work provided. Since I am a pilot, this also provided opportunities to keep up my flying skills and eliminate many of the overnight stays that would have been required with commercial travel. I visited many remote mountain tops both in the west and the east, investigating tower locations. And, with my strong interest in geology, I was able to see features that I had only read about in textbooks.

Walt still kids me about me asking to delay my start of employment from February 1 to March 1 so I could take a multi-country tour through Europe with a friend with whom I shared an office at the University. The friend was born in Poland and moved to Canada when he was four or five years old, just before the start of World War II. He had a lot of relatives in Warsaw and wanted to spend a week there. This seemed like a great opportunity, realizing that I would not have a chance again for that much travel after starting employment. Fortunately, Walt and Lee did not fire me before I had an opportunity to show them that they did not make a mistake in offering me employment.

The professionalism and opportunities that Walt has shown and presented to many of us have been outstanding. We, the profession and the community, have been very fortunate to have in our presence a person like Walt. His leadership, reserved management style, never-seeming-to-get-excited mannerisms, and always being available to discuss a problem you thought you might have, were great examples. He did not have to raise his voice to make a point, but you always knew when there was something you had better look into and get more concerned about. Thanks, Walt, for the opportunities you have provided me.

Richard W. "Dutch" Miller

I first met Walt Hanson when I interviewed for a position as a Geotechnical Engineer at the company office, in March of 1963. I had been asked to interview by Jack Healy, a fellow student at the University of Illinois, and a fellow M.S. graduate in February, 1962.

The University of Illinois used the text *Foundation Engineering*, so I was familiar with Walt's name prior to the interview, although I did not know much of Walt or the company. Upon entering the offices, I was immediately struck by the quiet, welcoming feeling of the place. Since the atmosphere of an office generally reflects the person at the top, it was a good feeling. I first interviewed with Leo Dondanville, who would be my immediate supervisor, and then with Walt.

Walt made everyone who met him feel at ease, and he quickly did so with me. He was soft spoken, seemed genuinely concerned about me and what my aspirations were as an engineer, rather than what I could do for the firm. He did, of course, inquire about my experience with a firm in Chicago where I had worked since graduation. I didn't realize it at the time, but in retrospect, he was probably finding out more about me and how I would relate to fellow employees and clients, rather than my technical competence.

Walt was a wonderful mentor. He had a unique ability to quickly review a problem or situation, ask a few key questions, and suggest a course of action in a calm, non-confrontational manner without making you feel incompetent. When he reviewed a technical report, he read it for content first, and then made constructive criticisms that allowed you, as the author, to use your own style of writing. He required concise writing and good logical thought. In my later career, I tried to handle young engineers and the development of their careers in the way Walt had related to me.

As the company grew, Walt became concerned about the future of the employees when it came time for him to think about retiring. He firmly believed that the people who helped make the company successful and profitable should share in the success and profits. This philosophy was reflected in the development of an employee stock-ownership transfer plan, as well as a profit sharing plan. He understood that the way to remain successful was to make sure that quality people wanted to remain in the organization and make it successful. He structured a management team that would carry on his corporate philosophy of treating the employees as high-quality individuals, rather than as people to be taken advantage of.

But, most important, treating people fairly was a basic ingrained part of him, and the corporate policies were simply an outgrowth of that part of the man.

Donald D. Oglesby

Walt Hanson's newly founded consulting firm was only one year old when I graduated from high school in 1955. Based on the recommendation of my high school mechanical drawing instructor, Walt offered me a draftsman position with his new firm, and I quickly accepted. In those early days, plan drawings were prepared by placing ink on vellum using a ruling pen for the linework and a scroll pen for hand lettering of the dimensions and notes. Also, the surface of the vellum had to be conditioned with a powder called "Pounce" to take the ink properly and to avoid slippage of the vellum during the printing process. Great care had to be taken to avoid mistakes, since removal of the ink was so difficult and excessive erasing could damage the vellum. In later years, pencil drawings rather than ink became the norm, but I quickly learned the importance of advance planning and coordination with the engineering designers to avoid false starts and rework. I owe my appreciation for planning and my very readable lettering of today, some fifty years later, to those early days of meeting Walt's high standards for the production of plans and drawings.

I came to enjoy my job with Walt's firm very much and decided in 1957 to enroll at the University of Illinois so that I could advance to engineering work. Walt encouraged me toward meeting this goal by offering to loan me money when funds for my studies were low and providing me with work on the second edition of *Foundation Engineering* as an additional source of income when in school. Finally, after eight years of intermittent attendance at the University of Illinois (during which time Walt offered me continued employment whenever I was out of school), I graduated from the University of Illinois in 1965 with a bachelor's degree in Civil Engineering and a master's degree in Soil Mechanics and Foundations. The combination of five years of university studies and five years of practical engineering work gained through employment by Walt certainly gave me an advantage in starting my engineering career.

Walt offered me full-time employment after graduation, and I again quickly accepted. Over the next forty years, Walt's company offered me the opportunity to work with some very talented engineers on some very exciting geotechnical projects. In addition to Walt, I benefited greatly from working under the leadership of Leo J. Dondanville, Gene R. Wilkinson, and John M. Healy. Some of the more notable projects I worked on include numerous AT&T communication facilities located in all fifty states; large earthen and rockfill dams in the Dominican Republic, providing crucial electrical power and irrigation; underground light rail projects in Cambridge, Massachusetts, Washington, D.C., and Pittsburgh, Pennsylvania; underpinning of the control building for a nuclear power plant in Midland, Michigan; soil mineralogy studies for the impervious clay core of the massive Richard B. Russell Dam between Georgia and South Carolina; design of a temporary bracing system to prevent failure of a 100 ft. deep lift station excavation in Austin, Texas; and detailed site characterizations studies in the states of Illinois and Vermont, for the potential locations of low-level radioactive waste disposal facilities. Two special projects which allowed me to work directly under Walt's leadership and gain important experience included 1) the investigation into base stability failures under taconite ore storage piles at the Burlington Northern transloading facility in Superior, Wisconsin, and 2) the geotechnical design of abutment foundations and cable anchorages for the Ruck-A-Chucky cable-stayed bridge proposed to span the American River in California. These latter projects also allowed me to work directly with Walt's co-author for *Foundation Engineering*, Ralph B. Peck, and the internationally known bridge designer T. Y. Lin.

During my career Walt always emphasized the need for good communication between geotechnical engineers such as myself, who provide the geotechnical parameters for foundation design, and those engineers responsible for the structural elements of the foundations. Walt fostered this communication by insisting that all of his geotechnical engineers spend at least a year of practice in his structural group. This proved to be an invaluable experience for me, resulting in obtainment of my license as a structural engineer in Illinois and gaining a much greater appreciation for the interactions between the ground and the structural foundations they support.

Since my retirement in 2002, I have continued my relationship with Walt, including the opportunity and privilege to co-author with him two structural magazine articles on limit state design for foundations.

John Hine

I became acquainted with Mr. Hanson in 1973. At that time I was working for the Illinois Department of Transportation as District #6 Planning Engineer. He contacted me to discuss joining Hanson Engineers as a partner in charge of Transportation Design. I accepted the offer after a series of discussions and continued that employment until retiring in January of 1990. This was the best employment decision of my life.

Mr. Hanson was most extraordinary in always standing up for all of his fellow employees. He believed and expressed his opinion about giving bonuses to each employee, especially to those who contributed to making a profit for the company. He also believed in stepping aside at retirement age and giving the younger engineers, who displayed brilliance, to continue the company into the future without a drain on profits to older managers.

I remember accompanying him on a trip to the Dominican Republic to prepare a submittal for roadway design in that country. He was very fond of the local Rodriguez firm that would assist us in this project. He didn't hesitate to end this proposal when it was evident that a pay-off would be required to obtain this assignment. He was always proud of providing a high quality of services to our clients but would never approve of spending company money on an individual to obtain work. He was a very honest person and a pleasure to work with on all projects.

Sergio "Satch" Pecori

I was about sixteen when I started working at Walter E. Hanson & Company and did everything from sweeping floors to running errands, doing whatever needed to be done. I recall when I started, Walt had me out to his house on Linden Lane, to help him work in the yard. As soon as I got there, Sue Hanson brought out cookies and milk, and Walt and I sat on the patio and probably talked for a half hour or forty-five minutes about what I was doing, what my interests were in high school, and that sort of thing. I think he wanted to find out what type of person I was, what kind of background I came from, and perhaps what type of values I had. I recall we discussed a wide variety of topics.

I would see Walt in the office occasionally. As time went on, working at W. E. Hanson got me interested in Civil Engineering and the University of Illinois. I attended the University of Illinois, and while I was there Walt would come over and visit me during his trips to campus. At the time, he may have been president of the Civil Engineering Alumni Association, and also during that time he started a company in the

Dominican Republic with Augusto Rodriguez, called Hanson-Rodriguez. He would look me up at the University, we'd have lunch, we'd visit, he would introduce me to some of the civil engineering professors.

I was fortunate to do pretty well there, and I ended up being president of the Civil Engineering alumni honorary fraternity, called Chi Epsilon. It just so happened that I was the master of ceremonies at several dinners during the fiftieth anniversary conclave. Actually, that honor society was founded at the University of Illinois, and Walt was a chapter Honor Member. He attended some of those events, and he introduced me to a friend of his, Professor Narbey Khachaturian. I never had him as an instructor, but that became a good relationship. It was all nurtured because of Walt's interest in helping me along in engineering. Walt helped many students along the way, and he was recognized by the civil engineering students for his teaching and mentoring skills.

After I joined the Hanson organization, he introduced me to a variety of people, and I worked with him on a variety of proposals. I spent a week in the Dominican Republic working on a proposal for the State Department. He and I would work during the day and have dinner at night, either just ourselves or with Augusto. We had some very interesting conversations, about Walt's thoughts on where the company was going. I found that to be very exciting. I look back now on some of the opportunities that I was exposed to, not only with him, because he was a visionary of national and international activity, but also that it gave me a great perspective of how to look at things in today's world. He had a global vision back in the '70s, long before some of the people who are "thinking global" now.

When I was promoted to an officer in the company, above others who were older, Walt commented to me something like this, "Some people won't be happy that you moved ahead of others. Just remember this: It was the right thing to do. In a few months, people aren't going to think anything of it; they will think that's the way it's been for a long time and that's the way it should be." I tell that philosophy to people here when we make a similar move. It's a great philosophical way of looking at things; it's true, and it's just so simple.

I have enjoyed visiting with him over the years, getting his perspective on things. I hope that when I get to be his age, if I make it that long, I will have his ambition to always continue to learn, to have an open mind. I think that's a trait that most people lose. Nothing frustrates me more than to hear someone say, "I can't wait to retire." If they're talking like that, they're retired already.

When I look back at the breaks I had—to do what I'm doing, and even to get into what I'm doing, it was because of Walt's initial interest.

I am an avid proponent of talking to young people and visiting with parents whose kids are interested in engineering or science. I tell them some of these same stories; how it happened to me. It wasn't just that I went to the best schools and studied very hard. Somebody helped me think about what was right and introduced me to people who would take an interest in me.

Walt is a gentlemen's gentleman.

Kathy Jo Watson

I first met Walter Hanson when I was employed by Walter E. Hanson Company on November 19, 1970. My initial role was to support the professional staff of the company as receptionist and word processor. I was a naïve country girl, with only two years of college, and I was quickly impressed by the projects the company undertook.

I was mentored by Walter's secretary, Claudie E. Daniels, C.P.S. She was an invaluable resource, and we worked very well together. While I was happy for her marriage to Nelson Morales in 1973, I was sad to see them leave the area for Nelson's home country, the Dominican Republic. However, Claudie's resignation opened up an opportunity for me. Prior to leaving the firm, she recommended me for her position as Executive Secretary. I was thrilled for the opportunity to work directly for Walter. After all, he was not only the Founder and Chief Executive Officer of Walter E. Hanson Company, he was a co-author of *Foundation Engineering*!

Of course, it was not all work and no play – Walter and his wife, Sue, hosted the Hanson Annual Summer Picnic at his lake home on Linden Lane for many years. We enjoyed boating, skiing, and always a superb picnic.

I am proud of my 36-year tenure with the firm and feel my commitment to the Hanson Company was very influential in guiding our youngest son, Kory, to the Civil Engineering program at the University of Illinois, where he will be a junior in Fall 2006.

I have never known such a fine gentleman as Walter. His professional knowledge, his business savvy, his fairness and his kindness are attributes I will always remember.

Narbey Khachaturian

My acquaintance with Professor Walter E. Hanson began in the summer of 1946, almost sixty years ago. During that summer, I was a senior in Civil Engineering at the University of Illinois at Urbana-Champaign. I was taking the course on bridge design, in which Professor Jamison Vawter was the lecturer and the three-hour design sessions were supervised by Professor Hanson. He was available to answer questions from the students.

Probably I was the student who asked Professor Hanson the most questions. He was always patient and thorough in answering them. As a good teacher, he was always available to help the students and was much admired by them and his colleagues.

In 1951 he resigned his academic position and joined the Illinois Division of Highways as Chief Bridge Engineer. He was intimately familiar with the department of Civil Engineering at the University of Illinois and knew that some of the structural teaching faculty were free during the summer. He suggested that available faculty members, if they so desired, could participate in the design and repairing of bridges. The leadership was under the supervision of Professor Eugene Daily, who was an experienced engineer, and several faculty members decided to participate in that program. I was among the participants and found it to be a unique opportunity to become familiar with the structural design process. This program, which lasted three summers, provided practical experience for the young faculty members, while the state may have benefited from the participation of the faculty.

About three years later Professor Hanson resigned from his position with the Illinois Division of Highways and established his own firm. The outstanding quality of his work in the fields of structural and geotechnical engineering resulted in expansion of his work load. During that period I was invited to make presentations of new areas of the profession. On some occasions I participated in writing reports on specific projects.

In 1976 he was appointed as a member of the Illinois Structural Engineer Examining Committee, and my membership coincided with his for a few years. His careful preparation of meaningful problems for the structural examination clearly demonstrated his professorial background.

Through the years, Professor Hanson has always encouraged his engineers to be on the cutting edge of technology and to follow new developments. He has emphasized the social responsibilities of engineers and the significance of commitment to engineering work.

He is truly a master of his profession, and I have benefited greatly through my association with him. I will always be grateful for the influence he has had on my career and on my life.

John D. Haltiwanger

I owe a debt of gratitude to Walt Hanson! At least indirectly, Walt had a profound and very rewarding influence on my career. I think it is safe to say that, had Walt not decided to leave his position on the University of Illinois Civil Engineering faculty in 1951, it is extremely unlikely that I would have had the opportunity to join that faculty in September of that year. In the late 1940s I had taken a Leave of Absence from the Alabama Polytechnic Institute (now Auburn University) to pursue an MS degree at the U of I and was fortunate to have Prof. Thomas C. Shedd as my advisor. After returning to Auburn for a few years, I received a call from Prof. Shedd in the Spring of 1951 asking if I would be interested in joining the U of I faculty. I'll never forget that telephone call; it took me all of 30 seconds to say yes to his offer, a decision that led to a most satisfying and rewarding career. And, as I noted at the outset, I owe a very large part of that opportunity to Walt Hanson, for it was his desk that I occupied that Fall.

While I may have occupied Walt's desk in Civil Engineering Hall, I would not presume to say that I replaced him on the faculty. I soon learned that he had been a highly regarded member of that faculty, and that his departure from it was viewed as a great loss. As time passed and I became more familiar with Walt's accomplishments here, I came to understand and appreciate the esteem in which he was held.

During the years following that fateful Fall of 1951, Walt developed into a highly regarded and widely admired practicing professional engineer, but more important, from my perspective, he did that while maintaining a strong and supportive relationship with the U of I CE Department. As part of that department, I saw first-hand his many contributions to it, and came to know him as a treasured personal friend.

Ralph C. Hahn

Walter Hanson has been an instructor, boss, competitor, friend and mentor to me for over fifty years. The company he founded, Hanson Engineers, even purchased my company, Ralph Hahn and Associates, Engineers, Architects and Consultants, when I retired.

My recollections begin in the classroom in the Civil Engineering Department at UIUC. He was my structural engineering instructor at least twice. In my opinion, he was the best instructor I ever had, and I had some good ones, including Walter's friends Professors Tom Shedd, Tom Thornburn and Ralph Peck. One memory of Walter was the absolute precision with which he printed and drew diagrams on the blackboard. He was able to explain the most complex principles with great clarity (and patience). If I remember correctly, he won several teaching awards.

After receiving my MS in Structural Engineering in 1952, I followed Walter to the Bridge Office of the Illinois Division of Highways, now the Illinois Department of Transportation, where he was Chief Bridge Engineer. He was an excellent and well-liked administrator. We were all disappointed and lost when he, Dean Collins, and Marc Rice resigned to found W. E. Hanson & Associates Consulting Engineers. Later, while I was still at the Bridge Office I arranged for Walter to teach a weekly class on foundation engineering to the Bridge Office engineers.

In 1961 I resigned to found my own company. Even though we were competitors, we loaned employees back and forth from time to time and combined forces on several projects, including the Capitol Complex Parking Deck across the street west of the Stratton Building.

Walter was a supporter and advisor when I successfully ran for and was elected four times to the University of Illinois Board of Trustees. As would be expected, he always retained his interest in higher education issues. While I was on the UI board, Hanson Engineers engineered a major structural renovation of Memorial Stadium.

In 1997, when considering retirement, my partners and I agreed that Hanson Engineers was the only company we were interested in joining. Walter was retired at that time, but his management skills and emphasis on quality engineering were carried on by the Hanson officers.

Walter was always a true gentleman. He was, and is today, well liked and respected in engineering circles as well as in the community. I am proud to have him as a friend and mentor.

Harry D. Rimbey

I was one of the fortunate students at the University of Illinois in Urbana/Champaign in the years of 1950 and 1951, because I had Associate Professor Walter E. Hanson as my instructor in two C.E. courses during my junior and senior years.

I will refer to him as Walt, because of my long acquaintance and friendship, but will always hold him in high esteem, not only because of what he has accomplished in his professional life, but also of what he did to help me develop my education while at the University. Also, I have learned and benefited from consulting with him during my involvement in the highway and heavy construction business for more than fifty years.

During the few hours spent in the classroom with Walt, he was able to teach me the fundamentals of how to solve a problem or analyze an assignment and complete the work in the most analytical and logical way—a procedure that made it so relatively clean and easy to understand. Walt is such a sterling person that he commanded one's attention from the time he walked into the classroom, always clean shaven and neatly dressed, until the study period was over. His knowledge of the subjects that he taught was the best. Since he co-authored one of the textbooks, that might have had some bearing on his knowledge of it content.

Soon after I graduated from the U. of I. in 1951 I began my career in the construction of highways and bridges for the state of Illinois. Walt became Engineer of Bridge and Traffic Structures for the State of Illinois Department of Public Works and Buildings, Division of Highways in Springfield. His office was in the old Centennial Building, now the Howlett Building, on Second and Edwards streets.

I recall one instance that occurred while I was acting as superintendent for McCann Construction Company in 1952. We were constructing a bridge carrying U.S. Route 66 highway over the C&IM Railroad and Illinois Route 104 south of Springfield. We were erecting the structural steel for the bridge, and after we had placed all of the steel beams on the piers and they seemed to fit so nicely, it was discovered by the resident engineer that the line of the beams and match marking on the erection plan did not agree with how the beams were to be erected. The resident engineer instructed me to remove the beams and re-erect them correctly. Since the work looked OK and it was going to cost our company several dollars to make this correction, I decided to take the issue to the Bridge Engineer, Walter Hanson, my old professor, to get him to agree that the work was OK and could be left as is.

Of course, I was disappointed when Walt explained to me that the state had paid a lot of money to have the Structural Steel Fabricating Company erect the beams for this structure in their shop, drill the holes for the rivets, and ream the holes, so that when the beams were erected, they would have the designed camber and would result in the bridge being constructed properly, as it was designed. We made the corrections, and I learned a lesson from Walt—that we, as professionals, must do the work in the correct way.

After Walt spent a couple of years as the Engineer of Bridges for the state, he decided to leave the state and form a consulting engineering company. He and two engineers from the Bridge office, Marc Rice and Dean Collins, opened up an office at the corner of Fourth Street and Capitol in Springfield. I believe they did a lot of work designing bridges on the Kansas Turnpike. I remained in contact with Walt and his engineering associates, as both of our companies grew into the 21st century. Walt's company grew in size and resulted in their moving into several larger offices, and finally to the present home of Hanson Professional Services. Today they are one of the highest respected and largest consulting engineering companies in the U.S.A. and doing work internationally.

One occasion in 1956 that I remember was when Walt helped me on the project we had building the bridges and retaining walls for several structures on the new Interstate Highway I-74 through downtown Peoria. We had to excavate for a large retaining wall to be constructed next to the YWCA Building. It was necessary for us to come up with a temporary retaining wall to protect the earth and foundation under the YWCA Building, while we built the new retaining wall for the Interstate highway. Since we had no room for error, we took the problem to Walt for his help in designing the temporary retaining wall that would be structurally designed and adequate to do the job. Walt designed a temporary retaining wall using a system of steel H-Piles, driven about 6 ft. apart, with wood planking placed between the beams to retain the earth and gravel that we encountered. The temporary retaining wall was built, held the earth back while we built the permanent retaining wall, and was removed. I must note that today, about 50 years later, this retaining wall is being removed and replaced due to the necessity of the reconstruction of I-74 through Peoria.

I have had many other occasions to work with Walt and his associates with several issues that we encountered in our construction business that involved consulting with him on items dealing with the settlement of claims, using his suggestion of mediation/arbitration as a means to settle claims, versus going to court, or binding arbitration.

We have also met on several occasions to help with the financial contributions that would better the future of the College of Engineering at the U of I, so that it could continue to provide the education for the students in the years ahead.

I am sure that Walt has helped many of his students, employees, associates, and friends to better themselves in life; and being the person that he is, he finds comfort in his life today, reminiscing and enjoying those treasured accomplishments.

Donald D. Fowler

My first contact with Walt was as one of his students in theory of simple structures at the University of Illinois. It was considered to be good luck to get him as an instructor, as he was known to be one of the best, if not the best, in the college of civil engineering. Later I was privileged to be his student in the first course I took on soils and foundations.

After graduation, a semester at LSU majoring in hydraulics, and a year in Korea in an infantry division, I returned to Illinois, joined the staff at the Illinois Department of Transportation as an engineer in the Bureau of Bridges and Structures, and was assigned to working on hydraulic requirements as well as foundations. I believe Walt was the first Chief Bridge Engineer who appreciated the hydraulics and, of course, he was an expert in all aspects of foundations.

Earl W. Henderson, Jr.

My first encounter with Walt Hanson must have occurred in 1950-51. As an Architectural student in the Engineering Option at the University of Illinois, one of my early courses was foundation engineering. The text book for the course was authored by Peck, Hanson and Thornburn, the Hanson being Walter E. Hanson. After the passing of half a century, I cannot honestly recall who taught the subject. It was probably not Walter.

The five-year degree for a B of Architecture (Engineering Option) left the summers open to gain practical experience. In the summer of 1951 or 1952 my employment was with the Division of Highways, at the time located in the Centennial Building in the Capitol complex in Springfield. I worked directly outside the offices of Frank Barker and Elmer Knight. My task for most of the summer employment was to sketch and build a model of a concrete bridge proposed to span the Kankakee River in Kankakee. The bridge office occupied most of the area surrounding my work station.

During that summer our paths could have crossed, although I was a summer-employed student and Walter was in charge of the bridge office. The model did attract attention, since it was the first time a three-dimensional model had been used to study the appearance of a proposed bridge. In that connection we could have met in the office.

I understand that the Hansons moved to Springfield in 1951 and associated with Westminster Presbyterian Church. When home for the summer, I attended Westminster, the church I had joined in 1943. Upon my graduation from the U of I in 1954 I essentially departed Springfield to gain experience in the world beyond.

In 1961 I returned to Springfield to form a partnership with Donald E. Ferry, Ferry and Henderson, Architects, Inc. Our first commission for a new building occurred that year. The modest project was to be a multi-unit apartment structure on a very narrow lot, at a prominent location—838 South Second Street, Springfield. I do not recall any hesitation by the partners about whom to approach to provide structural engineering services. The name we knew from school, certainly a person who by that time was recognized as a successful prominent professional (we needed all of the prominent backup we could muster) was Walter E. Hanson. By then I had made an effort to reintroduce myself into the community. Walter and I were on a first-name basis: Walter E. H. and E. Wallace H.

My foggy recollection of the meeting: I won't admit to intimidation, but on this first time it wasn't easy to negotiate with the man who wrote the book and was responsible for running the bridge office for the Division of Highways and now was the CEO of a major consulting engineering firm. I remember telling Walter that we welcomed him as part of our team for this project. The modest man that he is barely allowed him to acknowledge that the prestige he brought to the project was as valuable as the engineering services his firm would provide. Incidentally, the completed project won a Central Illinois AIA Design Award.

Over the years we associated on other projects, including the underground parking at the Old State Capitol and the Marine (now Chase) Bank in downtown Springfield

In all my years of associating with Walter Hanson, I have always welcomed his counsel, admired his patience and his professional acumen. He is truly a gentle man. I am pleased to call him a friend.

Michael Boer

It has been my good fortune to know Walt Hanson. We met shortly after I came to Springfield in 1984 to join the staff of the Greater Springfield Chamber of Commerce. Walt served on the Chamber Board soon after I became Chamber CEO. He was an outstanding Board member, one whose advice and counsel I valued highly.

When I think of Walt, the descriptors "kind," gentle," "modest," "intelligent," and "considerate of and caring for others," come to mind. He is forward-thinking, evidenced by the fact that he was one of the first to envision a "beltway" for Springfield's west side, which eventually came to fruition as Veterans Parkway.

Walt has set the bar high for his colleagues at Hanson Professional Services, serving as mentor and as a role model, as one who unselfishly gives back to his community, never seeking accolades. The extraordinary success of the firm which bears his name is a result of Walt's talent, dedication, and values. He is among the most respected corporate and community leaders in Springfield's storied history.

I am honored and blessed to have Walt and his fine family as friends.

James S. and Silvey W. Barge

It is an honor to share recollections of Walter and Sue Hanson and to celebrate the privilege of knowing and working with them in a variety of ways. It was February, 1965 when Walter and Sue came into our lives and thus began a wonderful friendship. A young family with two small sons, Jim had been called to become the Assistant Pastor of Westminster Presbyterian Church in Springfield, Illinois. Walter and Sue were "pillars" in the Westminster congregation, serving through the years as elders, deacons, trustees, and chairing innumerable committees. Through more than twenty years at Westminster as Jim moved from Assistant Pastor to Associate to Senior Pastor-Head of Staff (Sue Hanson chaired the search committee), Walter and Sue Hanson provided invaluable friendship, encouragement, support and mentoring to our family. To this day we feel richly blessed that their lives touched ours in so many beautiful ways.

One particular experience remains vivid in our minds when Walter combined his engineering expertise with his church commitments. In the early 1970's Walter served on a building committee to oversee the design, funding and construction of a new choir balcony at Westminster. Plans were developed and informational congregational meetings were held. During one of those meetings, a very elderly lady, one of the "saints" of the church, expressed concern that the balcony might not be strong enough to support an organ and choir, because the architectural drawings showed a very thin line for the balcony floor. In his usual patient, kindly way, Walter went into some detail about the construction of the balcony and assured Miss Kate that the balcony would support the anticipated weights. Miss Kate left the meeting supporting the balcony project, feeling her concerns had been taken seriously and professionally answered. The balcony was built and continues to serve the church well!

Another remembrance of Walter's vision was the development of a technical library for Hanson Engineers. Begun in the mid-1970s to serve the growing engineering staff, Walter invited Silvey to join the firm as a part-time technical librarian. Never having been a librarian, Silvey was very conscious of living up to Walter's expectations. For ten years it was an absolute delight to become acquainted with a talented engineering staff and to help organize the resources in the most helpful way. The job offer was more evidence of Walter's sensitivity to other people's needs, as that job supplemented the Barge family income to send to sons through college! Another impact on our lives — to this day we cannot drive over a bridge or down a highway, or look at a tower or dam, without real appreciation for the engineering skill that makes it all possible!

We salute Walter and Sue Hanson for their vision and integrity, for their friendship, for their generous contributions to the church and larger community, and most especially for their sense of humor and twinkle in the eye. In the New Testament book of Philemon, St. Paul wrote, "I thank my God always when I remember you. . . . For I have derived much joy and comfort from your love." Thank you, Walter and Sue Hanson, for the joy, comfort, and love you have shared with so many.

Sister Francis Marie Thrailkill, O.S.U.

Walter Hanson served on our Board of Trustees at Springfield College during my presidency and was a tremendous leader and champion for the college in the Springfield community. Walt was always a quiet (I would almost say self-effacing) gentleman— and each of those words is important! He never "put himself up" as an expert—even when he was a leader in the field. He never bragged about his book, his awards in bridge design, his position in his firm or on the Board. One had to ask him what he thought about something, then he would give his comments—which were always on point and very insightful.

I remember being at his officer one afternoon on a Springfield College matter and seeing in a hallway the design for a bridge that looked not only unusual, but spectacular. It was only upon my questioning him, that he told me about the bridge being over the fault line and how he had thought about the need to stabilize the structure by "hanging" (my word, not his) from the surrounding mountains to ensure its safety and strength in case of an earthquake. He then went on to tell me about the award it had won and the rest of the story. This was so typical of Walt—he never "tooted his own horn."

As a Board Chair, he was someone that I could turn to for advice knowing that he would consider the issue or situation very carefully, give me an analogous situation, talk about some options and support me in the decision I had to make. I learned to deeply appreciate this quality—sometimes when one asks for advice the person feels they are being asked to make the decision—Walt knew that the academic world is different, and ultimately he could give wise counsel, but that the decision had to come from the administration.

My memories of Walt are of a wise and gentle person, competent and smart, a quiet leader, whose words were heard not because they were loud, rather because they were well thought out.

Timothy J. Davlin

WHEREAS, Founded in 1954, Hanson Professional Services, Inc., a national employee-owned consulting firm, provides a full range of architectural, engineering, and management services, and as the tenth largest private employer in Springfield, Hanson is committed to the Springfield community, its business environment and economic development opportunities; and

WHEREAS, Hanson's impact on the local economy includes sustaining an estimated 850 jobs locally and generating more than $25.7 million in business within the area; and

WHEREAS, Hanson has completed projects nationwide and in many foreign countries, projects ranging from engineering studies to design projects, including the $92 million Clark Bridge over the Mississippi River near St. Louis, Missouri.

WHEREAS, Hanson has consistently appeared in the Top 500 Engineering News-Record Magazine's listing of premiere design firms in the United States for the last 17 years, and recently came in at No. 192 on the national list.

NOW THEREFORE, I, Timothy J. Davlin, Mayor of the City of Springfield, Illinois, do hereby proclaim Thursday, October 14, 2004 to be

HANSON PROFESSIONAL SERVICES, INC. DAY

in the City of Springfield, in celebration of the 50th Anniversary of this internationally respected organization that is one of Springfield,'s strongest assets.

IN WITNESS WHEREOF, I have hereunto set my hand and caused the Official Seal of the City of Springfield to be affixed this 14th day of October 2004.

INDEX

302